The Parish School Hymnal

Authorized by
The United Lutheran Church in America

PHILADELPHIA

THE BOARD OF PUBLICATION OF
THE UNITED LUTHERAN CHURCH IN AMERICA

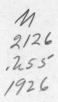

2126
.255
1926

420TH THOUSAND

77976
Mar. 1972

5128—50M—43

MADE IN THE UNITED STATES OF AMERICA

TABLE OF CONTENTS

THE ORDER OF SERVICE

¶ The School shall be called to reverent silence by a chord on the piano or other signal.

HYMN

¶ The Opening Hymn shall be one of adoration or praise, or it may be a morning hymn, or a hymn suitable to the Season. The School shall stand.

INVOCATION

¶ The Superintendent shall say:

IN the Name of the Father, and of the Son, and of the Holy Ghost.

School: *Amen.*

A - MEN.

OPENING VERSICLES

¶ Opening and Closing Versicles for use on Festivals and at other times will be found on p. 16, and may be used instead of the following.

Superintendent: I was glad when they said unto me:
School: *Let us go into the House of the Lord.*
   O come, let us worship the Lord:
     For He is our Maker.
   Every day will I praise Thee:
     And I will praise Thy Name forever and ever.
   The Lord is nigh unto all that call upon Him:
     To all that call upon Him in truth.
   O Lord, open Thou my lips:
     And my mouth shall show forth Thy praise.

¶ Then shall all sing the Gloria Patri.

GLORY be to the Father, and | to the | Son:
 And | to the | Holy | Ghost;
As it was in the beginning, is now, and | ever | shall be:
 World | without | end. A- | men.

5

I

II

J. Alcock

III

E. J. Hopkins

For Lent

IV

Arranged by J. Stainer

Glo - ry . be to the Fa - ther, and to the Son, and

to . the Ho - ly Ghost: As it { was in the be- } and
{ ginning, is now, }

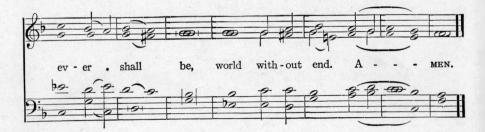

ev - er . shall be, world with - out end. A - - - men.

PRAYER

¶ The Pastor, or the Superintendent, shall offer the Prayer. A selection from the Prayers (p. 23) may be read by him and the School together.

Let us pray.

¶ Then shall be said the Prayer.

OUR Father, Who art in heaven; Hallowed be **Thy Name; Thy** kingdom come; Thy will be done on earth, as it is in heaven; Give us this day our daily bread; And forgive us our trespasses, as we forgive those who trespass against us; And lead us not into temptation; But deliver us from evil; For Thine is the kingdom, and the power, and the glory, for ever and ever. Amen.

HYMN

PSALM 67-38

¶ Then shall be read a Psalm responsively (p. 33), after which shall be sung the Gloria Patri. (Music, p. 6.)

SCRIPTURE LESSON

¶ A selection of Scripture (p. 49), may then be read in unison; or the Superintendent may read the Lesson for the Day.

CREED

¶ Then shall all say:

I BELIEVE in God the Father Almighty, Maker of heaven and earth. And in Jesus Christ His only Son, our Lord; Who was conceived by the Holy Ghost, Born of the Virgin Mary; Suffered under Pontius Pilate, Was crucified, dead, and buried; He descended into hell; The third day He rose again from the dead; He ascended into heaven, And sitteth on the right hand of God the Father Almighty; From thence He shall come to judge the quick and the dead. I believe in the Holy Ghost; The holy Christian Church, the Communion of Saints; the Forgiveness of sins; the Resurrection of the body; And the Life everlasting. Amen.

CATECHISM

¶ A Part of the Catechism (p. 51), may be read responsively.

HYMN

THE INSTRUCTION

¶ The Instruction shall be closed with a suitable signal.

HYMN

THE DAY'S REPORTS

CLOSING VERSICLES

¶ The School shall stand:

Pastor, (Superintendent) : We praise Thee, O God:
School: *We acknowledge Thee to be the Lord.*

All the earth doth worship Thee:
The Father everlasting.
Holy, Holy, Holy, Lord God of Sabaoth:
Heaven and earth are full of Thy glory.
Bless we the Father, and the Son, and the Holy Ghost:
We praise and magnify Him forever.
The fear of the Lord is the beginning of wisdom:
*A good understanding have all they that do His command-
ments.*
I will meditate in Thy precepts:
*And have respect unto Thy ways; I will not forget Thy
Word.*
Thy Word is a lamp unto my feet:
And a light unto my path.
O Lord, let Thy mercy be upon us:
As our trust is in Thee.
The Lord be with you:
And with thy spirit.
Let us pray.

¶ *Then shall all say one of the following Prayers:*

O GOD, Who hast prepared for them that love Thee such good
things as pass man's understanding: Pour into our hearts
such love toward Thee, that we, loving Thee above all things, may
obtain Thy promises which exceed all that we can desire; through
Jesus Christ, Thy Son, our Lord.   Amen.

O GOD, the Protector of all that trust in Thee, without Whom
nothing is strong, nothing is holy: Increase and multiply upon
us Thy mercy; that Thou being our Ruler and Guide, we may so
pass through things temporal, that we finally lose not the things
eternal; through Jesus Christ, Thy Son, our Lord.   Amen.

O MOST Merciful God, we beseech Thee, grant unto us, that we
may both earnestly desire and perfectly fulfill those things
which are well-pleasing in Thy sight, to the glory of Thy holy
Name; through Jesus Christ, Thy Son, our Lord.   Amen

Pastor (Superintendent): Bless we the Lord.

School: *Thanks be to God.*

BENEDICTION

¶ *The Pastor may say the Benediction.*
¶ *The School shall sing:*

A - MEN.

MATINS

¶ *The* Versicles *with the* Gloria Patri *shall be sung or said, the Congregation standing until the end of the* Venite.

¶ *The* Hallelujah *shall be omitted in Lent.*

THE VERSICLES

O LORD, open Thou my lips.
Response. And my mouth shall show forth Thy praise.
Make haste, O God, to deliver me.
℟. Make haste to help me, O Lord.
Glory be to the Father, and to the Son, and to the Holy Ghost:
℟. As it was in the beginning, is now, and ever shall be, **world** without end. Amen. Hallelujah.

¶ *Then may follow the* Invitatory *with the* Venite.

THE INVITATORY

O come, let us worship the Lord.
℟. For He is our Maker.

VENITE EXULTEMUS

O COME, let us sing unto the Lord: let us make a joyful noise to the Rock of our salvation.
Let us come before His presence with thanksgiving: and make a joyful noise unto Him with psalms.
For the Lord is a great God: and a great King above all gods.
In His hands are the deep places of the earth: the strength of the hills is His also.
The sea is His, and He made it: and His hands formed the dry land.
O come, let us worship and bow down: let us kneel before the Lord our Maker.
For He is our God: and we are the people of His pasture, and the sheep of His hand.
GLORY be to the Father, and to the Son, and to the Holy Ghost:
As it was in the beginning, is now, and ever shall be, world without end. Amen.

¶ *Then shall be sung the* Hymn.

THE HYMN

The musical setting for Matins will be found in the Common Service Book, Music Edition, page 29.

¶ *Then, all standing, shall be sung or said one or more* Psalms.

THE PSALM

¶ *At the end of each Psalm the Congregation shall sing or say the* Gloria Patri.

GLORIA PATRI

GLORY be to the Father, and to the Son, and to the Holy Ghost: as it was in the beginning, is now, and ever shall be, world without end. Amen.

THE LESSON

¶ *The* Scripture Lessons *shall then be read. After each Lesson shall be sung or said the* Response.

O Lord, have mercy upon us.
℟. Thanks be to God.

¶ *After the Lesson a* RESPONSORY *or a* HYMN *may be sung.*

¶ *A brief* SERMON *or the Instruction for the Day may then follow.*

THE CANTICLE

¶ *The Congregation shall rise and sing or say the* Canticle.

TE DEUM LAUDAMUS

WE praise Thee, O God: we acknowledge Thee to be the Lord.
All the earth doth worship Thee: the Father everlasting.
To Thee all Angels cry aloud: the heavens, and all the powers therein.
To Thee Cherubim and Seraphim: continually do cry,
Holy, Holy, Holy: Lord God of Sabaoth;
Heaven and earth are full of the Majesty: of Thy Glory.
The glorious company of the Apostles: praise Thee.
The goodly fellowship of the Prophets: praise Thee.
The noble army of Martyrs: praise Thee.
The holy Church throughout all the world: doth acknowledge Thee;
The Father: of an infinite Majesty;
Thine adorable, true: and only Son;
Also the Holy Ghost: the Comforter.

THOU art the King of glory: O Christ.
Thou art the everlasting Son: of the Father.
When Thou tookest upon Thee to deliver man: Thou didst humble Thyself to be born of a Virgin.
When Thou hadst overcome the sharpness of death: Thou didst open the kingdom of heaven to all believers.
Thou sittest at the right hand of God: in the glory of the Father.
We believe that Thou shalt come: to be our Judge.
We therefore pray Thee, help Thy servants: whom Thou hast redeemed with Thy precious blood.

10

Make them to be numbered with Thy saints: in glory everlasting.

O LORD, save Thy people: and bless Thine heritage.
Govern them: and lift them up for ever.
Day by day: we magnify Thee;
And we worship Thy Name: ever, world without end.
Vouchsafe, O Lord: to keep us this day without sin.
O Lord, have mercy upon us: have mercy upon us.
O Lord, let Thy mercy be upon us: as our trust is in Thee.
O Lord, in Thee have I trusted: let me never be confounded.

BENEDICTUS

BLESSED be the Lord God of Israel: for He hath visited and redeemed His people;
And hath raised up a horn of salvation for us: in the house of His servant David;
As He spake by the mouth of His holy prophets: which have been since the world began;
That we should be saved from our enemies: and from the hand of all that hate us;
To perform the mercy promised to our fathers: and to remember His holy covenant;
The oath which He sware to our father Abraham: that He would grant unto us;
That we, being delivered out of the hand of our enemies: might serve Him without fear,
In holiness and righteousness before Him: all the days of our life.
And thou, child, shalt be called the prophet of the Highest: for thou shalt go before the face of the Lord to prepare His ways;
To give knowledge of salvation unto His people: by the remission of their sins,
Through the tender mercy of our God: whereby the Dayspring from on high hath visited us;
To give light to them that sit in darkness and in the shadow of death: to guide our feet in to the way of peace.
GLORY be to the Father, and to the Son, and to the Holy Ghost:
As it was in the beginning, is now, and ever shall be, world without end. Amen.

THE PRAYER

¶ *Then shall be said the* Prayers.

¶ *The Minister shall say:*

Lord, have mercy upon us.

¶ *The Congregation shall sing or say:*

Lord, have mercy upon us.
Christ, have mercy upon us.
Lord, have mercy upon us.

¶ Then shall all say the **Lord's Prayer.**

OUR Father, Who art in heaven; Hallowed by Thy Name; Thy kingdom come; Thy will be done on earth, as it is in heaven; Give us this day our daily bread; And forgive us our trespasses, as we forgive those who trespass against us; And lead us not into temptation; But deliver us from evil; For Thine is the kingdom, and the power, and the glory, for ever and ever. Amen.

¶ Then may be sung or said:

The Lord be with you.
℟. And with thy spirit.

¶ The Minister shall say:

Let us pray.

¶ Then shall be said the **Collect for the Day.**

THE COLLECT FOR THE DAY

¶ Other Collects may then be said, and after them this Collect **for Grace,** *with which a* Versicle *may be used.*

℣. Let my mouth be filled with Thy praise.
℟. And with Thy honor all the day.

COLLECT FOR GRACE

O LORD, our Heavenly Father, Almighty and Everlasting God, Who hast safely brought us to the beginning of this day: Defend us in the same with Thy mighty power; and grant that this day we fall into no sin, neither run into any kind of danger; but that all our doings, being ordered by Thy governance, may be righteous in Thy sight; through Jesus Christ, Thy Son, our Lord, Who liveth and reigneth with Thee and the Holy Ghost, ever One God, world without end. Amen.

¶ Then may be sung or said the **Benedicamus.**

Bless we the Lord.
℟. Thanks be to God.

¶ Then shall the Minister say the **Benediction.**

THE Grace of our Lord Jesus Christ, and the Love of God, and the Communion of the Holy Ghost, be with you all. Amen.

✠

12

VESPERS

¶ *The* Versicles *with the* Gloria Patri *shall be sung or said, the Congregation stand-ing until the end of the* Psalm.

¶ *The* Hallelujah *shall be omitted in Lent.*

THE VERSICLES

O LORD, open Thou my lips.
Response. And my mouth shall show forth Thy praise.
Make haste, O God, to deliver me.
℟. Make haste to help me, O Lord.
Glory be to the Father, and to the Son, and to the Holy Ghost:
℟. As it was in the beginning, is now, and ever shall be, world without end. Amen. Hallelujah.

¶ *Then shall be sung or said one or more* Psalms.

THE PSALM

¶ *At the end of each Psalm the Congregation shall sing or say the* Gloria Patri.

GLORIA PATRI

G LORY be to the Father, and to the Son, and to the Holy Ghost: as it was in the beginning, is now, and ever shall be, world without end. Amen.

THE LESSON

¶ *The* Scripture Lessons *shall then be read. After each Lesson shall be sung or said the* Response.

O Lord, have mercy upon us.
℟. Thanks be to God.

¶ *After the Lesson a* Responsory *or a* Hymn *may be sung.*

¶ *A* Sermon *or the* Instruction *for the Day may then follow.*

¶ *The* Offering *may then be received and placed upon the Altar.*

¶ *Then shall be sung the* Hymn.

THE HYMN

¶ *The Congregation shall rise and sing or say the* Canticle.

The musical setting for Vespers will be found in the Common Service Book, Music Edition, page 40.

¶ *A* Versicle *shall be used with the Canticle.*

℣. Let my prayer be set forth before Thee as incense.

℟. And the lifting up of my hands as the evening sacrifice.

THE CANTICLE

MAGNIFICAT

MY soul doth magnify the Lord: and my spirit hath rejoiced in God my Saviour.

For He hath regarded: the low estate of His handmaiden.

For behold, from henceforth: all generations shall call me blessed.

For He that is mighty hath done to me great things: and holy is His Name.

And His mercy is on them that fear Him: from generation to generation.

He hath showed strength with His arm: He hath scattered the proud in the imagination of their hearts.

He hath put down the mighty from their seats: and exalted them of low degree.

He hath filled the hungry with good things: and the rich He hath sent empty away.

He hath holpen His servant Israel, in remembrance of His mercy: as He spake to our fathers, to Abraham, and to his seed for ever.

GLORY be to the Father, and to the Son, and to the Holy Ghost: As it was in the beginning, is now, and ever shall be, world without end. Amen.

NUNC DIMITTIS

LORD, now lettest Thou Thy servant depart in peace: according to Thy word;

For mine eyes have seen Thy salvation: which Thou hast prepared before the face of all people;

A light to lighten the Gentiles: and the glory of Thy people Israel.

Glory be to the Father, and to the Son, and to the Holy Ghost: As it was in the beginning, is now, and ever shall be, world without end. Amen.

THE PRAYER

¶ *Then shall be said the* Prayers.

¶ *The Minister shall say:*

Lord, have mercy upon us.

¶ *The Congregation shall sing or say:*

Lord, have mercy upon us.
Christ, have mercy upon us.
Lord, have mercy upon us.

¶ *Then shall all say the* Lord's Prayer.

OUR Father, Who art in heaven; Hallowed be Thy name; Thy kingdom come; Thy will be done on earth, as it is in heaven; Give us this day our daily bread; And forgive us our trespasses, as we forgive those who trespass against us; And lead us not into temptation; But deliver us from evil; For Thine is the kingdom, and the power, and the glory, for ever and ever. Amen.

¶ *Then may be sung or said:*

The Lord be with you.
℟. And with thy spirit.

¶ *The Minister shall say:*

Let us pray.

¶ *Then shall be said the* Collect for the Day.

THE COLLECT FOR THE DAY

¶ *Other Collects may then be said, and after them this* Collect for **Peace**, *with which a* Versicle *may be used.*

℣. The Lord will give strength unto His people.
℟. The Lord will bless His people with peace.

COLLECT FOR PEACE

O GOD, from Whom all holy desires, all good counsels, and all just works do proceed: Give unto Thy servants that peace, which the world cannot give; that our hearts may be set to obey Thy commandments, and also that by Thee, we, being defended from the fear of our enemies, may pass our time in rest and quietness; through the merits of Jesus Christ our Saviour, Who liveth and reigneth with Thee, and the Holy Ghost, ever One God, world without end. Amen.

¶ *Then may be sung or said the* Benedicamus.

Bless we the Lord.
℟. Thanks be to God.

¶ *Then shall the Minister say the* Benediction.

THE Grace of our Lord Jesus Christ, and the Love of God, and the Communion of the Holy Ghost, be with you all. Amen.

✠

VERSICLES

CHRISTMAS

OPENING VERSICLES

Superintendent: Unto us the Christ is born:
School: *O come, let us worship Him.*
The angel said: Fear not: for, behold, I bring you tidings of great joy, which shall be to all people.
For unto you is born this day in the city of David a Saviour, who is Christ the Lord.
And suddenly there was with the angel a multitude of the heavenly host praising God, and saying:
Glory to God in the highest, and on earth peace, good will toward men.
God so loved the world, that He gave His only-begotten Son,
That whosoever believeth in Him should not perish, but have everlasting life.
The *Gloria Patri.*

CLOSING VERSICLES

Pastor (Superintendent) : Unto us a Child is born:
School: *Unto us a Son is given.*
And the government shall be upon His shoulder:
And His Name shall be called Wonderful, Counsellor, The mighty God, The everlasting Father, The Prince of Peace.
My soul doth magnify the Lord:
And my spirit hath rejoiced in God my Saviour.
The Day-spring from on high hath visited us:
To give light to them that sit in darkness and in the shadow of death; to guide our feet into the way of peace.
Christ the Lord, our Saviour, Everlasting God, and Mary's Son:
We praise Thee evermore.
The Lord be with you:
And with thy spirit.
Let us pray.

EPIPHANY

OPENING VERSICLES

Superintendent: Christ hath appeared unto us:
School: *O come, let us worship Him.*
Arise, shine; for thy Light is come:
And the glory of the Lord is risen upon thee.

16

Behold, there came wise men from the east to Jerusalem, saying:
Where is He that is born king of the Jews? for we have seen His star in the east, and are come to worship Him.
And, lo, the star, which they saw in the east, went before them:
Till it came and stood over where the Young Child was.
And when they were come into the house, they saw the Young Child with Mary His mother, and fell down and worshiped Him:
And when they had opened their treasures, they presented unto Him gifts: gold, and frankincense, and myrrh.

The *Gloria Patri.*

CLOSING VERSICLES

Pastor (Superintendent) : O Lord, our Lord, how excellent is Thy Name in all the earth:
School: Who hast set Thy glory above the heavens.
God also hath highly exalted Him, and given Him a Name which is above every name:
That at the Name of Jesus every knee should bow, and every tongue should confess that Jesus Christ is Lord, to the glory of God the Father.
What shall I render unto the Lord for all His benefits to me?
I will take the cup of salvation, and call upon the Name of the Lord.
The Lord be with you:
And with thy spirit.
Let us pray.

LENT

OPENING VERSICLES

Superintendent: Behold the Lamb of God which taketh away the sin of the world:
School: O come, let us worship Him.
Christ glorified not Himself.
Though He was a Son, yet learned He obedience by the things which He suffered.
He was wounded for our transgressions:
He was bruised for our iniquities.
He humbled Himself, and became obedient unto death, even the death of the cross.
And being made perfect, He became the Author of eternal salvation unto all that obey Him.
God also hath highly exalted Him, and given Him a Name which is above every name:
That at the Name of Jesus every knee should bow, and every tongue should confess that Jesus Christ is Lord, to the glory of God the Father.
This is a faithful saying, and worthy of all acceptation:
That Christ Jesus came into the world to save sinners.

The *Gloria Patri.*

Pastor (Superintendent) : Worthy is the Lamb that was slain to receive power, and riches, and wisdom:

School: *And strength, and honor, and glory, and blessing.*

Blessing, and honor, and glory, and power, be unto Him that sitteth upon the throne:

And unto the Lamb for ever and ever.

The sacrifices of God are a broken spirit:

A broken and a contrite heart, O God, Thou wilt not despise.

Create in me a clean heart, O God:

And renew a right spirit within me.

Hear my prayer, O Lord:

And let my cry come unto Thee.

The Lord be with you:

And with thy spirit.

Let us pray.

EASTER

OPENING VERSICLES

Superintendent: The Lord is risen indeed:

School: *O come, let us worship Him.   Hallelujah!*

This is the day which the Lord hath made:

We will rejoice and be glad in it.

And very early in the morning, the first day of the week, they came unto the sepulchre at the rising of the sun.

And when they looked they saw that the stone was rolled away: for it was very great.

And entering into the sepulchre, they saw a young man sitting, clothed in a long white garment; and they were affrighted.

And he saith unto them, Be not affrighted: ye seek Jesus of Nazareth, who was crucified: He is risen; He is not here: behold the place where they laid Him.

Our Lord Jesus said: I am the Resurrection and the Life: he that believeth in Me, though he were dead, yet shall he live.

Lord, I believe that Thou art the Christ, the Son of God, who should come into the world.

The *Gloria Patri.*

CLOSING VERSICLES

Pastor (Superintendent) : O sing unto the Lord a new song:

School: *For He hath done marvelous things.*

Our Lord Jesus said: I am the Way, the Truth, and the Life:

No man cometh unto the Father, but by Me.

This is the victory that overcometh the world:

Even our faith.

I know whom I have believed:

And I am persuaded that He is able to guard that which I have committed unto Him against that day.

Unto Him that loved us, and washed us from our sins in His own blood, and hath made us kings and priests unto God and His Father:
> *To Him be glory and dominion for ever and ever. Amen.*

The Lord be with you:
> *And with thy spirit.*

Let us pray.

PENTECOST

OPENING VERSICLES

Superintendent: The Spirit of the Lord filleth the world:
> School: *O come, let us worship Him. Hallelujah.*

Our Lord Jesus said: The Comforter, who is the Holy Ghost, whom the Father will send in My Name:
> *He shall teach you all things, and bring all things to your remembrance.*

He shall testify of Me.
> *He will guide you into all truth. He shall glorify Me.*

And when the day of Pentecost was fully come, they were all with one accord in one place:
> *And suddenly there came a sound from heaven as of a rushing mighty wind, and it filled all the house where they were sitting.*

And there appeared unto them cloven tongues, like as of fire, and it sat upon each of them.
> *And they were all filled with the Holy Ghost and began to speak with other tongues, as the Spirit gave them utterance.*

Come, Holy Ghost, and fill the hearts of Thy faithful people:
> *And kindle in them the fire of Thy love.*

> The *Gloria Patri.*

CLOSING VERSICLES

Pastor (Superintendent): Who shall ascend into the hill of the Lord?
> School: *Or who shall stand in His holy place?*

He that hath clean hands and a pure heart.
> *Blessed are the pure in heart for they shall see God.*

As many as are led by the Spirit of God:
> *They are the sons of God.*

The Spirit itself beareth witness with our spirit, that we are the children of God:
> *And if children, then heirs; heirs of God, and joint heirs with Christ.*

The fruit of the Spirit is in all goodness, and righteousness, and truth.
> *If we live in the Spirit, let us also walk in the Spirit.*

The Lord be with you:
> *And with thy spirit.*

Let us pray.

REFORMATION

Superintendent: The Lord is in His holy temple:
School: O come, let us worship Him.
I was glad when they said unto me:
Let us go into the house of the Lord.
Great is the Lord, and greatly to be praised:
In the city of our God, in the mountain of His holiness.
Beautiful for situation, the joy of the whole earth, is mount Zion:
God is known in her palaces, for a refuge.
The *Gloria Patri.*

CLOSING VERSICLES

Pastor (Superintendent): Ye are fellow citizens with the saints, and of the household of God:
School: And are built upon the foundation of the apostles and prophets, Jesus Christ Himself being the chief cornerstone.
In whom all the building fitly framed together groweth unto an holy temple in the Lord:
In whom ye also are builded together for an habitation of God through the Spirit. For the temple of God is holy, which temple ye are.
Other foundation can no man lay than that is laid which is Jesus Christ.
But let every man take heed how he buildeth thereupon.
Other men have labored:
And ye are entered into their labors.
Be ye doers of the Word, and not hearers only.
Blessed are they that hear the Word of God, and keep it.
The Lord be with you:
And with thy spirit.
Let us pray.

HARVEST-THANKSGIVING

OPENING VERSICLES

Superintendent: Praise ye the Lord; praise God in His sanctuary:
School: O come, let us worship Him.
Enter into His gates with thanksgiving:
And into His courts with praise:
Bless the Lord, O my soul:
And all that is within me, bless His holy Name:
Bless the Lord, O my soul:
And forget not all His benefits.
Thou crownest the year with Thy goodness:
And Thy paths drop fatness.
Thou visitest the earth and waterest it:
Thou blessest the springing thereof.
O give thanks unto the Lord for He is good:
For His mercy endureth for ever.
The *Gloria Patri.*

CLOSING VERSICLES

Pastor (Superintendent) : I will extol Thee, my God, O King:
School: *Every day will I bless Thee.*
The eyes of all wait upon Thee:
And Thou givest them their meat in due season.
Thou openest Thine hand:
And satisfiest the desire of every living thing.
Thy mercies are new unto us every morning:
Great is Thy faithfulness.
Therefore take no thought saying, What shall we eat? or, What shall we drink? or, Wherewithal shall we be clothed?
For your heavenly Father knoweth that ye have need of all these things.
But seek ye first the kingdom of God, and His righteousness:
And all these things shall be added unto you.
The Lord be with you:
And with thy spirit.
Let us pray.

MISSIONS   OPENING VERSICLES

Superintendent: Christ hath appeared unto us:
School: *O come, let us worship Him.*
Arise, shine; for thy Light is come:
And the glory of the Lord is risen upon thee.
The Gentiles shall come to Thy Light:
And kings to the brightness of Thy rising.
Of the increase of His government and peace there shall be no end:
To order it, and to establish it with judgment and with justice from henceforth even for ever.
Our Lord Jesus said: Go ye into all the world:
And preach the Gospel to every creature.
Teaching them to observe all things whatsoever I have commanded you:
And, lo, I am with you alway, even unto the end of the world. Amen.
The *Gloria Patri.*

CLOSING VERSICLES

Pastor (Superintendent) : Bless we the Father, and the Son, and the Holy Ghost:
School: *We praise and magnify Him for ever.*
From the rising of the sun unto the going down of the same:
The Lord's Name is to be praised.
Whosoever shall call on the Name of the Lord shall be saved:
How then shall they call on Him in whom they have not believed?
And how shall they believe in Him of whom they have not heard?
And how shall they hear without a preacher?
And how shall they preach except they be sent?
As it is written, How beautiful are the feet of them that preach the Gospel of peace, and bring glad tidings of good things.

21

And the disciples went forth and preached everywhere:
The Lord working with them, and confirming the Word by the signs that followed.
The Lord be with you:
And with thy spirit.
Let us pray.

NATIONAL

Superintendent: O come, let us worship and bow down:
School: Let us kneel before the Lord our Maker.
For He is our God:
And we are the people of His pasture, and the sheep of His hand.
Thy kingdom is an everlasting kingdom:
And Thy dominion endureth throughout all generations.
Blessed is the nation whose God is the Lord:
And the people whom He hath chosen for His own inheritance.
We have heard with our ears, O God, our fathers have told us:
What work Thou didst in their days, in the times of old.
The mercy of the Lord is from everlasting to everlasting upon them that fear Him:
And His righteousness unto children's children;
To such as keep His covenant:
And to those that remember His commandments to do them.

The Gloria Patri.

CLOSING VERSICLES

Pastor (Superintendent): What doth the Lord require of thee, but to do justly, and to love mercy, and to walk humbly with thy God?
School: Our Lord Jesus said: Render unto Cæsar the things that are Cæsar's; and unto God the things that are God's.
I exhort that supplications, prayers, intercessions, and giving of thanks, be made for all men:
For kings, and for all that are in authority; that we may lead a quiet and peaceable life in all godliness and honesty.
Put them in mind to be in subjection to rulers, to authorities, to be obedient, to be ready to every good work,
To speak evil of no man, not to be contentious, to be gentle, showing all meekness toward all men.
For so is the will of God, that with well doing ye may put to silence the ignorance of foolish men:
As free, and not using your liberty for a cloak of maliciousness. but as the servants of God.
Blessed are the meek, for they shall inherit the earth.
Blessed are the peacemakers, for they shall be called the children of God.
The Lord be with you:
And with thy spirit.
Let us pray.

COLLECTS AND PRAYERS

1—*Advent.*

ALMIGHTY Father, by the Advent of Whose Son into the world the Kingdom of Heaven is open to all who believe in Him: Grant us Thy Holy Spirit so that we may believe in Him with our whole heart, and so serve Him in our daily lives that when He cometh again to make up His jewels, we may, by Thy mercy be gathered into the Kingdom which abideth eternal in the heavens; through Thy mercy, O our God, who livest and reignest One God, world without end. Amen.

2—*Christmas.*

OUR Father, of Whose love the angels sang when Jesus was born in Bethlehem, and through Whom we have learned the song of praise, Glory be to Thee in the highest: Accept our worship and our hymns of joy; and, as we celebrate the birthday of Thy Son, grant that in Him we may learn to know Thy love, to follow Him in obedience, and to offer ourselves to Thee in all things, that our lives may show us too to be Thy children in all our thoughts, words, and deeds; through the same Jesus Christ, Thy Son, our Lord. Amen.

3—*Old Year—New Year.*

O GOD, Who art ever the Same, and Whose years know no end: In Thy mercy we close another year of time and lay it away in Thy eternal storehouse. It has been filled with Thy goodness toward us, for this we humbly thank Thee; it has known our sins, and disobedience, and failures, for these we grieve and beseech Thy forgiveness; it has seen our feeble efforts in service of Thee and our fellowmen, purify this all and find, we humbly pray, something therein which may be to Thy glory. Grant us Thy grace so to enter this New Year that we may count every day a new privilege of life, and opportunity to learn of Thee, that through us Thy Name may be hallowed, in us Thy Kingdom come, and by us Thy Will be done; through Jesus Christ, Thy Son, our Lord. Amen.

4—*Epiphany.*

O GOD, our Heavenly Father, Whose guiding star led the Wise Men to our Lord's manger through a long, perilous, and unknown way: We pray Thee Who hast made Thy Son our Way through life, to keep us steadfast in following Him, to guide us and ever teach us by His example, to protect and counsel us by His Spirit, so that we may come safely to our heavenly home where all Thy children will ever adore Thee, the Father of love, through Jesus Christ, Thy Son, in Thy Holy Spirit. Amen.

5—*Epiphany Season.*

ALMIGHTY God, we humbly beseech Thee to hear the prayers of Thy children who call upon Thee, and grant that we may both see and know all such things as be pleasing unto Thee, and give us grace and a ready will always to perform the same; through Jesus Christ, our Lord. Amen.

6—*Lent.*

LET Thy blessing be upon us, Heavenly Father, as we pass through these holy days in which we remember the sufferings and death of our dear Lord, and grant that His holy example being ever before us, we may follow Him in willing obedience, learn His gracious humility, and, being filled with His love and spirit of self-sacrifice, learn the lessons of a life pleasing to Thee and helpful to our fellowmen; through Him Who loved us and gave Himself for us, even Jesus Christ, our Lord. Amen.

7—*Lent.*

WE beseech Thee, O God, by the mystery of our Saviour's fasting and temptation, to arm us with the same mind that was in Him, that we may resist evil and sin; and give us grace to keep our bodies in such holy discipline, that our minds may be ready always to shun evil, and to obey the guidance of Thy Holy Spirit; through Jesus Christ, our Lord. Amen.

8—*Palm Sunday.*

ALMIGHTY and Everlasting God, Who hast sent Thy Son, our Saviour Jesus Christ, to take upon Him our flesh, and to suffer death upon the Cross, that all mankind should follow the example of His great humility: Mercifully grant that we may both follow the example of His patience, and also be made partakers of His resurrection; through the same Jesus Christ, Thy Son, our Lord. Amen.

9—*Good Friday.*

ALMIGHTY God, we beseech Thee graciously to behold this Thy family, for which our Lord Jesus Christ was contented to be betrayed, and given up into the hands of wicked men, and to suffer death upon the Cross; through the same Jesus Christ, Thy Son, our Lord. Amen.

10—*Easter.*

ALMIGHTY God, our Heavenly Father, Who (on this day) didst bring again our Lord Jesus from the dead: Grant us by Thy grace to rise with Him to newness of life, that we may overcome the world with the victory of faith in Him, and, at the last, have part in the resurrection of the just; through the merits of Jesus Christ, our Saviour. Amen.

11—*Easter Season.*

O LORD Jesus Christ, Who didst rise victorious from the dead, conquering for us death and the grave and opening to us the gates to everlasting life: Receive, we pray Thee, our adoration and praise for this victory which Thou hast obtained for us, and grant that we may always follow Thee our Way, hold fast to Thee the Truth, and live now and eternally in Thee the Life, Who with the Father and the Holy Ghost, livest and reignest, ever One God, world without end. Amen.

12—*Pentecost.*

O GOD, Who (on this day) didst teach the hearts of Thy faithful people, by sending to them the light of Thy Holy Spirit: Grant us by the same Spirit to have a right judgment in all things, and evermore to rejoice in His holy comfort; through Jesus Christ, Thy Son, our Lord. Amen.

13—*Trinity.*

O UR Father, Who didst reveal and teach us the Way of Life in Thy Son Jesus and through Thy Holy Spirit dost enlighten our hearts and nourish us in this Truth: Receive, we humbly pray, our worship and thanksgiving for this Thy grace, and help us ever to call upon Thee, the Father of mercy and love, as we have been taught by Thy Son Jesus, our Lord. Amen.

14—*Reformation.*

A LMIGHTY God, Who, through the preaching of Thy servants, the blessed reformers, hast caused the light of the Gospel to shine forth: Grant, we beseech Thee, that, knowing its saving power, we may faithfully guard and defend it against all enemies, and joyfully proclaim it to the salvation of souls and the glory of Thy holy Name; through Jesus Christ, our Lord. Amen.

15—*Harvest.*

O ALMIGHTY and Everlasting God, Who hast given unto us the fruits of the earth in their season: We thank Thee for all these Thy blessings which Thou hast provided for the nourishment of our bodies, and we pray Thee to grant us grace ever to use the same to Thy glory, to the relief of those who are needy, and, thankfully, to our own comfort; through Jesus Christ, our Lord. Amen.

16—*Thanksgiving.*

A LMIGHTY God, our Heavenly Father, Whose mercies are new unto us every morning, and Who, though we have in no wise deserved Thy goodness, dost abundantly provide for all our wants of body and soul: Give us, we pray Thee, Thy Holy Spirit, that we may heartily acknowledge Thy merciful goodness toward us, give thanks for all Thy benefits, and serve Thee in willing obedience; through Jesus Christ, our Lord. Amen.

17—*National.*

A LMIGHTY God, Who hast given us a land wherein we are free to read and hear Thy Word, to confess Thy Name, and to labor together for the extension of Thy Kingdom: Grant, we beseech Thee, that the liberty vouchsafed unto us may be continued to our children and our children's children, and that the power of the Gospel may here abound, to the blessing of all the nations of the earth, and to Thine eternal glory; through Jesus Christ, Thy Son, our Lord. Amen.

18—*For Our Country.*

ALMIGHTY God, Heavenly Father, bless our country that it may be a blessing to the world: Grant us ideals and aspirations which accord with Thy will; grant us sound government and just laws; grant us good education, straightforwardness and justice in our relations with one another; grant us the spirit of service for others and devotion to Thee; preserve us from national wrongs and sins, and keep ever before us the faith and trust of our nation's founders. O God make this a land of Christian homes where Thou art ever loved and served and glorified; through Jesus Christ, Thy Son, our Lord. Amen.

19—*For Missions.*

O GOD, Who hast made of one blood all nations of men to dwell on the face of the whole earth, and didst send Thy blessed Son to preach to them that are far off and to them that are nigh: Grant that the message of the Gospel may be carried into all the world so that all nations and peoples and kindreds and tongues may be brought to the Great Shepherd and united in His fold; through the same Jesus Christ, our Lord. Amen.

20—*The Lord's Day.*

O GOD, our Father, Who art the Light of Life: We thank Thee for the light which greets us at the dawning of this day. Shine with Thy morning upon our souls. Search us as the sun searches the darkness. Scatter the shadows of our selfishness, and make the sky of our feelings and thought clear and bright. May our lives be full of quickening and gladdening light to others, that both we and they may be children of the light and of the day. We would go forth like Thy sun with brightness, seeking only to do good, to learn, obey, and love Thy will, to help and make happy our fellows. Bless to us this day, we pray, for Jesus' sake. Amen.

21—*Hallowing the Lord's Day.*

O LORD God, Heavenly Father, we beseech Thee so to rule and guide us by Thy Holy Spirit, that we hear and receive Thy Holy Word with our whole heart and hallow Thy Holy Day, in order that through Thy Word we also may be sanctified, learn to place all our trust and hope in Jesus Christ Thy Son, and following Him, be led safely through all evil, until through Thy grace, we come to everlasting life; through the same Jesus Christ, Thy Son, our Lord. Amen.

22—*A Morning Prayer.*

O LORD, our Heavenly Father, Almighty and Everlasting God, Who hast safely brought us to the beginning of this day: Defend us in the same with Thy mighty power; and grant that this day we fall into no sin, neither run into any kind of danger; but that all our doings, being ordered by Thy governance, may be righteous in Thy sight; through Jesus Christ, Thy Son, our Lord. Amen.

23—An Evening Prayer.

WE give thanks unto Thee, Heavenly Father, through Jesus Christ, Thy dear Son, that Thou hast this day so graciously protected us, and we beseech Thee to forgive us all our sins, and the wrong which we have done, and by Thy great mercy defend us from all the perils and dangers of this night. Into Thy hands we commend our bodies and souls, and all that is ours. Let Thy holy angel have charge concerning us, that the wicked one have no power over us. Amen.

24—Before the Lesson.

O LORD Jesus, Who hast begotten us by Thy Word, renewed us by Thy Spirit, and dost daily nourish us with Thy grace: Let Thy Holy Spirit be present with us and rest upon us as we read and study Thy Holy Word, that we may do it humbly and reverently, with a mind ready, desirous to learn and to obey, that we may be thoroughly furnished and instructed to every good work, and may strive to keep all Thy holy laws and commandments to the glory of Thy Name. Amen.

25—For the School.

O MERCIFUL and Loving Lord Jesus, bless, we pray Thee, all those in this parish who are diligent in Thy worship along with us in Thy holy house; especially do we invoke Thy blessing upon our school. Teach us all by faith to realize and treasure the blessings in which we are permitted to share, that we may be strengthened for the difficulties of our life in the world, and may be perfected according to Thy will, for the life which is to come. Amen.

26—For Pastors.

MOST Merciful Father, we beseech Thee to send Thy heavenly blessing upon Thy servants, the ministers of Thy Church, that they may be clothed with righteousness, and Thy Word spoken by their mouth may have such success that it may never be spoken in vain; through Jesus Christ, our Lord. Amen.

27—For Those who Teach.

O MOST Merciful God, Who art the Fountain of all truth and grace: Grant, we beseech Thee, to the teachers in this school the gift of the Holy Ghost, and daily increase in them Thy manifold gifts of grace; the spirit of wisdom and understanding, the spirit of counsel and might, the spirit of knowledge and the fear of the Lord; through the same Jesus Christ, our Lord. Amen.

28—For Those who Teach.

O LORD Jesus, lover of men, Who didst take little children in Thy arms and bless them: Grant to all who teach in this school so to love and tenderly protect the little ones committed to their care by word and example they may bring them to Thee, and teach them to know and love Thee and to trust in Thy protection. Amen.

29—*For the Holy Spirit.*

ALMIGHTY God, Who hast given us commandment to pray for the gift of the Holy Ghost: Most heartily we beseech Thee, through Jesus Christ our Advocate, to grant us Thy Holy Spirit, that He may quicken our hearts by Thy saving Word, and lead us into all truth, that He may guide, instruct, enlighten, govern, comfort, and sanctify us unto everlasting life; through the same Jesus Christ, Thy Son, our Lord. Amen.

30—*For Purity.*

ALMIGHTY God, unto Whom all hearts are open, all desires known, and from Whom no secrets are hid: Cleanse the thoughts of our hearts by the inspiration of Thy Holy Spirit, that we may perfectly love Thee, and worthily magnify Thy holy Name; through Jesus Christ, Thy Son, our Lord. Amen.

31—*For Divine Guidance.*

DIRECT us, O Lord, in all our doings, with Thy most gracious favor, and further us with Thy continual help; that in all our works begun, continued, and ended in Thee, we may glorify Thy holy Name; and finally, by Thy mercy, obtain everlasting life; through Jesus Christ, Thy Son, our Lord. Amen.

32—*For Divine Guidance.*

ALMIGHTY and Everlasting God, Who of Thy great mercy in Jesus Christ, Thy Son, dost grant us forgiveness of sin, and all things pertaining to life and godliness: Grant us, we beseech Thee, Thy Holy Spirit, that He may so rule our hearts, that we, being ever mindful of Thy fatherly mercy, may strive to mortify the flesh, and to overcome the world; and, serving Thee in holiness and pureness of living, may give Thee continual thanks for all Thy goodness; through Jesus Christ, Thy Son, our Lord. Amen.

33—*For Protection.*

O ALMIGHTY and most Merciful God, of Thy bountiful goodness keep us, we beseech Thee, from all things that may hurt us; that we, being ready, both in body and soul, may cheerfully accomplish those things that Thou wouldest have done; through Jesus Christ, our Lord. Amen.

34—*For Spiritual Enrichment.*

MOST Merciful Father, open our hearts, we beseech Thee, and grant us to desire with ardent mind those things which please Thee, to search for them wisely, to know them truly, and to fulfill them perfectly, to the honor and glory of Thy Holy Name; through Jesus Christ, our Lord. Amen.

35—*For Joyous Service.*

BLESSED Lord Jesus, Who art ever teaching us by Thy holy example that we are not living for ourselves alone: Help us to find the joy and fullness of right living in serving Thee in others, in finding and cheerfully doing our daily tasks, in helping those who need, in bringing Thee to those who know Thee not. Amen.

36—*For True Religion.*

O GOD, Who art the Author and Giver of all good things: Graft in our hearts the love of Thy Name, increase in us true religion, nourish us with all goodness, and of Thy great mercy keep us in the same; through Jesus Christ, our Lord. Amen.

37—*For Grace to Use the Holy Scriptures.*

ALMIGHTY God, Who hast granted us Thy Holy Word and revealed Thyself to us therein, and through it dost teach us the way of righteous living: Grant us ever to reverence, love, and treasure the Holy Scriptures; implant within us the desire and purpose constantly to read and study them; and as Thou hast promised wisdom to all who seek it, teach us by Thy Holy Spirit wisdom for this earthly life, so that we may grow in grace and in the knowledge of Jesus our Lord, and be made wise unto salvation; through the same Jesus Christ, our Lord. Amen.

38—*For Grace to do God's Will.*

ALMIGHTY God, give us grace that we may cast away the works of darkness, and put upon us the armor of light, now in the time of this mortal life, in which Thy Son Jesus Christ came to visit us in great humility; that in the last day, when He shall come again in His glorious majesty to judge both the quick and the dead, we may rise to the life immortal; through the same Jesus Christ, Our Lord. Amen.

39—*For Love Toward God.*

O GOD, Who hast prepared for them that love Thee such good things as pass man's understandings: Pour into our hearts such love toward Thee, that we, loving Thee above all things, may obtain Thy promises which exceed all that we can desire; through Jesus Christ, our Lord. Amen.

40—*For Grace to Obey God's Commandments.*

O GOD, Who declarest Thine almighty power chiefly in showing mercy and pity: Mercifully grant unto us such a measure of grace that we, running the way of Thy commandments, may obtain Thy gracious promises, and be made partakers of Thy heavenly treasure; through Jesus Christ, our Lord. Amen.

41—*For Right Thoughts and Deeds.*

GRANT to us, Lord, we beseech Thee, the Spirit to think and do always such things as are right; that we, who cannot do anything that is good without Thee, may by Thee be enabled to live according to Thy will; through Jesus Christ, our Lord. Amen.

42—*For Contentment.*

ALMIGHTY God, our Heavenly Father, Who dost feed the birds and clothe the flowers, and Who carest for us as a father for his children: We beseech Thee, guard us against distrust and vain over-carefulness, and help us, through Thy Holy Spirit, to live to the hallowing of Thy Name, the coming of Thy Kingdom, and the doing of Thy Will, so that we may cast all our care on Thee, and in unwavering faith abide trustingly in Thee; through Jesus Christ, our Lord. Amen.

43—*For the Sick or Sorrowing.*

OUR Father, we remember before Thee this day those who are absent from us because of *sickness* (*sorrow*) : Be present with them, we pray, and bless them in their need, that they and we may render thanks to Thee for Thy lovingkindness; through Jesus Christ our Lord. Amen.

44—*General (May be used on Children's Day).*

O LORD Jesus, Who didst love the little children and lay Thy hands upon them in blessing: We thank Thee for Thy love for us and pray Thee to help us daily to learn to love Thee more and more; open our hearts and dwell in them; fill our minds with Thy truth; keep our feet from wandering from Thy way; make our hands gentle, willing to give and bless; teach us to be obedient, truthful, pure, and faithful, so that in Thee we may be a blessing to others and live to Thy glory.

45—*For Catechumens.*

ALMIGHTY and Everlasting God, Who dost always multiply Thy Church, and with Thy light and grace dost strengthen the hearts of those whom Thou hast regenerated, confirming unto them Thy covenant and faithfulness: Grant unto our Catechumens increase both of faith and knowledge, that they may rejoice in their baptism and really and heartily renew their covenant with Thee; through Jesus Christ, Thy Son, our Lord. Amen.

46—*For Confirmands.*

O LORD Jesus, Who hast promised that Thou wilt confess before Thy Father in heaven those who confess Thee before men: Grant to those who have sealed their faith before Thy altar, and have been admitted into the fellowship of Thy religion, grace and strength ever to put away from them all things contrary to their profession and in humble and persevering faith to follow after all things pleasing to Thee; through Jesus Christ, our Lord. Amen.

47—*For Our Parents.*

ALMIGHTY God, Who hast strictly commanded us to honor our father and our mother next unto Thee: Grant us of Thy goodness and grace, so to love and honor our parents, to fear and to obey them, to help and to pray for them, as Thou in Thy holy Word hast directed and charged us to do, that both in their life, and at their death their souls may bless us, and by Thy fatherly mercy we may obtain that blessing which Thou hast promised to those that honor their father and their mother; and that Thou, seeing our reverence and love for them, mayest become our loving Father, and number us among those Thy children who are heirs of Thy glorious Kingdom; through Thy holy Child, Jesus Christ, our Lord. Amen.

48—*For Our Neighbors.*

OUR Heavenly Father, Who dost surround our daily life with familiar things and well-known faces, and dost teach us to love our neighbor as ourself: We pray for all those among whom we live, our neighbors and acquaintances, and for those with whom we work, or study, or play, as well as for our best friends and near relations, humbly committing them all to Thy favor and care, beseeching Thee to guard and preserve them and us from all dangers of body and soul, that by Thy grace and ever present help we may so live now that we may dwell with Thee in the life that knows no ending; through Jesus Christ, Thy Son, our Way and our Life. Amen.

49—*For the Holy Ministry.*

O ALMIGHTY God, look in mercy upon the world redeemed by the blood of Thy dear Son, and raise up in our school those who will offer themselves to Thee for Thy service and go forth in Thy Name to do the work of the ministry that perishing souls may be rescued and Thy glorious triumph hastened; through Jesus Christ, Thy Son, our Lord. Amen.

50—*For the Church and its Ministry.*

O LORD Jesus Christ, Who hast founded the Church for Thyself, and hast promised to dwell in it forever: Enlighten and sanctify it, we beseech Thee, by Thy Word and Spirit; endue all pastors with Thy grace that they may with confidence and joy guard and feed Thy sheep; bless all who serve Thee in the government of Thy Church, in the care of Thy poor, in the ministry of Thy praise, and in the teaching of the young. Strengthen them in their labors; give them courage to witness a good confession, and cause Thy Church to increase more and more that every knee may bow before Thee, and every tongue confess Thee, Lord to the glory of God the Father. Amen.

51—*For the Ministry of Mercy.*

O LORD Jesus Christ in Whose service holy women of old ministered to the needy: We beseech Thee to raise up those in our midst who will consecrate themselves in body, mind and soul to the labors of Christian love and mercy for the glory of Thy holy Name. Amen.

52—*A General Prayer.*

OUR Father, we pray Thee, give us clean hands, clean words, and clean thoughts; help us to stand for the hard right against the easy wrong; save us from habits that harm; teach us to work as hard and play as fair in Thy sight alone as if all the world were looking on; forgive us when we are unkind, and help us to forgive those who

31

are unkind to us; keep us ready to help others even though it be at some cost to ourselves; send us chances to do a little good every day, and to grow more like Thy dear Son; this we humbly ask in His Name. Amen.

53—A General Thanksgiving.

ALMIGHTY God, our Heavenly Father, we, Thine unworthy servants, do give Thee most humble and hearty thanks for all Thy goodness and lovingkindness to us, and to all men. We bless Thee for our creation, preservation, and all the blessings of this life; but above all, for Thine inestimable love in the redemption of the world by our Lord and Saviour Jesus Christ, for the means of grace, and for the hope of glory. And we beseech Thee, give us that due sense of all Thy mercies, that our hearts may be unfeignedly thankful, and that we may show forth Thy praise, not only with our lips, but in our lives; that walking before Thee in holiness and righteousness all our days, we may enjoy the testimony of a good conscience and the hope of Thy favor, be sustained and comforted under the troubles of this life, and finally be received into Thine everlasting kingdom, through Thine infinite mercy in Jesus Christ, our Lord. Amen.

54—For Answer to Prayer.

ALMIGHTY God, Who hast given us grace at this time with one accord to make our common supplications unto Thee; and dost promise that when two or three are gathered together in Thy Name, Thou wilt grant their requests: Fulfill now, O Lord, the desires and petitions of Thy servants, as may be most expedient for them; granting us in this world knowledge of Thy truth, and in the world to come life everlasting; Who livest and reignest with the Father and the Holy Ghost, One God, world without end. Amen.

✠

THE PSALMS

BLESSED is the man that walketh not in the counsel of the ungodly: nor standeth in the way of sinners, nor sitteth in the seat of the scornful.

But his delight is in the law of the LORD: and in His law doth he meditate day and night.

And he shall be like a tree planted by the rivers of water: that bringeth forth his fruit in his season;

His leaf also shall not wither: and whatsoever he doeth shall prosper.

The ungodly are not so: but are like the chaff which the wind driveth away.

Therefore the ungodly shall not stand in the judgment: nor sinners in the congregation of the righteous.

For the LORD knoweth the way of the righteous: but the way of the ungodly shall perish.

Psalm 8. *Domine, Dominus noster.*

O LORD, our Lord, how excellent is Thy Name in all the earth: Who hast set Thy glory above the heavens.

Out of the mouth of babes and sucklings hast Thou ordained strength because of Thine enemies: that Thou mightest still the enemy and the avenger.

When I consider Thy heavens, the work of Thy fingers: the moon and the stars, which Thou hast ordained;

What is man, that Thou art mindful of him: and the son of man, that Thou visitest him?

For Thou hast made him a little lower than the angels: and hast crowned him with glory and honor.

Thou madest him to have dominion over the works of Thy hands: Thou hast put all things under his feet;

All sheep and oxen: yea, and the beasts of the field;

The fowl of the air, and the fish of the sea: and whatsoever passeth through the paths of the seas.

O LORD our Lord: how excellent is Thy Name in all the earth.

Psalm 19. *Cœli enarrant.*

THE heavens declare the glory of God: and the firmament showeth His handywork.

Day unto day uttereth speech: and night unto night showeth knowledge.

There is no speech nor language: where their voice is not heard.

Their line is gone out through all the earth: and their words to the end of the world.

In them hath He set a tabernacle for the sun: which is as a bridegroom coming out of his chamber, and rejoiceth as a strong man to run a race.

His going forth is from the end of the heaven, and his circuit unto the ends of it: and there is nothing hid from the heat thereof.

The law of the LORD is perfect, converting the soul: the testimony of the LORD is sure, making wise the simple.

The statutes of the LORD are right, rejoicing the heart: the commandment of the Lord is pure, enlightening the eyes.

The fear of the LORD is clean, enduring forever: the judgments of the LORD are true and righteous altogether.

More to be desired are they than gold, yea, than much fine gold: sweeter also than honey and the honeycomb.

Moreover by them is Thy servant warned: and in keeping of them there is great reward.

Who can understand his errors: cleanse Thou me from secret faults.

Keep back Thy servant also from presumptuous sins, let them not have dominion over me: then shall I be upright, and I shall be innocent from the great transgression.

Let the words of my mouth, and the meditation of my heart, be acceptable in Thy sight: O LORD, my Strength, and my Redeemer.

PSALM 23. *Dominus regit me.*

THE LORD is my Shepherd: I shall not want.

He maketh me to lie down in green pastures: He leadeth me beside the still waters.

He restoreth my soul: He leadeth me in the paths of righteousness for His Name's sake.

Yea, though I walk through the valley of the shadow of death, I will fear no evil: for Thou art with me, Thy rod and Thy staff they comfort me.

Thou preparest a table before me in the presence of mine enemies: Thou anointest my head with oil, my cup runneth over.

Surely goodness and mercy shall follow me all the days of my life: and I will dwell in the house of the LORD for ever.

PSALM 24. *Domini est terra.*

THE earth is the LORD'S, and the fulness thereof: the world, and they that dwell therein.

For He hath founded it upon the seas: and established it upon the floods.

Who shall ascend into the hill of the LORD: or who shall stand in His holy place?

He that hath clean hands, and a pure heart: who hath not lifted up his soul unto vanity, nor sworn deceitfully.

He shall receive the blessing from the LORD: and righteousness from the God of his salvation.

This is the generation of them that seek Him: that seek thy face, O Jacob.

Lift up your heads, O ye gates, and be ye lift up, ye everlasting doors: and the King of glory shall come in.

Who is this King of glory: The LORD strong and mighty, the LORD mighty in battle.

Lift up your heads, O ye gates, even lift them up, ye everlasting doors: and the King of glory shall come in.

Who is this King of glory: The LORD of hosts, He is the King of glory.

PSALM 27. *Dominus illuminatio.*

THE LORD is my Light and my Salvation, whom shall I fear: the LORD is the strength of my life, of whom shall I be afraid?

When the wicked, even mine enemies and my foes, came upon me to eat up my flesh: they stumbled and fell.

Though an host should encamp against me, my heart shall not fear: though war should rise against me, in this will I be confident.

One thing have I desired of the LORD, that will I seek after: that I may dwell in the house of the LORD all the days of my life, to behold the beauty of the LORD, and to enquire in His temple.

For in the time of trouble He shall hide me in His pavilion: in the secret of His tabernacle shall He hide me, He shall set me up upon a rock.

And now shall mine head be lifted up: above mine enemies round about me;

Therefore will I offer in His tabernacle sacrifices of joy: I will sing, yea, I will sing praises unto the LORD.

Hear, O LORD, when I cry with my voice: have mercy also upon me, and answer me.

When Thou saidst, Seek ye My face: my heart said unto Thee, Thy face, LORD, will I seek.

Hide not Thy face far from me: put not Thy servant away in anger.

Thou hast been my help: leave me not, neither forsake me, O God of my salvation.

When my father and my mother forsake me: then the LORD will take me up.

Teach me Thy way, O LORD: and lead me in a plain path, because of mine enemies.

Deliver me not over unto the will of mine enemies: for false witnesses are risen up against me, and such as breathe out cruelty.

I had fainted: unless I had believed to see the goodness of the LORD in the land of the living.

Wait on the LORD: be of good courage, and He shall strengthen thine heart, wait, I say, on the LORD.

PSALM 32. *Beati quorum.*

[*A Penitential Psalm.*]

BLESSED is he whose transgression is forgiven: whose sin is covered.
Blessed is the man unto whom the LORD imputeth not iniquity: and in whose spirit there is no guile.

When I kept silence: my bones waxed old through my roaring all the day long.

For day and night Thy hand was heavy upon me: my moisture is turned into the drought of summer.

I acknowledged my sin unto Thee: and mine iniquity have I not hid

I said, I will confess my transgressions unto the LORD: and Thou forgavest the iniquity of my sin.

For this shall every one that is godly pray unto Thee in a time when Thou mayest be found: surely in the floods of great waters they shall not come nigh unto him.

Thou art my hiding place, Thou shalt preserve me from trouble: Thou shalt compass me about with songs of deliverance.

I will instruct thee and teach thee in the way which thou shalt go: I will guide thee with mine eye.

Be ye not as the horse, or as the mule, which have no understanding: whose mouth must be held in with bit and bridle, lest they come near unto thee.

Many sorrows shall be to the wicked: but he that trusteth in the LORD, mercy shall compass him about.

Be glad in the LORD, and rejoice, ye righteous: and shout for joy, all ye that are upright in heart.

PSALM 36. *Dixit injustus.*

THE transgression of the wicked saith within my heart: that there is no fear of God before his eyes.

For he flattereth himself in his own eyes: until his iniquity be found to be hateful.

The words of his mouth are iniquity and deceit: he hath left off to be wise, and to do good.

Thy mercy, O LORD, is in the heavens: and Thy faithfulness reacheth unto the clouds.

Thy righteousness is like the great mountains, Thy judgments are a great deep: O LORD, Thou preservest man and beast.

How excellent is Thy lovingkindness, O God: therefore the children of men put their trust under the shadow of Thy wings.

They shall be abundantly satisfied with the fatness of Thy house: and Thou shalt make them drink of the river of Thy pleasures.

For with Thee is the fountain of life: in Thy light shall we see light.

O continue Thy lovingkindness unto them that know Thee: and Thy righteousness to the upright in heart.

Let not the foot of pride come against me: and let not the hand of the wicked remove me.

There are the workers of iniquity fallen: they are cast down, and shall not be able to rise.

PSALM 46. *Deus noster refugium.*

GOD is our Refuge and Strength: a very present help in trouble.
Therefore will not we fear, though the earth be removed: and though the mountains be carried into the midst of the sea.

Though the waters thereof roar and be troubled: though the mountains shake with the swelling thereof.

There is a river, the streams whereof shall make glad the city of God: the holy place of the tabernacles of the Most High.

God is in the midst of her, she shall not be moved: God shall help her, and that right early.

The heathen raged, the kingdoms were moved: He uttered His voice, the earth melted.

The Lord of hosts is with us: the God of Jacob is our Refuge.

Come, behold the works of the LORD: what desolations He hath made in the earth.

He maketh wars to cease unto the end of the earth: He breaketh the bow, and cutteth the spear in sunder, He burneth the chariot in the fire.

Be still, and know that I am God: I will be exalted among the heathen, I will be exalted in the earth.

The LORD of hosts is with us: the God of Jacob is our Refuge.

PSALM 48. *Magnus Dominus.*

GREAT is the LORD, and greatly to be praised: in the city of our God, in the mountain of His holiness.

Beautiful for situation, the joy of the whole earth, is mount Zion: on the sides of the north, the city of the great King.

God is known in her palaces: for a refuge.

For, lo, the kings were assembled: they passed by together.

They saw it, and so they marveled: they were troubled, and hasted away.

Fear took hold upon them there, and pain: as of a woman in travail.

Thou breakest the ships of Tarshish: with an east wind.

As we have heard, so have we seen in the city of the LORD of hosts, in the city of our God: God will establish it for ever.

We have thought of Thy lovingkindness, O God: in the midst of Thy temple.

According to Thy Name, O God, so is Thy praise unto the ends of the earth: Thy right hand is full of righteousness.

Let mount Zion rejoice, let the daughters of Judah be glad: because of Thy judgments.

Walk about Zion, and go round about her: tell the towers thereof.

Mark ye well her bulwarks, consider her palaces: that ye may tell it to the generation following.

For this God is our God for ever and ever: He will be our Guide even unto death.

PSALM 63. *Deus, Deus meus.*

O GOD, Thou art my God: early will I seek Thee;

My soul thirsteth for Thee: my flesh longeth for Thee in a dry and thirsty land, where no water is;

To see Thy power and Thy glory: so as I have seen Thee in the sanctuary.

Because Thy lovingkindness is better than life: my lips shall praise Thee.

Thus will I bless Thee while I live: I will lift up my hands in Thy Name.

My soul shall be satisfied as with marrow and fatness: and my mouth shall praise Thee with joyful lips;

When I remember Thee upon my bed: and meditate on Thee in the night watches.

Because Thou hast been my help: therefore in the shadow of Thy wings will I rejoice.

My soul followeth hard after Thee: Thy right hand upholdeth me.

PSALM 67. *Deus misereatur nostri.*

GOD be merciful unto us, and bless us: and cause His face to shine upon us;

That Thy way may be known upon earth: Thy saving health among all nations.

Let the people praise Thee, O God: let all the people praise Thee.

O let the nations be glad and sing for joy: for Thou shalt judge the people righteously, and govern the nations upon earth.

Let the people praise Thee, O God: let all the people praise Thee.

Then shall the earth yield her increase: and God, even our own God shall bless us.

God shall bless us: and all the ends of the earth shall fear Him.

PSALM 72. *Deus, judicium.*

GIVE the king Thy judgments, O God: and Thy righteousness unto the king's son.

He shall judge Thy people with righteousness: and Thy poor with judgment.

The mountains shall bring peace to the people: and the little hills, by righteousness.

He shall judge the poor of the people, He shall save the children of the needy: and shall break in pieces the oppressor.

They shall fear Thee as long as the sun and moon endure: throughout all generations.

He shall come down like rain upon the mown grass: as showers that water the earth.

In His days shall the righteous flourish: and abundance of peace so long as the moon endureth.

He shall have dominion also from sea to sea: and from the river unto the ends of the earth .

They that dwell in the wilderness shall bow before Him: and His enemies shall lick the dust.

The kings of Tarshish and of the isles shall bring presents: the kings of Sheba and Seba shall offer gifts .

Yea, all kings shall fall down before Him: all nations shall serve Him.

For He shall deliver the needy when he crieth: the poor also, and him that hath no helper.

He shall spare the poor and needy: and shall save the souls of the needy.

He shall redeem their soul from deceit and violence: and precious shall their blood be in His sight.

And He shall live, and to Him shall be given of the gold of Sheba: prayer also shall be made for Him continually, and daily shall He be praised.

There shall be an handful of corn in the earth upon the top of the mountains: the fruit thereof shall shake like Lebanon, and they of the city shall flourish like grass of the earth.

His Name shall endure for ever, His Name shall be continued as long as the sun: and men shall be blessed in Him, all nations shall call Him blessed.

Blessed be the LORD God, the God of Israel: Who only doeth wondrous things.

And blessed be His glorious Name for ever: and let the whole earth be filled with His glory. Amen, and Amen.

PSALM 85. *Benedixisti, Domine.*

L ORD, Thou hast been favorable unto Thy land: Thou hast brought back the captivity of Jacob.

Thou hast forgiven the iniquity of Thy people: Thou hast covered all their sin.

Thou hast taken away all Thy wrath: Thou hast turned Thyself from the fierceness of Thine anger.

Turn us, O God of our salvation: and cause Thine anger toward us to cease.

Wilt Thou be angry with us for ever: wilt Thou draw out Thine anger to all generations?

Wilt Thou not revive us again: that Thy people may rejoice in Thee?

Show us Thy mercy, O LORD: and grant us Thy salvation.

I will hear what God the LORD will speak: for He will speak peace unto His people, and to His saints, but let them not turn again to folly.

Surely His salvation is nigh them that fear Him: that glory may dwell in our land.

Mercy and truth are met together: righteousness and peace have kissed each other.

Truth shall spring out of the earth: and righteousness shall look down from heaven.

Yea, the LORD shall give that which is good: and our land shall yield her increase.

Righteousness shall go before Him: and shall set us in the way of His steps.

PSALM 91. *Qui habitat.*

H E that dwelleth in the secret place of the Most High: shall abide under the shadow of the Almighty.

I will say of the LORD, He is my Refuge and my Fortress: my God; in Him will I trust.

Surely He shall deliver thee from the snare of the fowler: and from the noisome pestilence.

He shall cover thee with His feathers, and under His wings shalt thou trust: His truth shall be thy shield and buckler.

Thou shalt not be afraid for the terror by night: nor for the arrow that flieth by day;

Nor for the pestilence that walketh in darkness: nor for the destruction that wasteth at noonday.

A thousand shall fall at thy side, and ten thousand at thy right hand: but it shall not come nigh thee.

Only with thine eyes shalt thou behold: and see the reward of the wicked.

Because thou hast made the Lord, which is my Refuge: even the Most High, thy habitation;

There shall no evil befall thee: neither shall any plague come nigh thy dwelling.

For He shall give His angels charge over thee: to keep thee in all thy ways.

They shall bear thee up in their hands: lest thou dash thy foot against a stone.

Thou shalt tread upon the lion and adder: the young lion and the dragon shalt thou trample under feet.

Because he hath set his love upon Me, therefore will I deliver him: I will set him on high, because he hath known My Name.

He shall call upon Me, and I will answer him: I will be with him in trouble, I will deliver him, and honor him.

With long life will I satisfy him: and show him My salvation.

PSALM 92. *Bonum est confiteri.*

IT is a good thing to give thanks unto the LORD: and to sing praises unto Thy Name, O Most High.

To show forth Thy lovingkindness in the morning: and Thy faithfulness every night.

Upon an instrument of ten strings, and upon the psaltery: upon the harp with a solemn sound.

For Thou, LORD, hast made me glad through Thy work: I will triumph in the works of Thy hands.

O LORD, how great are Thy works: and Thy thoughts are very deep.

When the wicked spring as the grass, and when all the workers of iniquity do flourish: it is that they shall be destroyed for ever, but Thou, LORD, art most high for evermore.

For, lo, Thine enemies, O LORD, for, lo, Thine enemies shall perish: all the workers of iniquity shall be scattered.

The righteous shall flourish like the palm tree: he shall grow like a cedar in Lebanon.

Those that be planted in the house of the LORD: shall flourish in the courts of our God.

They shall still bring forth fruit in old age: they shall be fat and flourishing.

To show that the LORD is upright, He is my Rock: and there is no unrighteousness in Him.

PSALM 93. *Dominus regnavit.*

THE LORD reigneth, He is clothed with majesty: the LORD is clothed with strength, wherewith He hath girded Himself.

The world also is stablished: that it cannot be moved.

Thy throne is established of old: Thou art from everlasting.

The floods have lifted up, O LORD, the floods have lifted up their voice: the floods lift up their waves.

The LORD on high is mightier than the noise of many waters: yea, than the mighty waves of the sea.

Thy testimonies are very sure: holiness becometh Thine house, O LORD, for ever.

PSALM 95. *Venite, exultemus.*

O COME, let us sing unto the LORD: let us make a joyful noise to the Rock of our salvation.

Let us come before His presence with thanksgiving: and make a joyful noise unto Him with psalms.

For the LORD is a great God: and a great King above all gods.

In His hand are the deep places of the earth: the strength of the hills is His also.

The sea is His, and He made it: and His hands formed the dry land.

O come, let us worship and bow down: let us kneel before the LORD our Maker.

For He is our God: and we are the people of His pasture, and the sheep of His hand.

PSALM 98. *Cantate Domino.*

O SING unto the LORD a new song: for He hath done marvelous things;

His right hand, and His holy arm: hath gotten Him the victory.

The LORD hath made known His salvation: His righteousness hath He openly showed in the sight of the heathen.

He hath remembered His mercy and His truth toward the house of Israel: all the ends of the earth have seen the salvation of our God.

Make a joyful noise unto the LORD, all the earth: make a loud noise, and sing praise.

Sing unto the LORD with the harp: with the harp, and the voice of a psalm.

With trumpets and sound of cornet: make a joyful noise before the LORD, the King.

Let the sea roar, and the fulness thereof: the world, and they that dwell therein.

Let the floods clap their hands, let the hills be joyful together before the LORD: for He cometh to judge the earth;

With righteousness shall He judge the world: and the people with equity.

PSALM 100. *Jubilate Deo.*

MAKE a joyful noise unto the LORD, all ye lands: Serve the LORD with gladness, come before His presence with singing.

Know ye that the LORD He is God: it is He that hath made us, and not we ourselves, we are His people, and the sheep of His pasture.

Enter into His gates with thanksgiving, and into His courts with praise: be thankful unto Him, and bless His Name.

For the LORD is good, His mercy is everlasting: and His truth endureth to all generations.

PSALM 103. *Benedic, anima mea, Domino, et omnia.*

BLESS the LORD, O my soul: and all that is within me, bless His holy Name.

Bless the LORD, O my soul: and forget not all His benefits;

Who forgiveth all thine iniquities: Who healeth all thy diseases;

Who redeemeth thy life from destruction: Who crowneth thee with lovingkindness and tender mercies;

Who satisfieth thy mouth with good things: so that thy youth is renewed like the eagle's.

The LORD executeth righteousness and judgment: for all that are oppressed.

He made known His ways unto Moses: His acts unto the children of Israel.

The LORD is merciful and gracious: slow to anger, and plenteous in mercy.

He will not always chide: neither will He keep His anger forever.

He hath not dealt with us after our sins: nor rewarded us according to our iniquities.

For as the heaven is high above the earth: so great is His mercy toward them that fear Him.

As far as the east is from the west: so far hath He removed our transgressions from us.

Like as a father pitieth his children: so the LORD pitieth them that fear Him.

For He knoweth our frame: He remembereth that we are dust.

As for man, his days are as grass: as a flower of the field, so he flourisheth.

For the wind passeth over it, and it is gone: and the place thereof shall know it no more.

But the mercy of the LORD is from everlasting to everlasting upon them that fear Him: and His righteousness unto children's children;

To such as keep His covenant: and to those that remember His commandments to do them.

The LORD hath prepared His throne in the heavens: and His kingdom ruleth over all.

Bless the LORD, ye His angels, that excel in strength: that do His commandments, harkening unto the voice of His Word.

Bless ye the LORD, all ye His hosts: ye ministers of His, that do His pleasure.

Bless the LORD, all His works in all places of His dominion; bless the LORD, O my soul.

PSALM 111. *Confitebor tibi.*

PRAISE ye the LORD. I will praise the LORD with my whole heart: in the assembly of the upright, and in the congregation.

The works of the LORD are great: sought out of all them that have pleasure therein.

His work is honorable and glorious: and His righteousness endureth for ever.

He hath made His wonderful works to be remembered: the LORD is gracious and full of compassion.

He hath given meat unto them that fear Him: He will ever be mindful of His covenant.

He hath showed His people the power of His works: that He may give them the heritage of the heathen.

The works of His hands are verity and judgment: all His commandments are sure.

They stand fast for ever and ever: and are done in truth and uprightness.

He sent redemption unto His people: He hath commanded His covenant for ever, holy and reverend is His Name.

The fear of the LORD is the beginning of wisdom: a good understanding have all they that do His commandments, His praise endureth for ever.

PSALM 116. *Dilexi, quoniam.*

I LOVE the LORD: because He hath heard my voice and my supplications.

Because He hath inclined His ear unto me: therefore will I call upon Him as long as I live.

The sorrows of death compassed me, and the pains of hell gat hold upon me: I found trouble and sorrow.

Then called I upon the Name of the LORD: O LORD, I beseech Thee, deliver my soul.

Gracious is the LORD, and righteous: yea, our God is merciful.

The LORD preserveth the simple: I was brought low, and He helped me.

Return unto thy rest, O my soul: for the LORD hath dealt bountifully with thee.

For Thou hast delivered my soul from death: mine eyes from tears, and my feet from falling.

I will walk before the LORD: in the land of the living.

I believed, therefore have I spoken, I was greatly afflicted: I said in my haste, All men are liars.

What shall I render unto the LORD: for all His benefits toward me?

I will take the cup of salvation: and call upon the Name of the LORD.

I will pay my vows unto the LORD now: in the presence of all His people.

Precious in the sight of the LORD: is the death of His saints.

O LORD, truly I am Thy servant: I am Thy servant, and the son of Thine handmaid, Thou hast loosed my bonds.

I will offer to Thee the sacrifice of thanksgiving: and will call upon the Name of the LORD.

I will pay my vows unto the LORD now in the presence of all His people: in the courts of the LORD'S house, in the midst of thee, O Jerusalem. Praise ye the Lord.

PSALM 118. *Confitemini Domino.*

O GIVE thanks unto the LORD, for He is good: because His mercy endureth for ever.

Let Israel now say: that His mercy endureth for ever.

Let the house of Aaron now say: that His mercy endureth for ever.

Let them now that fear the LORD say: that His mercy endureth for ever.

I called upon the LORD in distress: the LORD answered me, and set me in a large place.

The LORD is on my side, I will not fear: what can man do unto me?

The LORD taketh my part with them that help me: therefore shall I see my desire upon them that hate me.

It is better to trust in the LORD: than to put confidence in man.

It is better to trust in the LORD: than to put confidence in princes.

All nations compassed me about: but in the Name of the LORD will I destroy them.

They compassed me about, yea, they compassed me about: but in the Name of the LORD I will destroy them.

They compassed me about like bees, they are quenched as the fire of thorns: for in the Name of the LORD I will destroy them.

Thou hast thrust sore at me that I might fall: but the LORD helped me.

The LORD is my strength and song: and is become my salvation.

The voice of rejoicing and salvation is in the tabernacles of the righteous: the right hand of the LORD doeth valiantly.

The right hand of the LORD is exalted: the right hand of the LORD doeth valiantly.

I shall not die, but live: and declare the works of the LORD.

The LORD hath chastened me sore: but He hath not given me over unto death.

Open to me the gates of righteousness: I will go into them, and I will praise the LORD:

This gate of the LORD: into which the righteous shall enter.

I will praise Thee, for Thou hast heard me: and art become my salvation.

The stone which the builders refused: is become the head stone of the corner.

This is the LORD'S doing: it is marvelous in our eyes.

This is the day which the LORD hath made: we will rejoice and be glad in it.

Save now, I beseech Thee, O LORD: O LORD, I beseech Thee, send now prosperity.

Blessed be He that cometh in the Name of the LORD: we have blessed you out of the house of the LORD.

God is the LORD, which hath showed us light: bind the sacrifice with cords, even unto the horns of the altar.

Thou art my God, and I will praise Thee: Thou art my God, I will exalt Thee.

O give thanks unto the LORD, for He is good: for His mercy endureth for ever.

PSALM 121. *Levavi oculos.*

I WILL lift up mine eyes unto the hills: from whence cometh my help.
My help cometh from the LORD: which made heaven and earth.

He will not suffer thy foot to be moved: He that keepeth thee will not slumber.

Behold, He that keepeth Israel: shall neither slumber nor sleep.

The LORD is thy keeper: the LORD is thy shade upon thy right hand.

The sun shall not smite thee by day: nor the moon by night.

The LORD shall preserve thee from all evil: He shall preserve thy soul.

The LORD shall preserve thy going out and thy coming in: from this time forth, and even for evermore.

PSALM 122. *Lœtatus sum.*

I WAS glad when they said unto me: Let us go into the house of the the LORD.

Our feet shall stand within thy gates: O Jerusalem.

Jerusalem is builded: as a city that is compact together;

Whither the tribes go up, the tribes of the LORD: unto the testimony of Israel, to give thanks unto the Name of the LORD.

For there are set thrones of judgment: the thrones of the house of David.

Pray for the peace of Jerusalem: they shall prosper that love thee.

Peace be within thy walls: and prosperity within thy palaces.

For my brethren and companions' sakes: I will now say, Peace be within thee.

Because of the house of the LORD our God: I will seek thy good.

PSALM 130. *De profundis.*

[A Penitential Psalm.]

O UT of the depths: have I cried unto Thee, O LORD.
LORD, hear my voice: let Thine ears be attentive to the voice of my supplications.

If Thou, LORD, shouldest mark iniquities: O LORD, who shall stand?

But there is forgiveness with Thee: that Thou mayest be feared.

I wait for the LORD, my soul doth wait: and in His Word do I hope.

My soul waiteth for the LORD more than they that watch for the morning: I say, more than they that watch for the morning.

Let Israel hope in the LORD, for with the LORD there is mercy: and with Him is plenteous redemption.

And He shall redeem Israel: from all his iniquities.

PSALM 145. *Exaltabo te, Deus.*

I WILL extol Thee, my God, O King: and I will bless Thy Name for ever and ever.

Every day will I bless Thee: and I will praise Thy Name for ever and ever.

Great is the LORD, and greatly to be praised: and His greatness is unsearchable.

One generation shall praise Thy works to another: and shall declare Thy mighty acts.

I will speak of the glorious honor of Thy majesty: and of Thy wondrous works.

And men shall speak of the might of Thy terrible acts: and I will declare Thy greatness.

They shall abundantly utter the memory of Thy great goodness: and shall sing of Thy righteousness.

The LORD is gracious, and full of compassion: slow to anger, and of great mercy.

The LORD is good to all: and His tender mercies are over all His works.

All Thy works shall praise Thee, O LORD: and Thy saints shall bless Thee.

They shall speak of the glory of Thy kingdom: and talk of Thy power;

To make known to the sons of men His mighty acts: and the glorious majesty of His kingdom.

Thy kingdom is an everlasting kingdom: and Thy dominion endureth throughout all generations.

The LORD upholdeth all that fall: and raiseth up all those that be bowed down.

The eyes of all wait upon Thee: and Thou givest them their meat in due season.

Thou openest Thine hand: and satisfiest the desire of every living thing.

The LORD is righteous in all His ways: and holy in all His works.

The LORD is nigh unto all them that call upon Him: to all that call upon Him in truth.

He will fulfill the desire of them that fear Him: He also will hear their cry, and will save them.

The LORD preserveth all them that love Him: but all the wicked will He destroy.

My mouth shall speak the praise of the LORD: and let all flesh bless His holy Name for ever and ever.

PSALM 146. *Lauda, anima mea.*

PRAISE ye the LORD: Praise the LORD, O my soul.

While I live will I praise the LORD: I will sing praises unto my God while I have any being.

Put not your trust in princes: nor in the son of man, in whom there is no help.

His breath goeth forth, he returneth to his earth: in that very day his thoughts perish.

Happy is he that hath the God of Jacob for his help: whose hope is in the LORD his God;

Which made heaven and earth, the sea, and all that therein is: which keepeth truth for ever;

Which executeth judgment for the oppressed: which giveth food to the hungry.

The LORD looseth the prisoners: the LORD openeth the eyes of the blind;

46

The LORD raiseth them that are bowed down: the LORD loveth the righteous;

The LORD preserveth the strangers, He relieveth the fatherless and widow: but the way of the wicked He turneth upside down.

The LORD shall reign for ever, even thy God, O Zion, unto all generations: Praise ye the LORD.

PSALM 148. *Laudate Dominum, de cœlis.*

PRAISE ye the LORD. Praise ye the LORD from the heavens: praise Him in the heights.

Praise ye Him, all His angels: praise ye Him, all his hosts.

Praise ye Him, sun and moon: praise Him, all ye stars of light.

Praise Him, ye heavens of heavens: and ye waters that be above the heavens.

Let them praise the Name of the LORD: for He commanded, and they were created.

He hath also stablished them for ever and ever: He hath made a decree which shall not pass.

Praise the LORD from the earth: ye dragons, and all deeps;

Fire, and hail, snow, and vapors: stormy wind fulfilling His Word;

Mountains, and all hills: fruitful trees, and all cedars;

Beasts, and all cattle: creeping things, and flying fowl;

Kings of the earth, and all people: princes, and all judges of the earth;

Both young men, and maidens: old men, and children;

Let them praise the Name of the LORD: for His Name alone is excellent, His glory is above the earth and heaven.

He also exalteth the horn of His people, the praise of all His saints: even of the children of Israel, a people near unto Him. Praise ye the LORD.

PSALM 150. *Laudate Dominum in sanctis ejus.*

PRAISE ye the LORD. Praise God in His sanctuary: praise Him in the firmament of His power.

Praise Him for His mighty acts: praise Him according to His excellent greatness.

Praise Him with the sound of the trumpet: praise Him with psaltery and harp.

Praise Him with the timbrel and dance: praise Him with stringed instruments and organs.

Praise Him upon the loud cymbals: praise Him upon the high sounding cymbals.

Let every thing that hath breath praise the LORD: Praise ye the LORD.

GLORY BE TO THE FATHER, AND TO THE SON, AND TO THE HOLY GHOST: AS IT WAS IN THE BEGINNING, IS NOW, AND EVER SHALL BE, WORLD WITHOUT END. AMEN.

TABLE OF PROPER PSALMS FOR FESTIVALS AND SEASONS

Festivals and Seasons	Psalms
ADVENT	8, 19, 24, 93, 98, 111, 122, 145
CHRISTMAS	19, 72, 93, 98, 148
CIRCUMCISION (NEW YEAR)	8, 72, 122
EPIPHANY	19, 46, 48, 67, 72, 100
TRANSFIGURATION	8, 93
SEPTUAGESIMA, SEXAGESIMA, QUINQUAGESIMA	27, 67, 116, 145
ASH WEDNESDAY	32, 130
LENT	27, 32, 34, 67, 91, 122, 130
PALM SUNDAY	24
HOLY WEEK	27, 67
EASTER DAY	8, 98, 111, 118
EASTERTIDE	23, 98, 100, 111, 118, 146, 148, 150
ASCENSION DAY	8, 24, 27, 148, 150
WHITSUNDAY	19, 48, 145
FESTIVAL OF THE HOLY TRINITY	8, 93, 111, 148, 150
FESTIVAL OF THE REFORMATION	24, 46, 48, 116
APOSTLES, EVANGELISTS AND MARTYRS	1, 19, 121, 146, 148
ST. MICHAEL	148
THE CHRISTIAN LIFE	1, 23, 32, 46, 48, 91, 121
CROSS AND COMFORT	23, 27, 91, 121, 130
DEATH AND BURIAL	23, 27, 116, 121, 130
MISSIONS	46, 67, 72, 100
CHRISTIAN EDUCATION	1, 91
HARVEST	67, 103, 118
THANKSGIVING	67, 92, 100, 103, 145, 148, 150
DAYS OF HUMILIATION AND PRAYER	130
NATIONAL OCCASIONS	46, 48, 67, 85, 100, 145, 148
PENITENTIAL PSALMS	32, 130

CANTICLES

THE TE DEUM ....p. 10

THE BENEDICTUS ....p. 11

THE MAGNIFICAT ....p. 14

THE NUNC DIMITTIS ....p. 14

✠

SCRIPTURE READINGS

THE LITURGICAL GOSPELS

Day	Gospel

Sundays in Advent:

1	Matt.	21:1-9
2	Luke	21:25-36
3	Matt.	11:2-10
4	John	1:19-28
Christmas Day	Luke	2:1-14
2 Christmas Day	Luke	2:15-20
Sunday after Christmas	Luke	2:33-40
New Year's Day	Luke	2:21
2 Sunday after Christmas	Matt.	2:13-23
Epiphany	Matt.	2:1-12

Sundays after Epiphany:

1	Luke	2:41-52
2	John	2:1-11
3	Matt.	8:1-13
4	Matt.	8:23-27
5	Matt.	13:24-30
6	Matt.	17:1-9
Septuagesima Sunday	Matt.	20:1-16
Sexagesima Sunday	Luke	8:4-15
Quinquagesima Sunday	Luke	18:31-43
Ash Wednesday	Matt.	6:16-21

Sundays in Lent:

1 Invocavit	Matt.	4:1-11
2 Reminiscere	Matt.	15:21-28
3 Oculi	Luke	11:14-28
4 Laetare	John	6:1-15
5 Judica	John	8:46-59
6 Palmarum	Matt.	21:1-9
Monday in Holy Week	John	12:1-23
Tuesday	John	12:24-43
Wednesday	Luke	22:1—23:42
Thursday	John	13:1-15
Good Friday	John	18:1—19:42
Easter Sunday	Mark	16:1-8
Easter Monday	Luke	24:13-35

Sundays after Easter:

1 Quasimodogeniti	John	20:19-31
2 Misericordias	John	10:11-16
3 Jubilate	John	16:16-23
4 Cantate	John	16:5-15
5 Rogate	John	16:23-30
Ascension Day	Mark	16:14-20
Sunday after Ascension	John	15:26—16:4
Whitsunday	John	14:23-31
Monday	John	3:16-21

Trinity Sunday ... John 3:1-15

Sundays after Trinity:

1	Luke	16:19-31
2	Luke	14:16-24
3	Luke	15:1-10
4	Luke	6:36-42
5	Luke	5:1-11
6	Matt.	5:20-26
7	Mark	8:1-9
8	Matt.	7:15-23
9	Luke	16:1-9
10	Luke	19:41-48
11	Luke	18:9-14
12	Mark	7:31-37
13	Luke	10:23-37
14	Luke	17:11-19
15	Matt.	6:24-34
16	Luke	7:11-17
17	Luke	14:1-11
18	Matt.	22:34-46
19	Matt.	9:1-8
20	Matt.	22:1-14
21	John	4:46-54
22	Matt.	18:23-35
23	Matt.	22:15-22
24	Matt.	9:18-26
25	Matt.	24:15-28
26	Matt.	25:31-46
27	Matt.	25:1-13

St. Thomas, Apostle	John	20:24-31
St. Stephen, Martyr	Matt.	23:34-39
St. John, Apostle	John	21:19-24
Conversion of St. Paul	Matt.	19:27-30
The Presentation of Christ	Luke	2:22-32
St. Matthias, Apostle	Matt.	11:25-30
The Annunciation	Luke	1:26-38
St. Mark, Evangelist	John	15:1-10
Sts. Philip & James, Apos.	John	14:1-14
St. John the Baptist	Luke	1:57-80
Sts. Peter & Paul, Apos.	Matt.	16:13-20
The Visitation	Luke	1:39-56
St. James the Elder, Apos.	Matt.	20:20-33
St. Bartholomew, Apos.	Luke	22:24-30
St. Matthew, Apostle	Matt.	9:9-13
St. Michael & All Angels	Matt.	18:1-11
St. Luke, Evangelist	Luke	10:1-9
Sts. Simon & Jude, Apos.	John	15:17-21
The Reformation	John	8:31-36
All Saints' Day	Matt.	5:1-12
St. Andrew, Apostle	Matt.	4:18-22

ADVENT
 Isaiah 11:1-6
 Malachi 3:1-4
 Luke 12:35-40

CHRISTMAS
 Matthew 1:18-23
 Luke 1:46-55
 John 1:1-14

NEW YEAR
 Isaiah 61:1-6
 Lamentations 3:22-26
 Luke 13:6-9

EPIPHANY
 Isaiah 2:2-5
 Isaiah 60:1-6
 Matthew 3:13-17
 Matthew 12:15-21
 I John 3: 1-6

LENT
 Isaiah 1:16-20
 Isaiah 53:4-9
 Matthew 16:21-23
 Luke 15:11-32
 I John 1:5-10

PALM SUNDAY
 Isaiah 63:1-9
 Mark 14:3-9
 Luke 23:24-47
 John 12:12-32

EASTER
 Matthew 28:1-8
 Luke 24:13-35
 John 20:11-18
 I Cor. 15:12-22

EASTER to ASCENSION
 Numbers 6:22-27
 Matthew 9:36-38
 John 21:1-17
 Acts 3:12-21
 I Peter 1:3-8
 I John 3:18-24

ASCENSION to PENTECOST
 John 14:15-21
 John 17:24-26
 Acts 2:42-47

TRINITY
 Matthew 28:18-20

REFORMATION
 John 6:66-71
 I Cor. 3:6-17
 Gal. 2:16-21
 Hebrews 13:7-9

HARVEST and THANKSGIVING
 Gen. 8:22
 Lev. 19:9-10
 Deut. 8: 1-20
 Deut. 26:1-11
 Isaiah 63:7-9
 II Cor. 9:6-11

CHILDREN'S SERVICE
 Eccl. 12:1-7, 13, 14
 Prov. 4:1-13

MISSIONS
 Isaiah 35:1-10
 Matthew 28:18-20
 Acts 1:6-8
 Rom. 1:14-17
 Rom. 10:8-17

CHARITY
 I Cor. 13.

TEMPERANCE
 Lev. 26:1-5, 14-20
 Gal. 5:13-26
 I Cor. 9:24-27
 I Cor. 13:16, 17

NATIONAL
 Exodus 20:1-20

THE SMALL CATECHISM

PART I

THE TEN COMMANDMENTS

In the plain form in which they are to be taught by the head of a family.

THE FIRST COMMANDMENT

I am the LORD thy God. Thou shalt have no other gods before Me.

[Thou shalt not make unto thee any graven image, or any likeness of anything that is in heaven above, or that is in the earth beneath, or that is in the water under the earth; thou shalt not bow down thyself to them, nor serve them: for I the LORD thy God am a jealous God, visiting the iniquity of the fathers upon the children unto the third and fourth generation of them that hate Me; and showing mercy unto thousands of them that love Me, and keep My commandments.]

What is meant by this Commandment?

Answer. We should fear, love, and trust in God above all things.

THE SECOND COMMANDMENT

Thou shalt not take the Name of the LORD thy God in vain; for the LORD will not hold him guiltless that taketh His Name in vain.

What is meant by this Commandment?

Answer. We should so fear and love God as not to curse, swear, conjure, lie, or deceive, by His Name, but call upon Him in every time of need, and worship Him with prayer, praise, and thanksgiving.

THE THIRD COMMANDMENT

Remember the Sabbath day, to keep it holy.

[Six days shalt thou labor, and do all thy work: but the seventh day is the sabbath of the LORD thy God: in it thou shalt not do any work, thou, nor thy son, nor thy daughter, thy manservant, nor thy maidservant, nor thy cattle, nor thy stranger that is within thy gates: for in six days the LORD made heaven and earth, the sea, and all that in them is, and rested the seventh day; wherefore the LORD blessed the sabbath day, and hallowed it.]

What is meant by this Commandment?

Answer. We should so fear and love God as not to despise His Word and the preaching of the Gospel, but deem it holy, and willingly hear and learn it.

THE FOURTH COMMANDMENT

Honor thy father and thy mother, that thy days may be long upon the land which the Lord thy God giveth thee.

What is meant by this Commandment?

Answer. We should so fear and love God as not to despise nor displease our parents and superiors, but honor, serve, obey, love, and esteem them.

THE FIFTH COMMANDMENT
Thou shalt not kill.

What is meant by this Commandment?

Answer. We should so fear and love God as not to do our neighbor any bodily harm or injury, but rather assist and comfort him in danger and want.

THE SIXTH COMMANDMENT
Thou shalt not commit adultery.

What is meant by this Commandment?

Answer. We should so fear and love God as to be chaste and pure in our words and deeds, each one also loving and honoring his wife or her husband.

THE SEVENTH COMMANDMENT
Thou shalt not steal.

What is meant by this Commandment?

Answer. We should so fear and love God as not to rob our neighbor of his money or property, nor bring it into our possession by unfair dealing or fraudulent means, but rather assist him to improve and protect it.

THE EIGHTH COMMANDMENT
Thou shalt not bear false witness against thy neighbor.

What is meant by this Commandment?

Answer. We should so fear and love God as not deceitfully to belie, betray, slander, nor raise injurious reports against our neighbor, but apologize for him, speak well of him, and put the most charitable construction on all his actions.

THE NINTH COMMANDMENT
Thou shalt not covet thy neighbor's house.

What is meant by this Commandment?

Answer. We should so fear and love God as not to desire by craftiness to gain possession of our neighbor's inheritance or home, or to obtain it under the pretext of a legal right, but be ready to assist and serve him in the preservation of his own.

THE TENTH COMMANDMENT
Thou shalt not covet thy neghbor's wife, nor his manservant, nor his maidservant, nor his ox, nor his ass, nor anything that is thy neighbor's.

What is meant by this Commandment?

Answer. We should so fear and love God as not to alienate our neighbor's wife from him, entice away his servants, nor let loose his cattle, but use our endeavors that they may remain and discharge their duty to him.

What does God declare concerning all these Commandments?

Answer. He says: I the LORD thy God am a jealous God, visiting the iniquity of the fathers upon the children unto the third and fourth generation of them that hate Me; and showing mercy unto thousands of them that love Me, and keep My commandments.

What is meant by this declaration?

Answer. God threatens to punish all those who transgress these commandments. We should, therefore, dread His displeasure, and not act contrarily to these commandments. But He promises grace and every blessing to all who keep them. We should, therefore, love and trust in Him, and cheerfully do what He has commanded us.

PART II

THE CREED

In the plain form in which it is to be taught by the head of a family.

THE FIRST ARTICLE

Of Creation

I believe in God the Father Almighty, Maker of heaven and earth.

What is meant by this Article?

Answer. I believe that God has created me and all that exists; that He has given and still preserves to me my body and soul, with all my limbs and senses, my reason and all the faculties of my mind, together with my raiment, food, home, and family, and all my property; that He daily provides me abundantly with all the necessaries of life, protects me from all danger, and preserves me and guards me against all evil; all which He does out of pure, paternal, and divine goodness and mercy, without any merit or worthiness in me; for all which I am in duty bound to thank, praise, serve, and obey Him. This is most certainly true.

THE SECOND ARTICLE

Of Redemption

And in Jesus Christ His only Son, our Lord; Who was conceived by the Holy Ghost, Born of the Virgin Mary; Suffered under Pontius Pilate, Was crucified, dead, and buried; He descended into hell; The third day He rose again from the dead; He ascended into heaven, And sitteth on the right hand of God the Father Almighty; From thence He shall come to judge the quick and the dead.

What is meant by this Article?

Answer. I believe that Jesus Christ, true God, begotten of the Father from eternity, and also true Man, born of the Virgin Mary, is my Lord; Who has redeemed me, a lost and condemned creature, secured and delivered me from all sins, from death, and from the power of the devil, not with silver and gold, but with His holy and precious blood, and with His innocent sufferings and death; in order that I might be His, live under Him in His kingdom, and serve Him in everlasting righteousness, innocence and blessedness; even as He is risen from the dead, and lives and reigns to all eternity. This is most certainly true.

THE THIRD ARTICLE

Of Sanctification

I believe in the Holy Ghost; the holy Christian Church, the Communion of Saints; The Forgiveness of sins; The Resurrection of the body; And the Life everlasting. Amen.

What is meant by this Article?

Answer. I believe that I cannot by my own reason or strength believe in Jesus Christ my Lord, or come to Him; but the Holy Ghost has called me through the Gospel, enlightened me by His gifts, and sanctified and preserved me in the true faith; in like manner as He calls, gathers, enlightens, and sanctifies the whole Christian Church on earth, and preserves it in union with Jesus Christ in the true faith; a which Christian Church He daily forgives abundantly all my sins, and the sins of all believers, and will raise up me and all the dead at the last day, and will grant everlasting life to me and to all who believe in Christ. This is most certainly true.

PART III

THE LORD'S PRAYER

In the plain form in which it is to be taught by the head of a family.

INTRODUCTION

Our Father, Who art in heaven.

What is meant by this Introduction?

Answer. God would thereby affectionately encourage us to believe that He i truly our Father, and that we are His children indeed, so that we may call upo Him with all cheerfulness and confidence, even as beloved children entreat thei affectionate parent.

FIRST PETITION

Hallowed be Thy Name.

What is meant by this Petition?

Answer. The Name of God is indeed holy in itself; but we pray in this petitio that it may be hallowed also by us.

How is this effected?

Answer. When the Word of God is taught in its truth and purity, and we, a the children of God, lead holy lives in accordance with it; to this may our blesse Father in heaven help us! But whoever teaches and lives otherwise than as God Word prescribes, profanes the Name of God among us; from this preserve u heavenly Father!

SECOND PETITION

Thy kingdom come.

What is meant by this Petition?

Answer. The kingdom of God comes indeed of itself, without our prayer; bu we pray in this petition that it may come unto us also.

When is this effected?

Answer. When our heavenly Father gives us His Holy Spirit, so that by Hi grace we believe His holy Word, and live a godly life here on earth, and in heave for ever.

THIRD PETITION

Thy will be done on earth, as it is in heaven.

What is meant by this Petition?

Answer. The good and gracious will of God is done indeed without our prayer but we pray in this petition that it may be done by us also.

When is this effected?

Answer. When God frustrates and brings to naught every evil counsel an purpose, which would hinder us from hallowing the Name of God, and prevent H kingdom from coming to us, such as the will of the devil, of the world, and of ou own flesh; and when He strengthens us, and keeps us steadfast in His word and i the faith, even unto our end. This is His gracious and good will.

FOURTH PETITION

Give us this day our daily bread.

What is meant by this Petition?

Answer. God gives indeed without our prayer, even to the wicked also the daily bread; but we pray in this petition that He would make us sensible of H benefits, and enable us to receive our daily bread with thanksgiving.

What is implied in the words: "Our daily bread"?

Answer. All things that pertain to the wants and the support of this present life; such as food, raiment, money, goods, house and land, and other property; a believing spouse and good children; trustworthy servants and faithful magistrates; favorable seasons, peace and health; education and honor; true friends, good neighbors, and the like.

FIFTH PETITION

And forgive us our trespasses, as we forgive those who trespass against us.

What is meant by this Petition?

Answer. We pray in this petition, that our heavenly Father would not regard our sins, nor deny us our requests on account of them; for we are not worthy of anything for which we pray, and have not merited it; but that He would grant us all things through grace, although we daily commit much sin, and deserve chastisement alone. We will therefore, on our part, both heartily forgive, and also readily do good to those who may injure or offend us.

SIXTH PETITION

And lead us not into temptation.

What is meant by this Petition?

Answer. God indeed tempts no one to sin; but we pray in this petition that God would so guard and preserve us, that the devil, the world, and our own flesh, may not deceive us, nor lead us into error and unbelief, despair, and other great and shameful sins; and that, though we may be thus tempted, we may nevertheless finally prevail and gain the victory.

SEVENTH PETITION

But deliver us from evil.

What is meant by this Petition?

Answer. We pray in this petition, as in a summary, that our heavenly Father would deliver us from all manner of evil, whether it affect the body or soul, property or character, and at last, when the hour of death shall arrive, grant us a happy end, and graciously take us from this world of sorrow to Himself in heaven.

CONCLUSION

For Thine is the kingdom, and the power, and the glory, for ever and ever. Amen.

What is meant by the word "Amen"?

Answer. That I should be assured that such petitions are acceptable to our heavenly Father, and are heard by Him; for He Himself has commanded us to pray in this manner, and has promised that He will hear us. Amen, Amen, that is, Yea, yea, it shall be so.

PART IV

THE SACRAMENT OF HOLY BAPTISM

In the plain form in which it is to be taught by the head of a family.

I. *What is Baptism?*

Answer. Baptism is not simply water, but it is the water comprehended in God's command, and connected with God's Word.

What is that Word of God?

Answer. It is that which our Lord Jesus Christ spake, as it is recorded in the last chapter of Matthew, verse 19: "Go ye, and teach all nations, baptizing them in the Name of the Father, and of the Son, and of the Holy Ghost."

II. *What gifts or benefits does Baptism confer?*

Answer. It worketh forgiveness of sins, delivers from death and the devil, and confers everlasting salvation on all who believe, as the Word and promise of God declare.

What are such words and promises of God?

Answer. Those which our Lord Jesus Christ spake, as they are recorded in the last chapter of Mark, verse 16: "He that believeth and is baptized, shall be saved; but he that believeth not shall be damned."

III. *How can water produce such great effects?*

Answer. It is not the water indeed that produces these effects, but the Word of God, which accompanies and is connected with the water, and our faith, which relies on the Word of God, connected with the water. For the water, without the Word of God, is simply water and no baptism. But when connected with the Word of God, it is a baptism, that is, a gracious water of life and a "washing of regeneration" in the Holy Ghost; as St. Paul says to Titus, in the third chapter, verses 5-8: "According to His mercy He saved us, by the washing of regeneration, and renewing of the Holy Ghost; which He shed on us abundantly through Jesus Christ our Saviour; that being justified by His grace, we should be made heirs according to the hope of eternal life. This is a faithful saying."

IV. *What does such baptizing with water signify?*

Answer. It signifies that the old Adam in us is to be drowned and destroyed by daily sorrow and repentance, together with all sins and evil lusts; and that again the new man should daily come forth and rise, that shall live in the presence of God in righteousness and purity for ever.

Where is it so written?

Answer. St. Paul, in the Epistle to the Romans, chapter 6, verse 4, says: "We are buried with Christ by baptism into death; that like as He was raised up from the dead by the glory of the Father, even so we also should walk in newness of life."

OF CONFESSION

What is Confession?

Answer. Confession consists of two parts: the one is, that we confess our sins; the other, that we receive absolution or forgiveness through the pastor as of God Himself, in no wise doubting, but firmly believing, that our sins are thus forgiven before God in heaven.

What sins ought we to confess?

Answer. In the presence of God we should acknowledge ourselves guilty of all manner of sins, even of those which we do not ourselves perceive; as we do in the Lord's Prayer. But in the presence of the pastor we should confess those sins alone, of which we have knowledge, and which we feel in our hearts.

Which are these?

Answer. Here reflect on your condition, according to the Ten Commandments, namely: Whether you are a father or mother, a son or daughter, a master or mistress, a manservant or maidservant—whether you have been disobedient, unfaithful, slothful—whether you have injured any one by words or actions—whether you have stolen, neglected, or wasted aught, or done other evil.

PART V

THE SACRAMENT OF THE ALTAR
OR
THE LORD'S SUPPER

In the plain form in which it is to be taught by the head of a family.

What is the Sacrament of the Altar?

Answer. It is the true Body and Blood of our Lord Jesus Christ, under the bread and wine, given unto us Christians to eat and to drink, as it was instituted by Christ Himself.

Where is it so written?

Answer. The holy Evangelists, Matthew, Mark, and Luke, together with St. Paul, write thus:

"Our Lord Jesus Christ, the same night in which He was betrayed, took bread: and when He had given thanks, He brake it, and gave it to the disciples, and said, Take, eat; this is My Body, which is given for you: this do, in remembrance of Me.

"After the same manner also He took the cup, when He had supped, gave thanks, and gave it to them, saying, Drink ye all of it; this cup is the New Testament in My Blood, which is shed for you, for the remission of sins: this do ye, as oft as ye drink it, in remembrance of Me."

What benefits are derived from such eating and drinking?

Answer. They are pointed out in these words: "Given and shed for you, for the remission of sins." Namely, through these words, the remission of sins, life and salvation are granted unto us in the Sacrament. For where there is remission of sins, there are also life and salvation.

How can the bodily eating and drinking produce such great effects?

Answer. The eating and the drinking, indeed, do not produce them, but the words which stand here, namely: "Given, and shed for you, for the remission of sins." These words are, besides the bodily eating and drinking, the chief things in the Sacrament; and he who believes these words, has that which they declare and set forth, namely, the remission of sins.

Who is it, then, that receives this Sacrament worthily?

Answer. Fasting and bodily preparation are indeed a good external discipline; but he is truly worthy and well prepared, who believes these words: "Given, and shed for you, for the remission of sins." But he who does not believe these words, or who doubts, is unworthy and unfit; for the words: "For you," require truly believing hearts.

✠

ADVENT

O Come, O Come, Emmanuel

VENI, VENI, EMMANUEL. 8 8, 8 8, 8 8.

Latin Antiphons, XI Century
Latin Hymn, XVIII Century
Tr. JOHN MASON NEALE, 1851, 1861

First Tune

Ancient Plain Song

1. O come, O come, Em - man - u - el, And ran-som cap-tive Is - ra - el,
2. O come, Thou Rod of Jes - se, free Thine own from Satan's' tyr - an - ny;
3. O come, Thou Day-Spring, come and cheer Our spir-its by Thine Ad - vent here;
4. O come, Thou Key of Da - vid, come, And o- pen wide our heav - enly home;

That mourns in lone-ly ex - ile here Un - til the Son of God ap - pear.
From depths of hell Thy peo - ple save And give them vic-tr'y o'er the grave.
And drive a - way the shades of night, And pierce the clouds and bring us light!
Make safe the way that leads on high, And close the path to mis - er - y.

Re - joice! re - joice! Em - man - u - el Shall come to thee, O Is - ra - el!
Re - joice! re - joice! Em - man - u - el Shall come to thee, O Is - ra - el!
Re - joice! re - joice! Em - man - u - el Shall come to thee, O Is - ra - el!
Re - joice! re - joice! Em - man - u - el Shall come to thee, O Is - ra - el! A-MEN.

O Come, O Come, Emmanuel

VENI, VENI, EMMANUEL. 8 8, 8 8, 8 8.

Latin Antiphons, XI Century
Latin Hymn, XVIII Century
Tr. John Mason Neale, 1851, 1861

Second Tune

Charles F. Gounod, 1872

1. O come, O come, Em-man - u - el, And ran - som cap - tive Is - ra - el, That mourns in lone - ly ex - ile here Un - til the Son of God ap - pear. Re - joice! re - joice! Em - man - u - el Shall come to thee, O Is - ra - el! A - MEN.

2. O come, Thou Rod of Jes - se, free Thine own from Sa - tan's tyr - an - ny; From depths of hell Thy peo - ple save And give them vic - t'ry o'er the grave. Re - joice! re - joice! Em -

3. O come, Thou Day - Spring, come and cheer Our spir - its by Thine Ad - vent here; And drive a - way the shades of night, And pierce the clouds and bring us light! Re - joice! re - joice! Em -

4. O come, Thou Key of Da - vid, come, And o - pen wide our heav'n - ly home; Make safe the way that leads on high, And close the path to mis - e - ry. Re - joice! re - joice! Em -

Come, Thou Long-Expected Jesus 2

ST. HILARY. 8 7, 8 7. D.

CHARLES WESLEY, 1744   Origin uncertain

1. Come, Thou long-ex-pect-ed Je-sus, Born to set Thy peo-ple free;
2. Born Thy peo-ple to de-liv-er; Born a Child, and yet a King;

From our fears and sins re-lease us; Let us find our rest in Thee.
Born to reign in us for-ev-er, Now Thy gra-cious king-dom bring.

Is-rael's Strength and Con-so-la-tion, Hope of all the earth Thou art,
By Thine own E-ter-nal Spir-it Rule in all our hearts a-lone;

Dear De-sire of ev-'ry na-tion, Joy of ev-'ry long-ing heart.
By Thine all-suf-fi-cient mer-it Raise us to Thy glo-rious throne. A-MEN.

3 Hark the Glad Sound! the Saviour Comes

CHESTERFIELD. C. M.

PHILIP DODDRIDGE, 1735

THOMAS HAWEIS, 1792

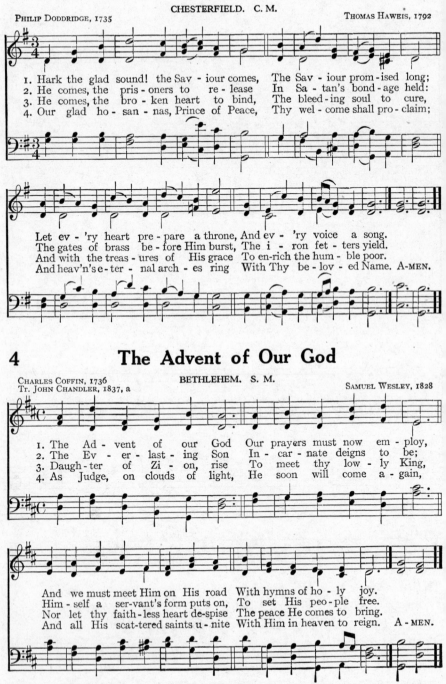

1. Hark the glad sound! the Sav - iour comes, The Sav - iour prom - ised long;
2. He comes, the pris - oners to re - lease In Sa - tan's bond - age held:
3. He comes, the bro - ken heart to bind, The bleed - ing soul to cure,
4. Our glad ho - san - nas, Prince of Peace, Thy wel - come shall pro - claim;

Let ev - 'ry heart pre - pare a throne, And ev - 'ry voice a song.
The gates of brass be - fore Him burst, The i - ron fet - ters yield.
And with the treas - ures of His grace To en - rich the hum - ble poor.
And heav'n's e - ter - nal arch - es ring With Thy be - lov - ed Name. A-MEN.

4 The Advent of Our God

BETHLEHEM. S. M.

CHARLES COFFIN, 1736
Tr. JOHN CHANDLER, 1837, a

SAMUEL WESLEY, 1828

1. The Ad - vent of our God Our prayers must now em - ploy,
2. The Ev - er - last - ing Son In - car - nate deigns to be;
3. Daugh - ter of Zi - on, rise To meet thy low - ly King,
4. As Judge, on clouds of light, He soon will come a - gain,

And we must meet Him on His road With hymns of ho - ly joy.
Him - self a ser - vant's form puts on, To set His peo - ple free.
Nor let thy faith - less heart de - spise The peace He comes to bring.
And all His scat - tered saints u - nite With Him in heaven to reign. A - MEN.

5 Before the dawning day
   Let sin's dark deeds be gone;
  The old man all be put away,
  The new man all put on!

6 All glory to the Son,
   Who comes to set us free,
  With Father, Spirit, ever One,
  Through all eternity.

Hosanna to the Living Lord   5

HOSANNA. 8 8, 8 8, 4 7.

REGINALD HEBER, 1811

JOHN B. DYKES, 1875

1. Ho - san - na to the liv - ing Lord! Ho - san - na to th' In-car-nate Word!
2. Ho - san - na, Lord! Thine an-gels cry; Ho - san - na, Lord! Thy saints re-ply;
3. O Sav - iour, with pro-tect-ing care, A - bide in this Thy house of prayer,

To Christ, Cre - a - tor, Sav-iour, King, Let earth, let heaven, Ho-san - na sing!
A - bove, be - neath us, and a - round, The dead and liv - ing swell the sound;
Where we Thy part-ing prom-ise claim, As - sem - bled in Thy sa - cred Name.

Ho - san - na! Lord! Ho - san - na in the high - est! A-MEN.

4 But, chiefest, in our cleansèd breast,
  Eternal! bid Thy Spirit rest,
  And make our secret soul to be
  A temple pure, and worthy Thee!
    Hosanna! Lord!
  Hosanna in the highest!

5 So, in the last and dreadful day,
  When earth and heaven shall melt away,
  Thy flock, redeemed from sinful stain,
  Shall swell the sound of praise again:
    Hosanna! Lord!
  Hosanna in the highest!

6 O How Shall I Receive Thee

ST. THEODULPH. 7 6, 7 6. D.

PAUL GERHARDT, 1653
Tr. ARTHUR TOZER RUSSELL, 1851, a

MELCHIOR TESCHNER, 1615

1. O how shall I re-ceive Thee, How greet Thee, Lord, a-right?
2. Thy Zi-on palms is strew-ing, And branch-es fresh and fair;
3. I lay in fet-ters groan-ing, Thou com'st to set me free!

All na-tions long to see Thee, My Hope, my heart's de-light!
My heart, its powers re-new-ing, An an-them shall pre-pare.
I stood, my shame be-moan-ing, Thou com'st to hon-or me!

O kin-dle, Lord, most ho-ly, Thy lamp with-in my breast,
My soul puts off her sad-ness Thy glo-ries to pro-claim;
A glo-ry Thou dost give me, A treas-ure safe on high,

To do in spir-it low-ly All that may please Thee best.
With all her strength and glad-ness She fain would serve Thy Name.
That will not fail nor leave me As earth-ly rich-es fly. A-MEN.

4 Love caused Thy Incarnation,
  Love brought Thee down to me,
Thy thirst for my salvation
  Procured my liberty.
O love beyond all telling,
  That led Thee to embrace,
In love all love excelling,
  Our lost and fallen race!

5 Rejoice then, ye sad-hearted,
  Who sit in deepest gloom,
Who mourn o'er joys departed,
  And tremble at your doom;
He Who alone can cheer you
  Is standing at the door;
He brings His pity near you,
  And bids you weep no more.

Rejoice, All Ye Believers

LANCASHIRE. 7 6, 7 6. D.

LAURENTIUS LAURENTI, 1700
Tr. SARAH BORTHWICK FINDLATER, 1854

HENRY SMART, 1836

1. Re - joice, all ye be - liev - ers, And let your lights ap - pear!
2. The watch - ers on the moun - tain Pro - claim the Bride-groom near;
3. Ye saints, who here in pa - tience Your cross and suf - f'rings bore,
4. Our Hope and Ex - pec - ta - tion, O Je - sus, now ap - pear;

The ev'n - ing is ad - vanc - ing And dark - er night is near.
Go meet Him as He com - eth, With hal - le - lu - jahs clear.
Shall live and reign for ev - er, When sor - row is no more.
A - rise, Thou Sun so longed for, O'er this be - night - ed sphere!

The Bride-groom is a - ris - ing, And soon will He draw nigh.
The mar - riage - feast is wait - ing, The gates wide o - pen stand;
A - round the throne of glo - ry The Lamb ye shall be - hold,
With hearts and hands up - lift - ed, We plead, O Lord, to see

Up! pray, and watch, and wres - tle — At mid - night comes the cry!
Up, up, ye heirs of glo - ry; The Bride-groom is at hand!
In tri - umph cast be - fore Him Your di - a - dems of gold!
The day of earth's re - demp - tion, That brings us un - to Thee! A-MEN.

8   On Jordan's Banks the Herald's Cry

CHARLES COFFIN, 1736
Tr. JOHN CHANDLER, 1837, a

ALSTONE. L. M.

CHRISTOPHER E. WILLING, 1868

1. On Jor-dan's banks the her-ald's cry   An-noun-ces that the Lord is nigh;
2. Then cleansed be ev-'ry breast from sin,   Make straight the way for God with-in,
3. For Thou art our sal-va-tion, Lord,   Our ref-uge and our great re-ward;

Come then and hearken, for he brings Glad ti-dings from the King of kings.
And let us all our hearts pre-pare For Christ to come and en-ter there.
With-out Thy grace we waste a-way, Like flow'rs that with-er and de-cay.   A-MEN.

4 Stretch forth Thy hand, to health restore,
  And make us rise, to fall no more;
  Once more upon Thy people shine,
  And fill the world with love divine.

5 All praise, Eternal Son, to Thee
  Whose Advent sets Thy people free,
  Whom, with the Father, we adore,
  And Holy Ghost for evermore.

9   The King Shall Come When Morning Dawns

JOHN BROWNLIE, 1907
Based on the Greek

FARRANT. C. M.

RICHARD FARRANT, (c. 1530-1585)

1. The King shall come when morn-ing dawns, And light tri-um-phant breaks;
2. Not as of old a lit-tle child To bear, and fight, and die,
3. O bright-er than the ris-ing morn When He, vic-to-rious, rose,

When beau-ty gilds the east-ern hills, And life to joy a-wakes.
But crowned with glo-ry like the sun That lights the morn-ing sky.
And left the lone-some place of death, De-spite the rage of foes;— A-MEN.

4 O brighter than that glorious morn
    Shall this fair morning be
When Christ, our King, in beauty comes,
    And we His face shall see.

5 The King shall come when morning dawns,
    And earth's dark night is past;
O haste the rising of that morn,
    The day that aye shall last.

6 And let the endless bliss begin,
    By weary saints foretold,
When right shall triumph over wrong,
    And truth shall be extolled.

7 The King shall come when morning dawns,
    And light and beauty brings;
Hail, Christ the Lord! Thy people pray,
    Come quickly, King of kings.

O'er the Distant Mountains Breaking 10

HOLYWOOD. 8 7, 8 7, 4 7.

JOHN S. B. MONSELL, 1863

J. F. WADE'S *Cantus Diversi*, 1751

1. O'er the dis - tant mountains break-ing Comes the reddening dawn of day;
2. O Thou long - ex - pect - ed! Wea - ry Waits my anx - ious soul for Thee;
3. Near - er is my soul's sal - va - tion, Spent the night, the day at hand;
4. With my lamp, well trimmed and burning, Swift to hear and slow to roam,

Rise, my soul, from sleep a - wak - ing, Rise and sing, and watch and pray;
Life is dark, and earth is drear - y, Where Thy light I do not see;
Keep me in my low - ly sta - tion, Watch-ing for Thee, till I stand,
Watch-ing for Thy glad re - turn - ing, To re - store me to my home.

'Tis thy Sav-iour, T'is thy Sav-iour, On His bright re - turn-ing way.
O my Sav-iour, O my Sav-iour, When wilt Thou re-turn to me?
O my Sav-iour, O my Sav-iour, In Thy bright, Thy promised land.
Come, my Sav-iour, Come, my Sav-iour, Thou hast promised. quickly come. A-MEN.

11 Thou Art Coming, O My Saviour

BEVERLY. Irregular.

FRANCES R. HAVERGAL, 1873

WILLIAM H. MONK, 1875

1. Thou art com-ing, O my Sav-iour, Thou art com-ing, O my King,
2. Thou art com-ing, Thou art com-ing; We shall meet Thee on Thy way,
3. Thou art com-ing; at Thy Ta-ble We are wit-ness-es for this;

In Thy beau-ty all re-splen-dent, In Thy glo-ry all tran-scend-ent;
We shall see Thee, we shall know Thee, We shall bless Thee, we shall show Thee
While re-mem-b'ring hearts Thou meet-est In com-mu-nion clear-est, sweet-est,

Well may we re-joice and sing: Com-ing! in the op'n-ing east Her-ald bright-ness
All our hearts could nev-er say: What an an-them that will be, Ring-ing out our
Earn-est of our com-ing bliss; Show-ing not Thy death a-lone, And Thy love ex-

rit. poco

slow-ly swells; Com-ing! O my glorious Priest, Hear we not Thy gold-en bells?
love to Thee, Pour-ing out our rap-ture sweet At Thine own all-glorious feet.
ceed-ing great, But Thy com-ing and Thy throne, All for which we long and wait. A-MEN.

4 Thou art coming; we are waiting
    With a hope that cannot fail;
Asking not the day or hour,
Resting on Thy word of power,
    Anchored safe within the veil:
Time appointed may be long,
    But the vision must be sure;
Certainty shall make us strong,
    Joyful patience can endure.

5 O the joy to see Thee reigning,
    Thee, my own beloved Lord!
Every tongue Thy Name confessing,
Worship, honor, glory, blessing,
    Brought to Thee with glad accord;
Thee, my Master and my Friend,
    Vindicated and enthroned:
Unto earth's remotest end,
    Glorified, adored, and owned.

Watchman, Tell Us of the Night   12

WATCHMAN. 7 7, 7 7. D.

JOHN BOWRING, 1825   LOWELL MASON, 1830

1. Watch-man, tell us of the night, What its signs of prom-ise are:
2. Watch-man, tell us of the night, High - er yet that star as-cends:
3. Watch-man, tell us of the night, For   the morn-ing seems to dawn:

Trav - 'ler, o'er yon moun-tain's height, See that glo - ry -beam - ing star;
Trav - 'ler, bless - ed - ness and light, Peace and truth, its course por-tends.
Trav - 'ler, dark - ness takes its flight, Doubt and ter - ror are with-drawn.

Watch-man, doth its beau - teous ray Aught of joy or hope fore-tell?
Watch-man, will its beams a - lone Gild the spot that gave them birth?
Watch-man, let thy wan - d'rings cease; Hie thee to thy qui - et home:

Trav - 'ler, yes; it brings the day, Prom-ised day of Is - ra - el.
Trav - 'ler, a - ges are its own, See, it bursts o'er all the earth.
Trav - 'ler, lo, the Prince of Peace, Lo, the Son of God is come. A-MEN.

13   Hark! the Herald Angels Sing

MENDELSSOHN. 77,77. D. With Refrain

CHARLES WESLEY, 1739. a

FELIX MENDELSSOHN BARTHOLDY, 1840
Arranged by WILLIAM H. CUMMINGS, 1855

1. Hark! the her - ald an - gels sing, "Glo - ry to the new-born King;
2. Christ, by high - est heaven a - dored, Christ, the ev - er - last - ing Lord:
3. Hail, the heaven-ly Prince of Peace, Hail, the Sun of Right - eous-ness!
4. Come, De - sire of na - tions, come, Fix in us Thy hum - ble home;

Peace on earth and mer - cy mild, God and sin - ners re - con-ciled":
Late in time be - hold Him come, Off - spring of a vir - gin's womb!
Light and life to all He brings, Ris'n with heal - ing in His wings.
O, to all Thy - self im - part, Formed in each be - liev - ing heart!

Joy - ful all ye na - tions rise, Join the tri - umph of the skies,
Veiled in flesh, the God - head see, Hail th' in - car - nate De - i - ty!
Mild He lays His glo - ry by, Born that man no more may die;
Hark! the her - ald an - gels sing, "Glo - ry to the new-born King;

With th' an-gel - ic host pro - claim, "Christ is born in Beth - le - hem".
Pleased as Man with men to appear, Je - sus, our Im - manu - el here!
Born to raise the sons of earth; Born to give them sec - ond birth.
Peace on earth, and mer - cy mild, God and sin - ners re - con-ciled!"

REFRAIN

Hark! the her-ald an-gels sing "Glo-ry to the new-born King." A-MEN.

Good News from Heaven the Angels Bring 14

VOM HIMMEL HOCH. L. M.

MARTIN LUTHER, 1535
TRS. ARTHUR T. RUSSELL, 1848. a
CATHERINE WINKWORTH, 1855

Geistliche Lieder, Leipzig, 1539
Melody of secular origin

1. Good news from heav'n the an-gels bring, Glad ti-dings to the earth they sing:
2. This is the Christ, our God and Lord, Who in all need shall aid af-ford;
3. All hail, Thou no-ble Guest, this morn, Whose love did not the sin-ner scorn;
4. Were earth a thou-sand times as fair, Be-set with gold and jew-els rare,

To us this day a Child is given, To crown us with the joy of heaven.
He will Him-self our Sav-iour be, From all our sins to set us free.
In my dis-tress Thou com'st to me; What thanks shall I re-turn to Thee?
She yet were far too poor to be A nar-row cra-dle, Lord, for Thee. A-MEN.

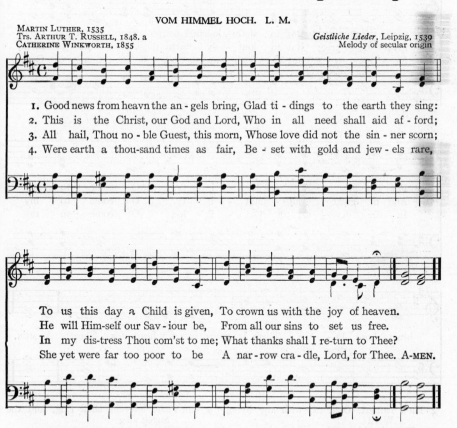

5 Ah, dearest Jesus, Holy Child,
Make Thee a bed, soft, undefiled,
Within my heart, that it may be
A quiet chamber kept for Thee.

6 Praise God upon His heavenly throne,
Who gave to us His only Son;
For this His hosts, on joyful wing,
A blest New Year of mercy sing.

15 Thou Didst Leave Thy Throne

MARGARET. Irregular.

EMILY E. S. ELLIOTT, 1864   TIMOTHY R. MATTHEWS, 1876

1. Thou didst leave Thy throne and Thy king-ly crown When Thou cam-est to earth for me; But in Beth-le-hem's home there was found no room For Thy ho-ly Na-tiv-i-ty. O come to my heart, Lord Je-sus: There is room in my heart for Thee. A-MEN.

2. Heav-en's arch-es rang, when the an-gels sang, Pro-claim-ing Thy royal de-gree; But in low-ly birth didst Thou come to earth, And in great hu-mil-i-ty, O come to my

3. The foxes found rest, and the bird had its nest In the shade of the for-est tree; But Thy couch was the sod, O Thou Son of God, In the des-ert of Gal-i-lee, O come to my

4 Thou camest, O Lord, with the living Word
That should set Thy children free;
But with mocking scorn, and with crown of thorn
They bore Thee to Calvary.
O come to my heart, Lord Jesus:
There is room in my heart for Thee.

5 When the heavens shall ring, and the angels sing
At Thy coming to victory,
Let Thy voice call me home, saying,
"Yet there is room,
There is room at My side for thee."
And my heart shall rejoice, Lord Jesus:
There is room in my heart for Thee.

Come Hither, Ye Faithful

ADESTE FIDELES. 11 11, 11 11.

Latin Hymn XVII Century
Tr. Edward Caswall, 1849. a

John F. Wade's *Cantus Diversi*, 1751

1. Come hith - er, ye faith - ful, tri - umph-ant - ly sing; Come see in the
2. True Son of the Fa - ther, He comes from the skies; To be born of a
3. Hark, hark, to the an - gels, all sing - ing in heaven, "To God in the
4. To Thee, then, O Je - sus, this day of Thy birth, Be glo - ry and

man - ger the an - gels' dread King! To Beth - le - hem hast - en, with
Vir - gin He does not de - spise; To Beth - le - hem hast - en, with
high - est all glo - ry be given!" To Beth - le - hem hast - en, with
hon - or through heav - en and earth; True God - head in - car - nate, om -

joy - ful ac - cord; O come ye, come hith - er, to wor - ship the
joy - ful ac - cord; O come ye, come hith - er, to wor - ship the
joy - ful ac - cord: O come ye, come hith - er, to wor - ship the
ni - po - tent Word! O come, let us hast - en to wor - ship the

Lord! O come ye, come hith - er, to wor - ship the Lord!
Lord! O come ye, come hith - er, to wor - ship the Lord!
Lord! O come ye, come hith - er, to wor - ship the Lord!
Lord! O come, let us hast - en to wor - ship the Lord! A-men.

17   Once in Royal David's City

IRBY. 87,87,77.

CECIL F. ALEXANDER, 1848   HENRY J. GAUNTLETT, 1849

1. Once in roy - al Da - vid's cit - y   Stood a low - ly cat - tle - shed,
2. He came down to earth from heav-en,   Who is God and Lord of all,
3. And, through all His won- drous child-hood, He would hon - or, and o - bey,
4. For He is our child-hood's Pat-tern, Day by day like us He grew:

Where a moth - er laid her Ba - by   In a man - ger for His bed;
And His shel - ter was a sta - ble,   And His cra - dle was a stall;
Love, and watch the low - ly maid - en   In whose gen - tle arms He lay;
He was lit - tle, weak, and help-less, Tears and smiles like us He knew;

Ma - ry was that moth - er mild, Je - sus Christ her lit - tle Child.
With the poor, and mean, and lowly, Lived on earth our Sav - iour holy.
Chris - tian chil - dren all must be Mild, o - bed - ient, good as He.
And He feel - eth for our sadness, And He shar - eth in our gladness. A-MEN.

5 And our eyes at last shall see Him,
Through His own redeeming love;
For that Child so dear and gentle
Is our Lord in heaven above;
And He leads His children on
To the place where He is gone.

6 Not in that poor lowly stable,
With the oxen standing by,
We shall see Him, but in heaven,
Set at God's right hand on high;
When like stars His children crowned,
All in white shall wait around.

The New-born King Who Comes Today 18

MATERNA. C. M. D.

SAMUEL A. WARD, 1882

1. The new-born King Who comes to-day Brings ti-dings of great joy,
2. He comes not as a king of earth, In pomp and pride to reign;
3. For us He leaves His Father's throne, His sap-phire throne on high,

Which sin can nev - er take a - way Nor death nor hell de - stroy.
He seeks a poor and hum - ble birth, But free from sin - ful stain;
And comes to dwell on earth a - lone, For fall - en man to die.

Re - joice, ye Gen - tile lands, re - joice, And hail this glo-rious dawn;
Re - joice, ye Gen - tile lands, re - joice, Glad hymns of tri - umph sing:
Re - joice, ye Gen - tile lands, re - joice, All hail Mes - si - ah's dawn;

For God comes down, frail man to crown—The Lord of Life is born!
The Won - der - ful, the Coun - sel - lor, He comes, your God and King!
Our God comes down, earth's joy and crown: The King of Love is born. A - MEN.

4 Glad Gentiles in their eastern home
    His radiant star behold;
To God, their King, they joy to bring
    Sweet incense, myrrh, and gold.
Rejoice, ye Gentile lands, rejoice,
    In heaven your praises sing,
Before Him fall, the Lord of all,
    Your Maker and your King!

5 We join your song, celestial throng,
    Whose anthems never cease,
We tune our lyres, with angel choirs,
    To hail the Prince of Peace!
Rejoice, ye Gentile lands, rejoice,
    And hail Immanuel's morn;
For God comes down, frail man to crown:
    To us a Child is born.

19   Joy to the World! the Lord is Come

ANTIOCH. C. M.

Isaac Watts, 1719   T. Hawkes' *Collection of Tunes*, 1833

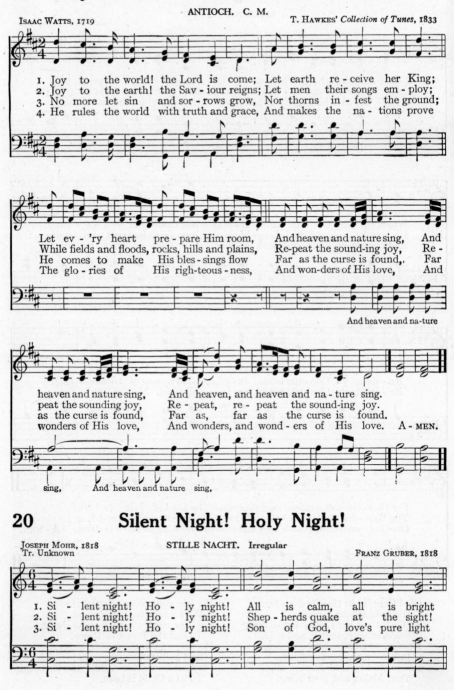

1. Joy to the world! the Lord is come; Let earth re - ceive her King;
2. Joy to the earth! the Sav - iour reigns; Let men their songs em - ploy;
3. No more let sin and sor - rows grow, Nor thorns in - fest the ground;
4. He rules the world with truth and grace, And makes the na - tions prove

Let ev - 'ry heart pre - pare Him room, And heaven and nature sing, And
While fields and floods, rocks, hills and plains, Re - peat the sound - ing joy, Re -
He comes to make His bles - sings flow Far as the curse is found, Far
The glo - ries of His righ - teous - ness, And won - ders of His love, And

And heaven and na-ture

heaven and nature sing, And heaven, and heaven and na - ture sing.
peat the sounding joy, Re - peat, re - peat the sound - ing joy.
as the curse is found, Far as, far as the curse is found.
wonders of His love, And wonders, and wond - ers of His love. A - MEN.

sing, And heaven and nature sing,

20   Silent Night! Holy Night!

STILLE NACHT. Irregular

Joseph Mohr, 1818
Tr. Unknown   Franz Gruber, 1818

1. Si - lent night! Ho - ly night! All is calm, all is bright
2. Si - lent night! Ho - ly night! Shep - herds quake at the sight!
3. Si - lent night! Ho - ly night! Son of God, love's pure light

Round yon Vir - gin Moth-er and Child. Ho - ly In - fant, so ten - der and mild,
Glo - ries stream from heav-en a - far, Heaven-ly hosts sing: Al - le - lu - ia,
Ra - diant beams from Thy ho - ly face, With the dawn of re - deem - ing grace,

Sleep in heav - en - ly peace. Sleep in heav - en - ly peace.
Christ, the Sav - iour, is born! Christ, the Sav - iour, is born!
Je - sus, Lord, at Thy birth. Je - sus, Lord, at Thy birth.

Hark! How the Angels Sing 21

GEORGE H. TRABERT, 1923   TRABERT. 6 4, 6 4, 6 6 4.   J. F. OHL, 1923

1. Hark! how the an - gels sing   On Christ - mas morn;   What is the
2. Shep-herds near Beth - le - hem   Saw a great light,   Bright-ness sur -
3. There in a man - ger, see   An In - fant lie;   The Son of
4. Let us re - joice and sing   On Christ - mas morn,   Je - sus our

news they bring? Je - sus is born. It rings through-out the sky:
round-ed them, Though it was night; An an - gel spake to them,
God is He, Sent from on high; There see God's love re - vealed,
Lord and King For us is born. That He might save from sin

Glo - ry to God on high, Je - sus is born, Je - sus is born.
Go, there in Beth - le - hem Je - sus is born, Je - sus is born.
His Word is now ful-filled, Je - sus is born, Je - sus is born.
And we might glo - ry win Je - sus is born, Je - sus is born. A - MEN.

22   Come! Ye Lofty, Come! Ye Lowly

ARCHER T. GURNEY, 1852

J. F. OHL, 1926

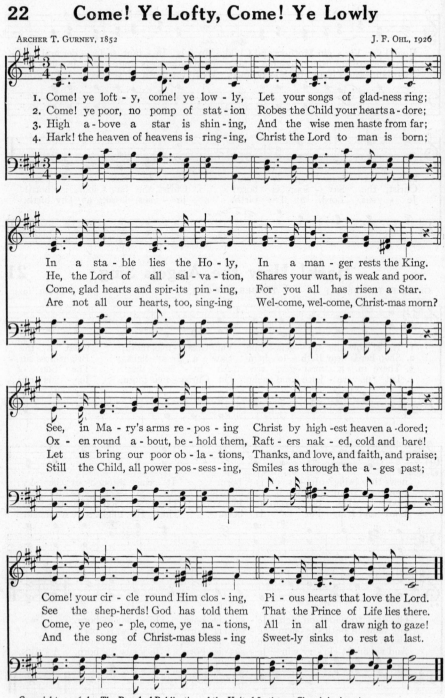

1. Come! ye loft - y, come! ye low - ly, Let your songs of glad-ness ring;
2. Come! ye poor, no pomp of stat - ion Robes the Child your hearts a - dore;
3. High a - bove a star is shin - ing, And the wise men haste from far;
4. Hark! the heaven of heavens is ring - ing, Christ the Lord to man is born;

In a sta - ble lies the Ho - ly, In a man - ger rests the King.
He, the Lord of all sal - va - tion, Shares your want, is weak and poor.
Come, glad hearts and spir-its pin - ing, For you all has risen a Star.
Are not all our hearts, too, sing-ing Wel-come, wel-come, Christ-mas morn?

See, in Ma - ry's arms re - pos - ing Christ by high -est heaven a -dored;
Ox - en round a - bout, be - hold them, Raft - ers nak - ed, cold and bare!
Let us bring our poor ob - la - tions, Thanks, and love, and faith, and praise;
Still the Child, all power pos - sess - ing, Smiles as through the a - ges past;

Come! your cir - cle round Him clos - ing, Pi - ous hearts that love the Lord.
See the shep-herds! God has told them That the Prince of Life lies there.
Come, ye peo - ple, come, ye na - tions, All in all draw nigh to gaze!
And the song of Christ-mas bless - ing Sweet-ly sinks to rest at last.

O Little Town of Bethlehem 23

PHILLIPS BROOKS, 1868

LEWIS H. REDNER, 1868

1. O lit - tle town of Beth - le - hem, How still we see thee lie!
2. For Christ is born of Ma - ry; And, gath - ered all a - bove,
3. How si - lent - ly, how si - lent - ly, The won - drous gift is given!
4. O Ho - ly Child of Beth - le - hem, De - scend to us, we pray;

A - bove thy deep and dream-less sleep, The si - lent stars go by;
While mor-tals sleep, the an - gels keep Their watch of won - d'ring love.
So God im - parts to hu - man hearts The bless - ings of His heaven.
Cast out our sin, and en - ter in, Be born in us to - day.

Yet in thy dark streets shin - eth The ev - er - last - ing Light:
O morn - ing stars, to - geth - er Pro - claim the ho - ly Birth!
No ear may hear His com - ing, But in this world of sin,
We hear the Christ - mas an - gels The great glad ti - dings tell;

The hopes and fears of all the years Are met in thee to - night.
And prais - es sing to God the King, And peace to men on earth.
Where meek souls will re - ceive Him still The dear Christ en - ters in.
O come to us, a - bide with us, Our Lord Im - man - u - el.

24 While Shepherds Watched Their Flocks

NAHUM TATE, 1700

Based on a melody by G. W. FINK, 1842
In SULLIVAN'S *Church Hymns*, 1874

1. While shep-herds watched their flocks by night, All seat-ed on the ground,
2. "To you, in Da-vid's town this day, Is born of Da-vid's line
3. Thus spake the ser-aph, and forth-with Ap-peared a shin-ing throng

The an-gel of the Lord came down, And glo-ry shone a-round.
A Sav-iour, Who is Christ, the Lord, And this shall be the sign:—
Of an-gels, prais-ing God, who thus Ad-dressed their joy-ful song:—

"Fear not," said he,— for might-y dread Had seized their trou-bled mind,—
The heaven-ly Babe you there shall find To hu-man view dis-played,
"All glo-ry be to God on high, And to the earth be peace;

"Glad ti-dings of great joy I bring To you and all man-kind."
All mean-ly wrapped in swath-ing bands, And in a man-ger laid."
Good-will hence-forth from heaven to men Be-gin and nev-er cease!"

It Came Upon the Midnight Clear

EDWARD H. SEARS, 1850, a.   RICHARD S. WILLIS, 1850

1. It came up-on   the mid-night clear, That glo-rious song of old,
2. Still through the clo-ven skies they come, With peace-ful wings un-furled,
3. And ye, be-neath life's crush-ing load, Whose forms are bend-ing low,
4. For lo, the days are hast-'ning on, By proph-ets seen of old,

From an-gels bend-ing near the earth   To touch their harps of gold:
And still their heavenly mu-sic floats   O'er all the wea-ry world;
Who toil a-long the climb-ing way   With pain-ful steps and slow;—
When with the ev-er-circ-ling years   Shall come the time fore-told,

"Peace on the earth, good will to men,   From heaven's all-gra-cious King":
A-bove its sad and low-ly plains They bend on hov-'ring wing,
Look now! for glad and gold-en hours Come swift-ly on the wing;
When the new heaven and earth shall own The Prince of Peace their King,

The world in sol-emn still-ness lay,   To hear the an-gels sing.
And ev-er o'er its Ba-bel-sounds The bless-ed an-gels sing.
O rest be-side the wea-ry road,   And hear the an-gels sing.
And the whole world send back the song Which now the an-gels sing.

26 Joy Fills Our Inmost Hearts Today

WM. CHATTERTON DIX, 1865

SAMUEL SMITH, 1874

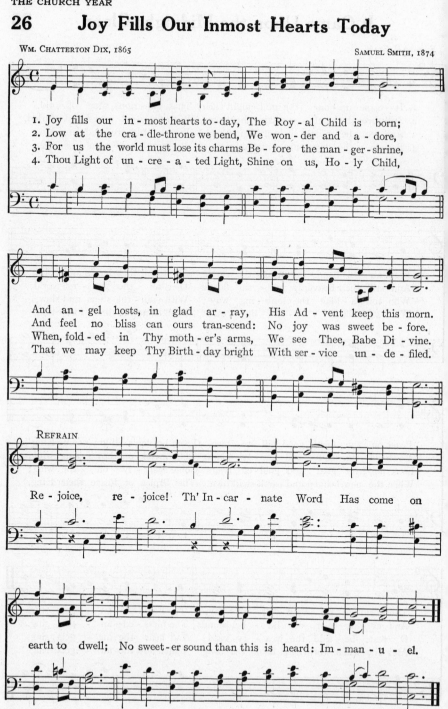

1. Joy fills our in - most hearts to - day, The Roy - al Child is born;
2. Low at the cra - dle-throne we bend, We won - der and a - dore,
3. For us the world must lose its charms Be - fore the man - ger - shrine,
4. Thou Light of un - cre - a - ted Light, Shine on us, Ho - ly Child,

And an - gel hosts, in glad ar - ray, His Ad - vent keep this morn.
And feel no bliss can ours tran-scend: No joy was sweet be - fore.
When, fold - ed in Thy moth - er's arms, We see Thee, Babe Di - vine.
That we may keep Thy Birth - day bright With ser - vice un - de - filed.

REFRAIN

Re - joice, re - joice! Th' In - car - nate Word Has come on

earth to dwell; No sweet - er sound than this is heard: Im - man - u - el.

The Joyful Morn Is Breaking   27

BENJAMIN GOUGH, 1873   EDWARD J. HOPKINS (1818–1901)

1. The joy - ful morn is break - ing, The bright - est morn of earth,
2. High strains of praise are swell - ing From an - gel hosts on high,
3. His chil - dren's songs shall name Him In man - y a tongue to - day;

Thro' all cre - a - tion wak - ing The joy of Je - sus' birth.
And one soft voice is tell - ing Glad ti - dings from the sky;
His Church shall yet pro - claim Him To peo - ple far a - way;

His star a - bove is glist - 'ning, Where Je - sus cra - dled lies,
Ti - dings of free sal - va - tion, Of peace on earth be - low;
Till i - dols fall be - fore Him, Till strife and wrong shall cease,

And all the earth is list - 'ning The car - ol of the skies.
Thro' ev - 'ry land and na - tion The bless - ed word shall go!
Till all the earth a - dore Him, Th'e - ter - nal Prince of Peace!

28   See, Amid the Winter's Snow

EDWARD CASWALL, 1851   JOHN GOSS, 1870

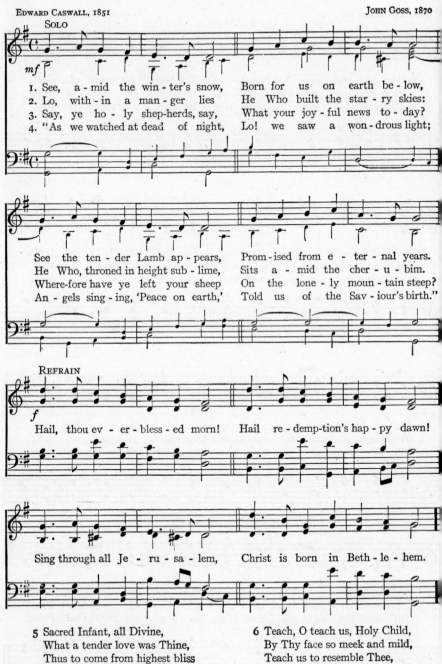

1. See, a-mid the win-ter's snow, Born for us on earth be-low,
2. Lo, with-in a man-ger lies He Who built the star-ry skies:
3. Say, ye ho-ly shep-herds, say, What your joy-ful news to-day?
4. "As we watched at dead of night, Lo! we saw a won-drous light;

See the ten-der Lamb ap-pears, Prom-ised from e-ter-nal years.
He Who, throned in height sub-lime, Sits a-mid the cher-u-bim.
Where-fore have ye left your sheep On the lone-ly moun-tain steep?
An-gels sing-ing, 'Peace on earth,' Told us of the Sav-iour's birth."

REFRAIN

Hail, thou ev-er-bless-ed morn! Hail re-demp-tion's hap-py dawn!

Sing through all Je-ru-sa-lem, Christ is born in Beth-le-hem.

5 Sacred Infant, all Divine,
What a tender love was Thine,
Thus to come from highest bliss
Down to such a world as this!

6 Teach, O teach us, Holy Child,
By Thy face so meek and mild,
Teach us to resemble Thee,
In Thy sweet humility.

Like Silver Lamps in a Distant Shrine 29

WM. CHATTERTON DIX, 1867   CHARLES STEGGALL, 1867

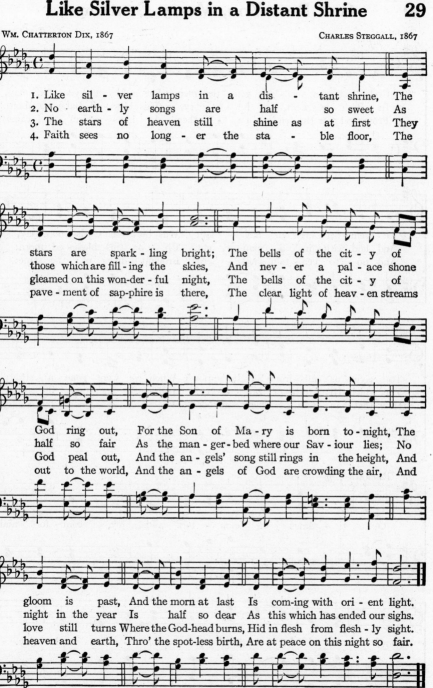

1. Like sil-ver lamps in a dis-tant shrine, The stars are spark-ling bright; The bells of the cit-y of God ring out, For the Son of Ma-ry is born to-night, The gloom is past, And the morn at last Is com-ing with ori-ent light.

2. No earth-ly songs are half so sweet As those which are fill-ing the skies, And nev-er a pal-ace shone half so fair As the man-ger-bed where our Sav-iour lies; No night in the year Is half so dear As this which has ended our sighs.

3. The stars of heaven still shine as at first They gleamed on this won-der-ful night, The bells of the cit-y of God peal out, And the an-gels' song still rings in the height, And love still turns Where the God-head burns, Hid in flesh from flesh-ly sight.

4. Faith sees no long-er the sta-ble floor, The pave-ment of sap-phire is there, The clear light of heav-en streams out to the world, And the an-gels of God are crowding the air, And heaven and earth, Thro' the spot-less birth, Are at peace on this night so fair.

30 God Rest You, Merry Gentlemen

4 "Fear not then," said the angel,
   "Let nothing you affright,
This day is born a Saviour
   Of a pure Virgin bright,
To free all those who trust in Him
   From Satan's power and might."

5 The shepherds at those tidings
   Did much rejoice in mind,
And left their flocks a-feeding,
   In tempest, storm, and wind:
And went to Bethlehem straightway,
   The Son of God to find.

6 And when they came to Bethlehem
   Where our dear Saviour lay,
They found Him in a manger,
   Where oxen feed on hay;
His Mother Mary kneeling down,
   Unto the Lord did pray.

7 Now to the Lord sing praises,
   All you within this place,
And with true love and brotherhood
   Adore our Saviour's grace;
This holy tide of Christmas
   All others doth deface.

Stars All Bright Are Beaming 31

RICHARD R. CHOPE (1830–)   W. R. HOLT

1. Stars all bright are beam-ing   From the skies a-bove, Na-ture's face all
2. Here for us   a-bid-ing,   Cra-dled in   a   stall, All His glo-ry
3. Born that He might lead   us   From this des-ert home,—Guide our way, and

REFRAIN

gleam-ing,   Shines with Heaven's own love.
hid-ing,   See   the   Lord of   all!   Wake and sing, good Chris-tians,
feed   us,   Till   the   end shall come.

On this birth-day morn, Heaven and earth are tell-ing God for man is born.

4 Thousand thousand blessings
   Sing we for His love,
Choral hymns addressing
   To our Lord above.

5 Glory in the highest,
   For this wondrous birth;
Choir of heaven! thou criest
   "Peace to all on earth!"

32 In the Silence of the Night

A. MARY R. DOBSON

A. MARY R. DOBSON

UNISON

1. In the si - lence of the night, Long, long years a - go,.......
From the star - ry heaven - ly height, Came the Christ be - low;......
He was born that men might know Joy in an - guish, rest in woe;
Yea, this Child did come to give Peace on earth that men might live.

2. Shep-herds from the far hill-side, Sought that man-ger rude;..... With the
3. Wise men on the de - sert track Hailed that bea - con bright, ... On - ward
4. We no an - gel's voice have heard, And no star we see, ... Yet we

an - gel's word to guide, They their way pur - sued...... Saw the low - ing
pressed and turned not back, Guid - ed by its light...... For to seek the
fain would trust Thy word, Yield - ing all to Thee...... Lo, we come with

ox - en nigh, Where the lit - tle Child did lie; Da - vid's Son come down to
King they came, All their hearts with love a - flame, Low - ly kneel - ing they a -
hearts a - glow, Through the cold-ness of the snow, For, dear Lord, Thou still dost

give Peace on earth, that men might live.
dored, For that Child was Christ the Lord. ORGAN. pp
give Peace on earth, that men may live.

33   Come and Hear the Grand Old Story

HORATIUS BONAR, 1861   J. F. OHL, 1886

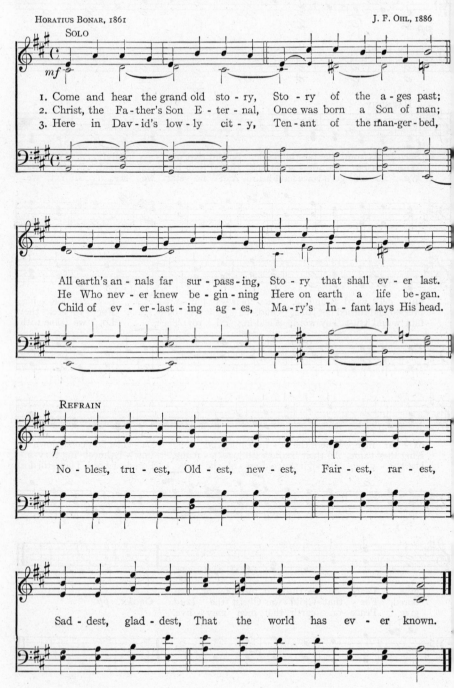

SOLO

1. Come and hear the grand old sto - ry, Sto - ry of the a - ges past;
2. Christ, the Fa - ther's Son E - ter - nal, Once was born a Son of man;
3. Here in Dav - id's low - ly cit - y, Ten - ant of the man - ger - bed,

All earth's an - nals far sur - pass - ing, Sto - ry that shall ev - er last.
He Who nev - er knew be - gin - ning Here on earth a life be - gan.
Child of ev - er - last - ing ag - es, Ma - ry's In - fant lays His head.

REFRAIN

No - blest, tru - est, Old - est, new - est, Fair - est, rar - est,

Sad - dest, glad - dest, That the world has ev - er known.

Good Christian Men, Rejoice

From the Latin
Tr. JOHN MASON NEALE, 1853

Pre-Reformation Melody

1. Good Chris-tian men, re - joice, With heart and soul and voice,
2. Good Chris-tian men, re - joice, With heart and soul and voice,
3. Good Chris-tian men, re - joice, With heart and soul and voice,

fz fz

Give ye heed to what we say: News! News! Je - sus Christ is born to - day!
Now ye hear of end - less bliss: Joy! Joy! Je - sus Christ was born for this!
Now ye need not fear the grave: Peace! Peace! Je - sus Christ was born to save!

Ox and ass be - fore Him bow, And He is in the
He hath oped the heaven - ly door, And man is bless - ed
Calls you one and calls you all, To gain His ev - er -

ff

man - ger now. Christ is born to - day! Christ is born to - day!
ev - er - more. Christ was born for this! Christ was born for this!
last - ing hall: Christ was born to save! Christ was born to save!

35   The First Noel the Angel Did Say

Traditional   Traditional

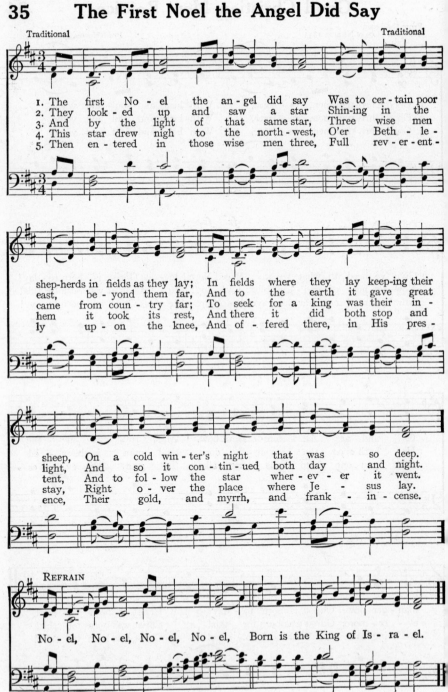

1. The first No - el the an - gel did say Was to cer - tain poor shep-herds in fields as they lay; In fields where they lay keep-ing their sheep, On a cold win - ter's night that was so deep.

2. They look - ed up and saw a star Shin-ing in the east, be - yond them far, And to the earth it gave great light, And so it con - tin - ued both day and night.

3. And by the light of that same star, Three wise men came from coun - try far; To seek for a king was their in - tent, And to fol - low the star wher - ev - er it went.

4. This star drew nigh to the north - west, O'er Beth - le - hem it took its rest, And there it did both stop and stay, Right o - ver the place where Je - sus lay.

5. Then en - tered in those wise men three, Full rev - er - ent - ly up - on the knee, And of - fered there, in His pres - ence, Their gold, and myrrh, and frank - in - cense.

REFRAIN

No - el, No - el, No - el, No - el, Born is the King of Is - ra - el.

There Dwelt in Old Judea

Traditional

ROBERT JACKSON (1840–)

In Unison

1. There dwelt in old Ju - de - a, A maid - en fair to see;
2. And as the In - fant Je - sus Lay on His low - ly bed,
3. The shep - herds bowed be - fore Him, While an - gels swift did fly

The Moth - er mild and un - de-filed, Of a bless - ed Babe was she.
A cir - cle bright of heaven - ly light Shone round a - bout His head.
On blest em-ploy, with songs of joy, To fill the star - ry sky.

REFRAIN. In Harmony

Sing No - el, sing No - el, And mer - ry be al - way;

For Christ was born, in the ear - ly morn, All on a Christ-mas Day.

4 For this was Prince Emmanuel,
　Who laid aside His crown;
　And all to win our souls from sin
　Unto the earth came down.

5 Now Christ, my dear Redeemer,
　I give my heart to Thee;
　For, by my word, this loving Lord
　Shall be the Lord of me.

37 When Christ Was Born of Mary Free

Traditional

J. F. OHL, 1926

f Allegro commodo

mf

1. When Christ was born of Ma - ry free In Beth - le - hem, that
2. Herdsmen be - held those an - gels bright. To them ap-pear - ing
3. This King is come to save man-kind, In Scrip - ture prom - ised
4. Grant us, O Lord, for Thy great grace, In heaven the bliss to

fair cit - ie, The an - gels sang with mirth and glee, "In ex-cel - sis glo - ri - a."
with great light, And said, "God's Son is born this night, In ex-cel - sis glo - ri - a."
as we find. We there-fore have this song in mind, "In ex-cel - sis glo - ri - a."
see Thy face, That we may sing to Thy so - lace—"In ex-cel - sis glo - ri - a."

f

"In - ex - cel - sis glo - ri - a, In ex - cel - sis glo - ri - a,

In ex - cel - sis, In ex - cel - sis glo - ri - a."

After the last stanza

ff

"In ex - cel - sis glo - ri - a, In ex - cel - sis glo - ri - a,

ff

In ex - cel - sis, In ex - cel - sis glo - ri - a."

38 Sing, Sing for Christmas

J. H. Egar

W. W. Rousseau

1. Sing, sing for Christ-mas! Wel-come hap-py day! For Christ is born, our Sav-iour,
2. Tell, tell the sto-ry Of the won-drous night When shep-herds who were watch-ing
3. Soft, soft-ly shin-ing, Stars were in the sky, And sil-ver fell the moon-light

To take our sins a-way. Sing, sing a joy-ful song, Loud and clear to-day,
Their flocks till morn-ing light, Saw an-gel hosts from heaven, Heard the an-gel voice,
On hill and moun-tain high, When sud-den-ly the night Outshone the bright midday

To praise our Lord and Sav-iour, Who in the man-ger lay.
And so were told the ti-dings, Which make the world re-joice.
With an-gel hosts who her-ald The reign of peace for aye.

CHORUS

Sing, sing for Christ-mas! Wel-come hap-py day! For

Christ is born, our Sav-iour, To take our sins a-way.

4 Hark, hear them singing,
   Singing in the sky,
"Be worship, honor, glory,
   And praise to God on high!
Peace, peace, good-will to men,
   Born the Child from heaven!
The Christ, the Lord, the Saviour.
   The Son to you is given!"

5 Sing, sing for Christmas.
   Echo, earth, the cry
Of worship, honor, glory,
   And praise to God on high!
Sing, sing the joyful song,
   Let it never cease,
Of glory in the highest,
   On earth, good-will and peace.

Child Jesus Came from Heaven to Earth 39

From the Danish of
HANS CHRISTIAN ANDERSEN (1805–1875)

J. F. OHL, 1886

mf

1. Child Je - sus came from heaven to earth, The Fa - ther's mer - cy show - ing;
2. O soul with sin and grief cast down, For - get thy bit - ter sad - ness!

In sta - ble mean He had His birth, No bet - ter cra - dle know - ing;
A Child is come to Dav - id's town, To bring thee joy and glad - ness!

Trebles only   *Trebles and Altos*

A star smiled down the Babe to greet, The hum - ble ox - en
O let us haste the Child to find, And child - like be in

Full

f

kissed His feet: Al - le - lu - ia, Al - le - lu - ia, Child Je - sus!
heart and mind: Al - le - lu - ia, Al - le - lu - ia, Child Je - sus!

40 Away in a Manger

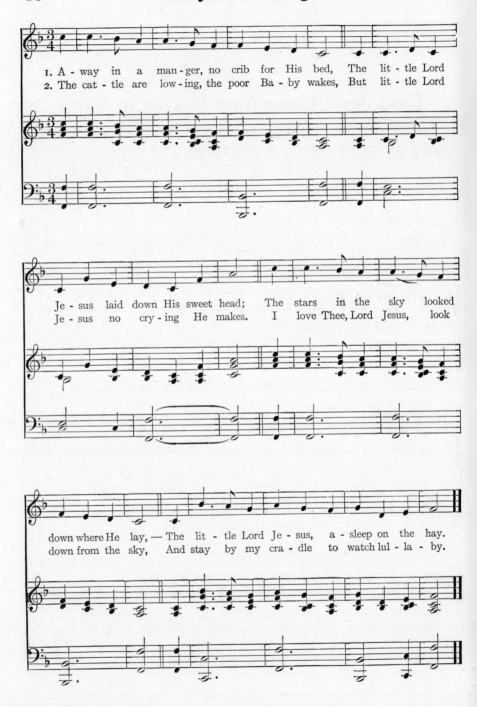

1. A - way in a man - ger, no crib for His bed, The lit - tle Lord
2. The cat - tle are low - ing, the poor Ba - by wakes, But lit - tle Lord

Je - sus laid down His sweet head; The stars in the sky looked
Je - sus no cry - ing He makes. I love Thee, Lord Jesus, look

down where He lay, — The lit - tle Lord Je - sus, a - sleep on the hay.
down from the sky, And stay by my cra - dle to watch lul - la - by.

'Tis Christmas Day

S. ARCHER GIBSON

J. F. OHL, 1926

1. Oh, what mean these songs they're sing-ing? 'Tis Christ - mas Day!
2. See these gifts that we're re - ceiv - ing; 'Tis Christ - mas Day!
3. Glo - ry be to God in heav - en, 'Tis Christ - mas Day!

Oh, what mean these bells they're ring - ing? 'Tis Christ - mas Day!
To - ken of God's won - drous giv - ing, 'Tis Christ - mas Day!
Who for us His Son has giv - en, 'Tis Christ - mas Day!

Oh, what mean these or - gans peal - ing, What this news that they're re - veal - ing,
Oh, that we may not for - sake Him, Oh, that we our - selves may take Him,
Loud we raise our hap - py voi - ces, Na - ture adds har - mo - nious noi - ses,

Tens of thou - sands low - ly kneel - ing? 'Tis Christ - mas Day!
On - ly gift that we can make Him! 'Tis Christ - mas Day!
All His world in Him re - joic - es! 'Tis Christ - mas Day!

42 Carol, Sweetly Carol

FANNY J. CROSBY (1823–1915)

The Children's Hymn Book, London

1. Car - ol, sweet - ly car - ol, A Sav - iour born to - day;
2. Car - ol, sweet - ly car - ol, As when the An - gel throng,
3. Car - ol, sweet - ly car - ol, The hap - py Christ - mas time:

Bear the joy - ful ti - dings, Oh, bear them far a - way! Car - ol, sweet - ly
O'er the vales of Ju - dah, A - woke the heavenly song: Car - ol, sweet - ly
Hark! the bells are peal - ing Their mer - ry, mer - ry chime: Car - ol, sweet - ly

car - ol, Till earth's re - mot - est bound Shall hear the might - y cho - rus,
car - ol, Good-will, and peace, and love, Glo - ry in the high - est
car - ol, Ye shin - ing ones a - bove, Sing in loud - est num - bers,

CHORUS

And ech - o back the sound. Car - ol, sweet - ly car - ol, Car - ol
To God who reigns a - bove.
Oh, sing re - deem - ing love.

Car - ol, car - ol, Car - ol

sweet - ly to - day; Bear the joy - ful ti - dings, Oh, bear them far a - way!
ol, car - ol;

sweet - ly to - day;

At the Name of Jesus

BOHEMIA. 6 5, 6 5. D.

CAROLINE M. NOEL, 1870

Adapted from the Melody
"Laus Tibi, Christe," XIV Century

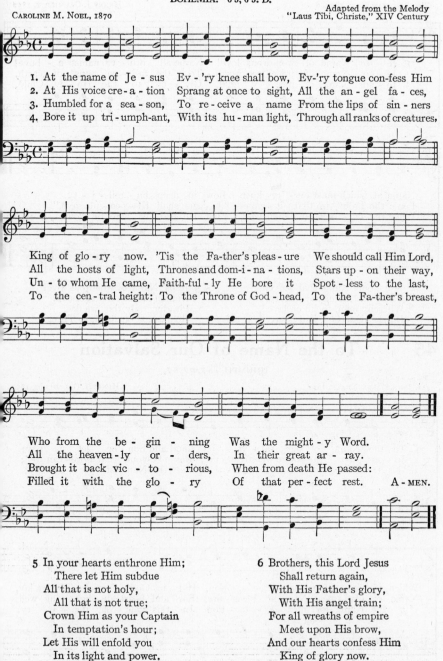

1. At the name of Je - sus Ev - 'ry knee shall bow, Ev-'ry tongue con-fess Him
2. At His voice cre-a-tion Sprang at once to sight, All the an-gel fa-ces,
3. Humbled for a sea-son, To re-ceive a name From the lips of sin-ners
4. Bore it up tri-umph-ant, With its hu-man light, Through all ranks of creatures,

King of glo-ry now. 'Tis the Fa-ther's pleas-ure We should call Him Lord,
All the hosts of light, Thrones and dom-i-na-tions, Stars up-on their way,
Un-to whom He came, Faith-ful-ly He bore it Spot-less to the last,
To the cen-tral height: To the Throne of God-head, To the Fa-ther's breast,

Who from the be-gin-ning Was the might-y Word.
All the heaven-ly or-ders, In their great ar-ray.
Brought it back vic-to-rious, When from death He passed:
Filled it with the glo-ry Of that per-fect rest. A-MEN.

5 In your hearts enthrone Him;
There let Him subdue
All that is not holy,
All that is not true;
Crown Him as your Captain
In temptation's hour;
Let His will enfold you
In its light and power.

6 Brothers, this Lord Jesus
Shall return again,
With His Father's glory,
With His angel train;
For all wreaths of empire
Meet upon His brow,
And our hearts confess Him
King of glory now.

44   Jesus! Name of Wondrous Love

UNIVERSITY COLLEGE. 7 7, 7 7.

WM. WALSHAM HOW, 1854, a   HENRY J. GAUNTLETT, 1852

1. Je - sus! Name of won-drous love! Name all oth - er names a - bove!
2. Je - sus! Name of price - less worth To the fall - en sons of earth,
3. Je - sus! Name of mer - cy mild, Giv - en to the Ho - ly Child,

Name at which must ev - 'ry knee Bow in deep hu - mil - i - ty.
For the prom - ise that it gave— "Je - sus shall His peo - ple save."
When the cup of hu - man woe First He tast - ed here be - low. A - MEN.

4 Jesus! only Name that's given
Under all the mighty heaven,
Whereby man, to sin enslaved,
Bursts his fetters, and is saved.

5 Jesus! Name of wondrous love!
Human Name of God above!
Pleading only this, we flee,
Helpless, O our God, to Thee.

45   To the Name of Our Salvation

TRIUMPH. 8 7, 8 7, 8 7.

From the Latin
Tr. JOHN MASON NEALE, 1851   HENRY J. GAUNTLETT, 1852

1. To the Name of our sal - va - tion Laud and hon - or let us pay;
2. Je - sus is the Name we treas - ure, Name be-yond what words can tell;
3. 'Tis the Name for ad - o - ra - tion; 'Tis the Name of vic - to - ry;

Which, for ma - ny a gen - er - a - tion, Hid in God's fore - knowl-edge lay,
Name of glad - ness, Name of pleas - ure, Ear and heart de - light - ing well;
'Tis the Name for med - i - ta - tion In this vale of mis - e - ry;

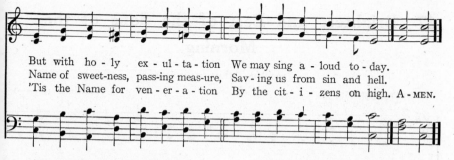

But with ho - ly ex - ul - ta - tion We may sing a - loud to - day.
Name of sweet-ness, pass-ing meas-ure, Sav - ing us from sin and hell.
'Tis the Name for ven - er - a - tion By the cit - i - zens on high. A - MEN.

4 'Tis the Name by right exalted
  Over every other name;
That, when we are sore assaulted,
  Puts our enemies to shame;
Strength to them who else had halted,
  Eyes to blind, and feet to lame.

5 Jesus, we, Thy Name adoring,
  Long to see Thee as Thou art;
Of Thy clemency imploring
  So to write it in our heart,
That hereafter, upward soaring,
  We with angels may have part.

How Sweet the Name of Jesus Sounds 46

ST. PETER. C. M.

JOHN NEWTON, 1779

ALEXANDER R. REINAGLE, 1830

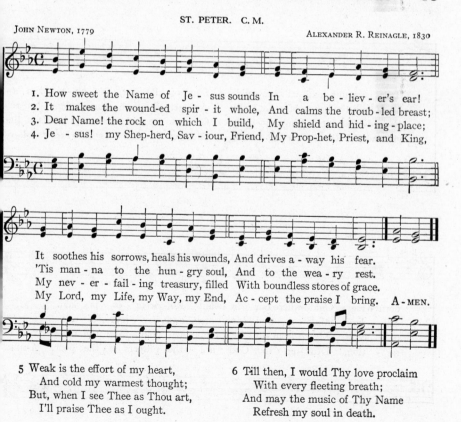

1. How sweet the Name of Je - sus sounds In a be - liev - er's ear!
2. It makes the wound-ed spir - it whole, And calms the troub-led breast;
3. Dear Name! the rock on which I build, My shield and hid - ing - place;
4. Je - sus! my Shep-herd, Sav - iour, Friend, My Proph-et, Priest, and King,

It soothes his sorrows, heals his wounds, And drives a - way his fear.
'Tis man - na to the hun - gry soul, And to the wea - ry rest.
My nev - er - fail - ing treasury, filled With boundless stores of grace.
My Lord, my Life, my Way, my End, Ac - cept the praise I bring. A - MEN.

5 Weak is the effort of my heart,
  And cold my warmest thought;
But, when I see Thee as Thou art,
  I'll praise Thee as I ought.

6 Till then, I would Thy love proclaim
  With every fleeting breath;
And may the music of Thy Name
  Refresh my soul in death.

47 Brightest and Best of the Sons of the Morning

MORNING STAR. 11 10, 11 10.

REGINALD HEBER, 1811

J. P. HARDING (1861———)

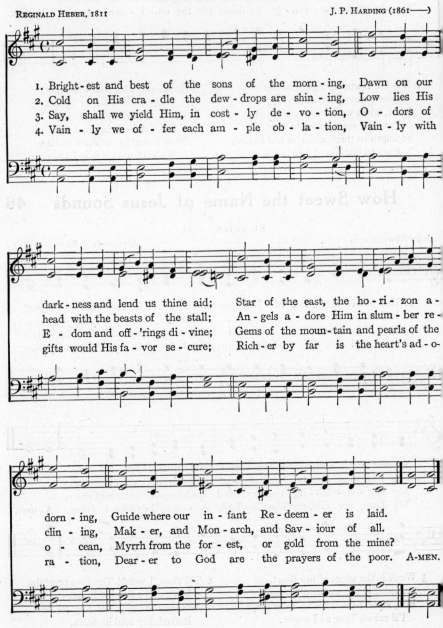

1. Bright-est and best of the sons of the morn-ing, Dawn on our
2. Cold on His cra-dle the dew-drops are shin-ing, Low lies His
3. Say, shall we yield Him, in cost-ly de-vo-tion, O-dors of
4. Vain-ly we of-fer each am-ple ob-la-tion, Vain-ly with

dark-ness and lend us thine aid; Star of the east, the ho-ri-zon a-
head with the beasts of the stall; An-gels a-dore Him in slum-ber re-
E-dom and off-'rings di-vine; Gems of the moun-tain and pearls of the
gifts would His fa-vor se-cure; Rich-er by far is the heart's ad-o-

dorn-ing, Guide where our in-fant Re-deem-er is laid.
clin-ing, Mak-er, and Mon-arch, and Sav-iour of all.
o-cean, Myrrh from the for-est, or gold from the mine?
ra-tion, Dear-er to God are the prayers of the poor. A-MEN.

As With Gladness Men of Old

DIX. 7 7, 7 7, 7 77.

WM. CHATTERTON DIX, 1860

CONRAD KOCHER, 1836

1. As with glad-ness men of old Did the guid-ing star be-hold;
2. As with joy-ful steps they sped To that low-ly man-ger-bed,
3. As they of-fered gifts most rare At that man-ger rude and bare;

As with joy they hailed its light, Lead-ing on-ward, beam-ing bright;
There to bend the knee be-fore Thee Whom heaven and earth a - dore;
So may we, with ho-ly joy, Pure, and free from sin's al - loy,

So, most gra-cious God, may we Ev - er - more be led to Thee.
So may we, with will-ing feet, Ev - er seek Thy mer - cy - seat.
All our cost-liest treas-ures bring, Christ, to Thee, our heavenly King. A-MEN.

4 Holy Jesus! every day
Keep us in the narrow way,
And, when earthly things are past,
Bring our ransomed souls at last
Where they need no star to guide,
Where no clouds Thy glory hide.

5 In the heavenly country bright
Need they no created light;
Thou its Light, its Joy, its Crown,
Thou its Sun which goes not down;
There for ever may we sing
Hallelujahs to our King.

49   O Thou, Who By a Star Didst Guide

ST. LEONARD. C. M. D.

JOHN MASON NEALE, 1842   HENRY HILES, 1867

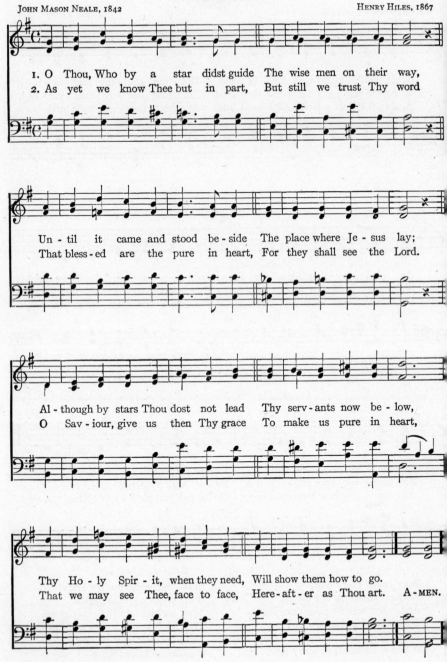

1. O Thou, Who by a star didst guide The wise men on their way,
2. As yet we know Thee but in part, But still we trust Thy word

Un - til it came and stood be - side The place where Je - sus lay;
That bless - ed are the pure in heart, For they shall see the Lord.

Al - though by stars Thou dost not lead Thy serv - ants now be - low,
O Sav - iour, give us then Thy grace To make us pure in heart,

Thy Ho - ly Spir - it, when they need, Will show them how to go.
That we may see Thee, face to face, Here - aft - er as Thou art. A - MEN.

Hail to the Lord's Anointed

AURELIA. 7 6, 7 6. D.

James Montgomery, 1821

Samuel S. Wesley, 1864

1. Hail to the Lord's A - noint - ed, Great Da - vid's great - er Son!
2. He comes with suc - cor speed - y To those who suf - fer wrong;
3. He shall come down like show - ers Up - on the fruit - ful earth;
4. Kings shall fall down be - fore Him, And gold and in - cense bring;

Hail, in the time ap - point - ed, His reign on earth be - gun!
To help the poor and need - y, And bid the weak be strong;
And love, joy, hope, like flow - ers, Spring in His path to birth.
All na - tions shall a - dore Him, His praise all peo - ple sing.

He comes to break op - pres - sion, To set the cap - tive free;
To give them songs for sigh - ing; Their dark - ness turn to light,
Be - fore Him on the moun - tains Shall peace, the her - ald, go;
To Him shall prayer un - ceas - ing And dai - ly vows as - cend;

To take a - way trans - gres - sion, And rule in e - qui - ty.
Whose souls, condemned and dy - ing, Were pre - cious in His sight.
Of right - eous - ness the fount - ains From hill to val - ley flow.
His king - dom still in - creas - ing, A king - dom with-out end. A-MEN.

51 From the Eastern Mountains

ST. THERESA. 6 5, 6 5. D. With Refrain.

GODFREY THRING, 1873

ARTHUR S. SULLIVAN, 1874

VOICES IN UNISON

1. From the east-ern moun-tains, Press-ing on they come, Wise men in their
2. There their Lord and Sav-iour Meek and low-ly lay, Wondrous Light that
3. Thou Who in a man-ger Once hast low-ly lain, Who dost now in

wis - dom, To His hum-ble home; Stirred by deep de - vo - tion,
led them On-ward on their way, Ev - er now to light - en
glo - ry O'er all king-doms reign, Gath - er in the heath - en,

Hast-ing from a - far, Ev - er journ'ying on-ward, Guid-ed by a star.
Na - tions from a - far, As they journey home-ward By that guid-ing star.
Who in lands a - far Ne'er have seen the brightness Of Thy guid-ing star.

REFRAIN

Light of Life, that shin - est Ere the world be - gan,

Draw Thou near and light - en Ev - 'ry heart of man. A - MEN.

4 Gather in the outcasts,
    All who've gone astray,
  Throw Thy radiance o'er them,
    Guide them on their way,
  Those who never knew Thee,
    Those who've wandered far,
  Lead them by the brightness
    Of Thy guiding star.

5 Until every nation,
    Whether bond or free,
  'Neath Thy starlit banner,
    Jesus, follows Thee
  O'er the distant mountains
    To that heavenly home,
  Where no sin nor sorrow
    Evermore shall come.

52   There Came Three Kings

GERARD MOULTRIE (1829–1854)

R. F. SMITH
In CHOPE'S *Carols for Use in Church*, 1875

1. There came three kings, ere break of day, All on E - piph - a - nie;
2. The star shone bright - ly o - ver - head, The air was calm and still,
3. An old man knelt at a man - ger low, A Babe lay in the stall;

Their gifts they bare, both rich and rare, All, all, Lord Christ for Thee;
O'er Beth-lehem's fields its rays were shed, The dew lay on the hill.
The star - light played on the In - fant brow, Deep sil - ence lay o'er all;

Gold, frank - in - cense, and myrrh are there. Where is the King? O
We see no throne, no pal - ace fair, Where is the King? O
A maiden bent o'er the Babe in prayer:— There is the King! O

where? O where? O where is the King? O where?
where? O where? O where is the King? O where?
there! O there! O there is the King! O there!

We Three Kings of Orient Are 53

JOHN H. HOPKINS, 1857   JOHN H. HOPKINS, 1857

UNISON

1. We three kings of O - ri-ent are, Bear - ing gifts we trav-erse a - far,
2. Born a King on Bethlehem's plain, Gold I bring to crown Him a - gain,
3. Frank - in-cense to of - fer have I, In - cense owns a De - i - ty nigh;

Field and foun - tain, moor and moun-tain, Follow-ing yon - der star.
King for - ev - er, ceas - ing nev - er O - ver us all to reign.
Prayer and prais - ing, all men rais - ing, Wor-ship Him, God on high.

REFRAIN

O star of won - der, star of night, Star with roy - al beau - ty bright,

West - ward lead - ing, still pro-ceed - ing, Guide us to thy per - fect light.

4 Myrrh is mine; its bitter perfume
  Breathes a life of gathering gloom:
Sorrowing, sighing, bleeding, dying,
  Sealed in the stone-cold tomb.

5 Glorious now behold Him arise,
  King, and God, and Sacrifice;
Alleluia, alleluia!
  Earth to heaven replies.

54 There's a Beautiful Star

ROSSITER W. RAYMOND (1840–1918)   FREDERICK SCHILLING

1. There's a beau-ti-ful star, a beau-ti-ful star, That
2. In the land of the East, in the shad-ows of night, We
3. We have gold for trib-ute and gifts for prayer, Sweet

wea-ry trav'lers have fol-lowed a-far; Shin-ing so bright-ly
saw the glo-ry of thy new light; Tell-ing to us, in our
in-cense, myrrh, and spi-ces rare: All that we have we

all the way, Till it stood o'er the place where the young Child lay.
dis-tant home, The Lord, our Re-deem-er, to earth had come!
hith-er bring, To lay it with joy at the feet of the King.

REFRAIN

Star, star, beau-ti-ful star! Pil-grims wea-ry we are;

To Je-sus, to Je-sus, We fol-low thee from a-far.

There's a Song in the Air

55

J. G. HOLLAND, 1872

J. F. OHL, 1926

1. There's a song in the air! There's a star in the sky!
2. There's a tu - mult of joy O'er the won - der - ful birth,
3. In the light of that star Lie the a - ges im-pearled;
4. We re - joice in the light, And we ech - o the song

There's a moth - er's deep prayer, And a ba - by's low cry!
For the Vir - gin's sweet boy Is the Lord of the earth.
And that song from a - far Has swept o - ver the world.
That comes down through the night From the heav - en - ly throng.

And the star rains its fire while the beau - ti - ful sing,
Ay! the star rains its fire while the beau - ti - ful sing,
Ev - ery hearth is a - flame, and the beau - ti - ful sing
Ay! we shout to the love - ly e - van - gel they bring,

For the man - ger of Beth - le - hem cra - dles a King!
For the man - ger of Beth - le - hem cra - dles a King!
In the homes of the na - tions that Je - sus is King!
And we greet in His cra - dle our Sav - iour and King!

56 In the Cross of Christ I Glory

RATHBUN. 8 7, 8 7.

JOHN BOWRING, 1825

ITHAMAR CONKEY, 1851

1. In the Cross of Christ I glo-ry, Tow'r-ing o'-er the wrecks of time;
2. When the woes of life o'er-take me, Hopes de-ceive and fears an-noy,
3. When the sun of bliss is beam-ing Light and love up-on my way,
4. Bane and bless-ing, pain and pleas-ure, By the Cross are sanc-ti-fied;

All the light of sa-cred sto-ry Gath-ers round its head sub-lime.
Nev-er shall the Cross for-sake me; Lo! it glows with peace and joy.
From the Cross the radiance stream-ing Adds more lus-tre to the day.
Peace is there that knows no meas-ure, Joys that through all time a-bide. A-MEN.

57 Sweet the Moments, Rich in Blessing

BATTY. 8 7, 8 7

JAMES ALLEN, 1757
WALTER SHIRLEY, 1770

Adapted from *Ringe recht wenn Gottes Gnade*, 1745

1. Sweet the mo-ments, rich in bless-ing, Which be-fore the Cross we spend;
2. Here we rest in won-der, view-ing All our sins on Je-sus laid;
3. Here we find the dawn of heav-en, While up-on the Cross we gaze;
4. O that near the Cross a-bid-ing, We may to the Sav-iour cleave;

Life and health and peace pos-sess-ing, From the sin-ner's dy-ing Friend.
Here we see re-demp-tion flow-ing From the sac-ri-fice He made.
See our tres-pass-es for-giv-en, And our songs of tri-umph raise.
Naught with Him our hearts di-vid-ing, All for Him con-tent to leave. A-MEN.

Hail, Thou Once Despised Jesus

SUPPLICATION. 8 7, 8 7. D.

JOHN BAKEWELL, 1757
MADAN'S *Collection*, 1760
AUGUSTUS M. TOPLADY, 1776

WILLIAM H. MONK (1823-1889)

1. Hail, Thou once de - spis - ed Je - sus! Hail, Thou Gal - i - le - an King!
2. Pas - chal Lamb, by God ap - point - ed, All our sins on Thee were laid;
3. Je - sus, hail, en-throned in glo - ry, There for ev - er to a - bide!
4. Wor - ship, hon - or, pow'r, and bless - ing Thou art worth - y to re-ceive;

Thou didst suf - fer to re - lease us; Thou didst free sal - va - tion bring.
By al - might - y love a - noint - ed, Thou hast full a - tone - ment made.
All the heaven-ly hosts a - dore Thee, Seat - ed at Thy Fa - ther's side;
Loud - est prais - es, with - out ceas - ing, Meet it is for us to give.

Hail, Thou ag - o - niz - ing Sav - iour, Bear - er of our sin and shame!
All Thy peo - ple are for - giv - en Through the vir - tue of Thy Blood;
There for sin - ners Thou art plead - ing, There Thou dost our place pre - pare,
Help, ye bright an - gel - ic spir - its, Bring your sweet - est, no-blest lays,

By Thy mer - its we find fa - vor; Life is given through Thy Name.
O - pened is the gate of heav-en; Peace is made 'twixt man and God.
Ev - er for us in - ter - ced - ing, Till in glo - ry we ap - pear.
Help to sing our Sav-iour's mer-its, Help to chant Im-man - uel's praise. A-MEN.

59

I Adore Thee

W. J. SPARROW SIMPSON

ADORATION. 8 7, 8 8, 7.

From *The Crucifixion*
JOHN STAINER (1840–1901)

1. I a - dore Thee, I a - dore Thee! Glo - rious ere the
2. I a - dore Thee, I a - dore Thee! Thank - ful at Thy
3. I a - dore Thee, I a - dore Thee, Born of wo - man,

world be - gan; Yet more won - der - ful Thou shin - est, Tho' di -
feet to be; I have heard Thy ac - cent thrill - ing, Lo! I
yet Di - vine: Stained with sins I kneel be - fore Thee, Sweet - est

vine, yet still di - vin - est In Thy dy - ing love for man.
come, for Thou art will - ing Me to par - don, ev - en me.
Je - sus, I im - plore Thee, Make me ev - er on - ly Thine. A - MEN.

60

Holy Jesus, By Thy Passion

W. J. SPARROW SIMPSON

PLEAD FOR ME. 8 7, 8 7, 7 7.

From *The Crucifixion*
JOHN STAINER (1840–1901)

1. Ho - ly Je - sus, by Thy Pas - sion, By the woes which none can share,
2. By the treach - er - y and tri - al, By the blows and sore dis - tress,
3. By Thy look so sweet and low - ly, While they smote Thee on the face,
4. By the hour of con - dem - na - tion, By the blood which trick - led down,

Borne in more than king - ly fash - ion, By Thy love be - yond com - pare:
By de - ser - tion and de - ni - al, By Thine aw - ful lone - li - ness:
By Thy pa - tience, calm and ho - ly, In the midst of keen dis - grace:
When, for us and our sal - va - tion, Thou didst wear the robe and crown:

Cru - ci - fied, I turn to Thee, Son of Ma - ry, plead for me. A - MEN

Wide Open Are Thy Hands 61

SALVE JESU. S. M. D.

BERNARD OF CLAIRVAUX (?), d. 1153
Tr. CHARLES PORTERFIELD KRAUTH, 1870, a

HAROLD LEWARS, 1914

1. Wide o - pen are Thy hands, Pay - ing with more than gold
2. Wide o - pen are Thine arms, A fall - en world to em - brace;
3. Draw all my mind and heart Up to Thy throne on high,

The aw - ful debt of guilt - y men, For - ev - er and of old.
To take to love and end - less rest Our whole for - sak - en race.
And let Thy sa - cred Cross ex - alt My spir - it to the sky.

Ah, let me grasp those hands, That we may nev - er part,
Lord, I am sad and poor, But bound - less is Thy grace;
To these, Thy might - y hands, My spir - it I re - sign:

And let the pow - er of their blood Sus - tain my faint - ing heart.
Give me the soul-trans-form-ing joy For which I seek Thy face.
Liv - ing, I live a - lone to Thee, Dy - ing, a - lone am Thine. A - MEN.

62 **Lord of Mercy and of Might**

IRENE. *7 7 7, 5.*

REGINALD HEBER, 1811, a   CLEMENT C. SCHOLEFIELD, 1874

1. Lord of mer-cy and of might, Of man-kind the Life and Light,
2. Strong Cre - a - tor, Sav-iour mild, Hum-bled to a mor - tal child,
3. Throned a-bove ce - les - tial things, Borne a - loft on an-gels' wings,
4. Soon to come to earth a - gain, Judge of an-gels and of men,

Mak - er, Teach-er, In - fi - nite: Je - sus, hear and save!
Cap - tive, beat-en, bound, re - viled: Je - sus, hear and save!
Lord of lords, and King of kings: Je - sus, hear and save!
Hear us now, and hear us then: Je - sus, hear and save! A-MEN.

63 **Jesus, and Shall it Ever Be**

BRESLAU. L. M.

JOSEPH GRIGG, 1765
Revised by BENJAMIN FRANCIS, 1787   Melody in *As Hymnodus Sacer,* Leipzig, 1625

1. Je - sus, and shall it ev - er be, A mor-tal man a-shamed of Thee?
2. A-shamed of Je - sus! soon - er far Let eve-ning blush to own a star;
3. A-shamed of Je - sus! just as soon Let mid-night be a-shamed of noon:
4. A-shamed of Je - sus! that dear Friend On whom my hopes of heaven de-pend!

Ashamed of Thee, Whom angels praise, Whose glories shine through endless days?
He sheds the beams of light di-vine O'er this be-night-ed soul of mine.
'Tis mid-night with my soul, till He, Bright Morning Star, bid darkness flee.
No; when I blush, be this my shame, That I no more re-vere His Name. A - MEN.

5 Ashamed of Jesus! yes, I may,
When I've no guilt to wash away,
No tear to wipe, no good to crave,
No fears to quell, no soul to save.

6 Till then—nor is my boasting vain—
Till then I boast a Saviour slain!
And O, may this my glory be,
That Christ is not ashamed of me.

O Lamb of God, Still Keep Me 64

ST. CHRISTOPHER. 7 6, 7 6, D.

JAMES G. DECK, 1842

FREDERICK C. MAKER, 1881

1. O Lamb of God, still keep me Near to Thy wound-ed side!
2. 'Tis on-ly in Thee hid-ing, I feel my life se-cure;
3. Soon shall my eyes be-hold Thee, With rap-ture, face to face;

'Tis on-ly there in safe-ty And peace I can a-bide.
On-ly in Thee a-bid-ing, The con-flict can en-dure:
One half hath not been told me Of all Thy power and grace;

What foes and snares sur-round me, What lusts and fears with-in!
Thine arm the vic-t'ry gain-eth O'er ev-ery hurt-ful foe;
Thy beau-ty, Lord, and glo-ry, The won-ders of Thy love,

The grace that sought and found me A-lone can keep me clean.
Thy love my heart sus-tain-eth In all its care and woe.
Shall be the end-less sto-ry Of all Thy saints a-bove. A-MEN.

65   Jesus, Meek and Lowly

- ST. MARTIN.   6 6, 6 6. Trochaic.

HENRY COLLINS, 1854   C. ETT's *Cantica Sacra*, 1840

1. Je - sus, meek and low - ly,   Sav - iour, pure and ho - ly,
2. Prince of life and pow - er,   My sal - va - tion's tow - er,
3. There be - hold me gaz - ing   At the sight a - maz - ing;
4. By Thy red wounds stream - ing,   With Thy life - blood gleam - ing,

On Thy love re - ly - ing,   Hear me hum - bly cry - ing.
On the Cross I view Thee   Call - ing sin - ners to Thee.
Bend - ing low be - fore Thee,   Help - less, I a - dore Thee.
Blood for sin - ners flow - ing,   Par - don free be - stow - ing;   A-MEN

5 By that fount of blessing,
Thy dear love expressing,
All my aching sadness
Turn Thou into gladness.

6 Lord, in mercy guide me;
Be Thou e'er beside me;
In Thy ways direct me,
'Neath Thy wings protect me.

66   Art Thou Weary, Art Thou Languid

STEPHANOS.   8 5, 8 3.

JOHN MASON NEALE, 1853
Based on the Greek   HENRY W. BAKER, 1868

1. Art thou wea - ry, art thou lan - guid,   Art thou sore dis - tressed?
2. Hath He marks to lead me to Him,   If He be my Guide?
3. Hath He di - a - dem, as Mon - arch,   That His brow a - dorns?

"Come to Me," saith One, "and com - ing,   Be at rest."
"In His feet and hands are wound-prints   And His side."
"Yea, a crown in ver - y sure - ty,   But of thorns."   A-MEN

4 If I find Him, if I follow,
   What His guerdon here?
. "Many a sorrow, many a labor,
   Many a tear."

5 If I still hold closely to Him,
   What hath He at last?
   "Sorrow vanquished, labor ended,
   Jordan passed."

6 If I ask Him to receive me,
   Will He say me nay?
   "Not till earth and not till heaven
   Pass away."

7 Finding, following, keeping, struggling,
   Is He sure to bless?
   "Saints, apostles, prophets, martyrs,
   Answer, 'Yes.'"

Jesus, Tender Saviour 67

MAGDALENE. 6 5, 6 5. D.

Anonymous

JOHN B. DYKES, 1857

1. Je-sus, ten-der Sav-iour, Hast Thou died for me? Make me ver-y thank-ful
2. Now I know Thou liv-est And dost plead for me; Make me ver-y thank-ful

In my heart to Thee. When the sad, sad sto-ry Of Thy grief I read,
In my prayers to Thee. Soon I hope in glo-ry At Thy side to stand:

Make me ver-y sor-ry For my sins in-deed.
Make me fit to meet Thee In that hap-py land. A-MEN.

68 Thy Life Was Given for Me

WALTHAM. 6 6, 6 6, 6 6.

FRANCES RIDLEY HAVERGAL, 1858, a

WILLIAM H. MONK, 1889

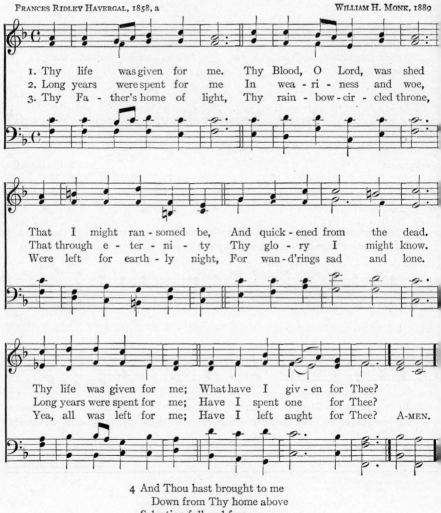

1. Thy life was given for me. Thy Blood, O Lord, was shed
2. Long years were spent for me In wea - ri - ness and woe,
3. Thy Fa - ther's home of light, Thy rain - bow - cir - cled throne,

That I might ran - somed be, And quick - ened from the dead.
That through e - ter - ni - ty Thy glo - ry I might know.
Were left for earth - ly night, For wan - d'rings sad and lone.

Thy life was given for me; What have I giv - en for Thee?
Long years were spent for me; Have I spent one for Thee?
Yea, all was left for me; Have I left aught for Thee? A-MEN.

4 And Thou hast brought to me
  Down from Thy home above
Salvation full and free,
  Thy pardon and Thy love.
Great gifts Thou broughtest me;
What have I brought to Thee?

5 O let my life be given,
  My years for Thee be spent;
World-fetters all be riven,
  And joy with suffering blent.
Thou gav'st Thyself for me,
  I give myself to Thee.

Jesus, Keep Me Near the Cross

NEAR THE CROSS

FANNY J. CROSBY, 1869

WILLIAM H. DOANE, 1869

1. Je - sus, keep me near the Cross, There a pre - cious foun - tain,
2. Near the Cross, a trem - bling soul, Love and mer - cy found me;
3. Near the Cross! O Lamb of God, Bring its scenes be - fore me;
4. Near the Cross I'll watch and wait, Hop - ing, trust - ing ev - er,

Free to all, a heal - ing stream, Flows from Cal-vary's moun - tain.
There the Bright and Morn - ing Star Shed His beams a - round me.
Help me walk from day to day, With it's shad - ows o'er me.
Till I reach the gold - en strand, Just be - yond the riv - er.

REFRAIN

In the Cross, in the Cross Be my glo - ry ev - er;

Till my rap - tured soul shall find Rest be - yond the riv - er. A - MEN.

70   All Glory, Laud, and Honor

ST. THEODULPH. 76,76. D.

Theodulph of Orleans, d. 821
Tr. John Mason Neale, 1854, 1859

Melchior Teschner, 1615

The first stanza

1. {All glo - ry, laud, and hon - or   To Thee, Re - deem - er, King,
To Whom the lips of chil - dren   Made sweet ho - san - nas ring.}

The second and following stanzas

2. Thou art the King of Is - rael, Thou Da - vid's roy - al Son,
3. The com - pan - y of an - gels Are prais - ing Thee on high,
4. The peo - ple of the He - brews With palms be - fore Thee went;

Who in the Lord's Name com - est, The King and Bless - ed One!
And mor - tal men and all things Cre - a - ted make re - ply.
Our praise and prayer and an - thems Be - fore Thee we pre - sent.

After each stanza except the first

{All glo - ry, laud, and hon - or   To Thee, Re - deem - er, King;
To Whom the lips of chil - dren   Made sweet ho - san - nas ring.} A-MEN.

5 To Thee before Thy Passion
    They sang their hymns of praise;
To Thee, now high exalted,
    Our melody we raise.

6 Thou didst accept their praises;
    Accept the praise we bring,
Who in all good delightest,
    Thou good and gracious King.

When, His Salvation Bringing

ROTTERDAM. 7 6, 7 6, D.

71

John King, 1830

Berthold Tours, 1875

1. When, His sal - va - tion bring - ing, To Zi - on Je - sus came,
2. And since the Lord re - tain - eth His love for child - ren still,
3. For should we fail pro - claim - ing Our great Re - deem - er's praise,

The child - ren all stood sing - ing Ho - san - na to His Name.
Though now as King He reign - eth On Zion's heav - en - ly hill,
The stones, our sil - ence sham - ing, Would their ho - san - nas raise.

Nor did their zeal of - fend Him, But, as He rode a - long,
We'll flock a - round His ban - ner, Who sits up - on the throne,
But shall we on - ly ren - der The tri - bute of our words?

He let them still at - tend Him, And smiled to hear their song.
And cry a - loud, "Ho - san - na To Da - vid's Roy - al Son!"
No! while our hearts are tend - er, They, too, shall be the Lord's. A-MEN.

72 Hosanna We Sing

HOSANNA. Irregular.

GEORGE S. HODGES, 1875

JOHN B. DYKES, 1875

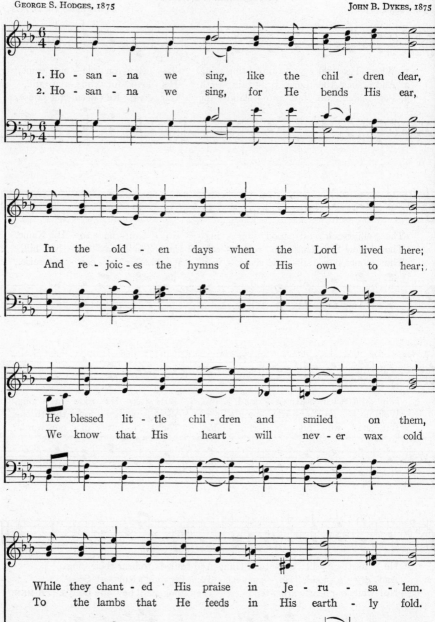

1. Ho - san - na we sing, like the chil - dren dear,
2. Ho - san - na we sing, for He bends His ear,

In the old - en days when the Lord lived here;
And re - joic - es the hymns of His own to hear;

He blessed lit - tle chil - dren and smiled on them,
We know that His heart will nev - er wax cold

While they chant - ed His praise in Je - ru - sa - lem.
To the lambs that He feeds in His earth - ly fold.

Al - le - lu - ia we sing, like the chil - dren bright
Al - le - lu - ia we sing, in the Church we love,

With their harps of gold and their rai - ment white,
Al - le - lu - ia re - sounds in the Church a - bove;

As they fol - low their Shep - herd with lov - ing eyes,
To Thy lit - tle ones, Lord, may such grace be given,

Through the beau - ti - ful val - leys of Par - a - dise.
That we lose not our part in the song of heaven. A - MEN.

73   Hosanna! Loud Hosanna!

ABERDOUR. 7 6, 7 6. D.

JEANNETTE THRELFALL, 1873   GEORGE ESSEX (1839——)

1. Ho - san - na! loud ho - san - na! The lit - tle chil - dren sang;
2. From Ol - i - vet they fol - lowed, 'Midst an ex - ult - ant crowd,
3. Fair leaves of sil - v'ry ol - ive They strewed up - on the ground,
4. "Ho - san - na in the high - est!" That an - cient song we sing;

Through pil - lar'd court and tem - ple The glo - rious an - them rang;
Wav - ing the vic - tor palm - branch, And shout - ing clear and loud;
Whilst Sa - lem's cir - cling moun - tains Ech - oed the joy - ful sound;
For Christ is our Re - deem - er, The Lord of heaven, our King.

To Je - sus Who had blessed them, Close fold - ed to His breast,
Bright an - gels joined the cho - rus Be - yond the cloud - less sky:
The Lord of men and an - gels Rode on in low - ly state,
Oh! may we ev - er praise Him With heart, and life, and voice,

The chil - dren sang their prais - es, The sim - plest and the best.
"Ho - san - na in the high - est: Glo - ry to God on high!"
Nor scorned that lit - tle chil - dren Should on His bid - ding wait.
And in His bliss - ful pres - ence E - ter - nal - ly re - joice.! A - MEN.

O Thou, Who Through This Holy Week 74

CONFIDENCE. C. M.

John Mason Neale, 1842

Christopher F. Herrmann, 1881

1. O Thou, Who through this Ho - ly Week Did'st suf - fer for us all;
2. We can - not un - der - stand the woe Thy love was pleased to bear;
3. Thy feet the path of suff - 'ring trod; Thy hands the vic - t'ry won;

The sick to heal, the lost to seek, To raise up them that fall.
O Lamb of God, we on - ly know That all our hopes are there.
What shall we ren - der to our God For all that He hath done? A-MEN.

There is a Green Hill Far Away 75

GREEN HILL. C. M.

Cecil F. Alexander, 1848

J. Comley

1. There is a green hill far a - way, Out - side a cit - y wall,
2. We may not know, we can - not tell, What pains He had to bear;
3. He died that we might be for - given, He died to make us good,

Where the dear Lord was cru - ci - fied, Who died to save us all.
But we be - lieve it was for us He hung and suf-fered there.
That we might go at last to heaven, Saved by His pre - cious Blood. A-MEN.

4 There was no other good enough
  To pay the price of sin;
He only could unlock the gate
  Of heaven, and let us in.

5 O, dearly, dearly has He loved,
  And we must love Him too,
And trust in His redeeming Blood,
  And try His works to do.

76   When I Survey the Wondrous Cross

BRESLAU. L. M.

First Tune

ISAAC WATTS, 1707, a   Melody in *As Hymnodus Sacer*, Leipzig, 1625

1. When I sur - vey the won-drous Cross On which the Prince of Glo - ry died,
2. For - bid it, Lord, that I should boast, Save in the Death of Christ, my God;
3. See, from His head, His hands, His feet, Sor - row and love flow min - gled down!
4. Were the whole realm of na - ture mine, That were a trib - ute far too small:

My rich-est gain I count but loss, And pour con-tempt on all my pride.
All the vain things that charm me most, I sac - ri - fice them to His Blood.
Did e'er such love and sor-row meet, Or thorns com-pose so rich a crown?
Love so a - maz-ing, so di - vine, De-mands my soul, my life, my all. A - MEN.

Second Tune

ROCKINGHAM. L. M.

EDWARD MILLER'S *Psalms of David*, 1790

1. When I sur - vey the won-drous Cross On which the Prince of Glo - ry died,

My rich - est gain I count but loss, And pour con-tempt on all my pride. A - MEN.

O Come and Mourn With Me Awhile 77

ST. CROSS. L. M.

FREDERICK W. FABER, 1849, a

JOHN B. DYKES, 1861

1. O come and mourn with me a - while; O come ye to the Sav-iour's side;
2. Have we no tears to shed for Him, While sol-diers scoff and Jews de-ride?
3. O love of God! O sin of man! In this dread act your strength is tried;

O come, to-geth - er let us mourn; Je - sus, our Lord, is cru - ci - fied.
Ah! look how pa-tient - ly He hangs; Je - sus, our Lord, is cru - ci - fied.
And vic-to-ry re - mains with love; For He, our Love, is cru - ci - fied! A-MEN.

Glory Be to Jesus 78

CASWALL. 6 5, 6 5.

From the Italian
Tr. EDWARD CASWALL, 1857

FRIEDRICH FILITZ, 1847

1. Glo - ry be to Je - sus, Who, in bit - ter pains,
2. Grace and life e - ter - nal In that Blood I find;
3. Blest through end - less a - ges Be the pre - cious stream
4. A - bel's blood for ven - geance Plead - ed to the skies;

Poured for me the life - blood From His sa - cred veins!
Blest be His com - pas - sion, In - fi - nite - ly kind!
Which from end - less tor - ments Doth the world re - deem!
But the Blood of Je - sus For our par - don cries! A-MEN.

5 Oft as earth exulting
   Wafts its praise on high,
   Angel-hosts rejoicing
   Make their glad reply.

6 Lift we then our voices,
   Swell the mighty flood;
   Louder still, and louder
   Praise the precious Blood!

79   O Sacred Head, Now Wounded

PASSION CHORAL. 7 6, 7 6. D.

Paul Gerhardt, 1656, Based on the Latin
Tr. James W. Alexander, 1830, a

Hans Leo Hassler, 1601

1. O Sa-cred Head, now wound-ed, With grief and shame weighed down,
2. How art Thou pale with an-guish, With sore a-buse and scorn!
3. Lo, here I fall, my Sav-iour! 'Tis I de-serve Thy place!

Now scorn-ful-ly sur-round-ed With thorns, Thy on-ly crown!
How does that vis-age lan-guish, Which once was bright as morn!
Look on me with Thy fa-vor, Vouch-safe to me Thy grace.

O Sa-cred Head, what glo-ry, What bliss, till now, was Thine!
What Thou, my Lord, hast suf-fered, Was all for sin-ners' gain;
Re-ceive me, my Re-deem-er; My Shep-herd, make me Thine!

Yet, though de-spised and gor-y, I joy to call Thee mine.
Mine, mine was the trans-gres-sion, But Thine the dead-ly pain.
Of ev-'ry good the Foun-tain, Thou art the Spring of mine! A-men.

4 What language shall I borrow
    To thank Thee, dearest Friend,
For this Thy dying sorrow,
    Thy pity without end!
O make me Thine for ever,
    And should I fainting be,
Lord, let me never, never,
    Outlive my love to Thee.

5 Be near when I am dying;
    O! show Thy Cross to me;
Lord, on Thy help relying
    Come Thou and set me free;
These eyes, new faith receiving,
    From Thee shall never move;
For he who dies believing
    Dies safely in Thy love.

Into the Woods My Master Went

LANIER. Irregular.

SYDNEY LANIER, 1880

Arranged from H. M. HANSEN

1. In - to the woods my Mas - ter went, Clean for - spent, for - spent.
2. Out of the woods my Mas - ter went, And He was well con - tent.

In - to the woods my Mas - ter came, For - spent with love and shame.
Out of the woods my Mas - ter came, Con - tent with death and shame.

But the ol - ives they were not blind to Him, The lit-tle gray leaves were kind to Him:
When death and shame would woo Him last From un-der the trees they drew Him last,

The thorn-tree had a mind to Him When in - to the woods He came.
'Twas on a tree they slew Him last, When out of the woods He came.

81 The Day of Resurrection

LANCASHIRE. 7 6, 7 6. D.

John of Damascus, VIII Century
Tr. John Mason Neale, 1862, a

Henry Smart, 1863

1. The day of Res - ur - rec - tion! Earth, tell it out a - broad!
2. Our hearts be pure from e - vil, That we may see a - right
3. Now let the heavens be joy - ful! Let earth her song be - gin!

The Pass - o - ver of glad - ness! The Pass - o - ver of God!
The Lord in rays e - ter - nal Of res - ur - rec - tion - light;
Let all the world keep tri - umph, And all that is there - in;

From death to life e - ter - nal, From earth un - to the sky,
And, list - 'ning to His ac - cents, May hear, so calm and plain,
In grate - ful ex - ul - ta - tion Their notes let all things blend,

Our Christ hath brought us o - ver With hymns of vic - to - ry.
His own "All hail!"—and, hear - ing, May raise the vic - tor - strain.
For Christ the Lord hath ris - en, Our Joy, that hath no end! A - men.

Christ, the Lord, is Risen Today   82

ST. GEORGE'S, WINDSOR. 77,77.D.

CHARLES WESLEY, 1739, a

GEORGE J. ELVEY, 1858

1. Christ, the Lord, is risen to-day, Sons of men and an-gels say;
2. Vain the stone, the watch, the seal; Christ hath burst the gates of hell!
3. Soar we now where Christ hath led, Follow-ing our ex-alt-ed Head:

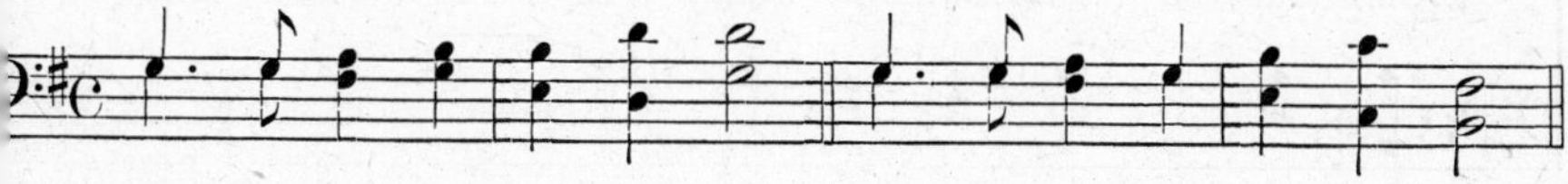

Raise your joys and tri-umphs high; Sing, ye heavens, and earth, re-ply,
Death in vain for-bids His rise; Christ hath o-pened Par-a-dise.
Made like Him, like Him we rise; Ours the cross, the grave, the skies.

Love's re-deem-ing work is done, Fought the fight, the bat-tle won;
Lives a-gain our glo-rious King; Where, O death, is now Thy sting?
Hail, the Lord of earth and heaven! Praise to Thee by both be given;

Lo! the Sun's e-clipse is o'er; Lo! He sets in blood no more.
Once He died our souls to save; Where thy vic-to-ry, O grave?
Thee we greet tri-umph-ant now; Hail, the Res-ur-rec-tion Thou! A-MEN.

83   Christ, the Lord, is Risen Today

RESURRECTION HYMN. 77,77. With Alleluia.

Medieval Sequence
Tr. JANE ELIZA LEESON, 1851

HENRY J. GAUNTLETT (1806–1876)

1. Christ, the Lord, is ris'n to-day: Al - - - le - lu - ia!
2. For the sheep the Lamb hath bled, Al - - - le - lu - ia!
3. Christ, the Vic - tim un - de - filed, Al - - - le - lu - ia!
4. Chris-tians, on this hap - py day Al - - - le - lu - ia!

Chris-tians, haste your vows to pay; Al - - - le - lu - ia!
Sin - less in the sin - ner's stead; Al - - - le - lu - ia!
God and man hath rec - on - ciled; Al - - - le - lu - ia!
Haste with joy your vows to pay; Al - - - le - lu - ia!

Of - fer ye your prais - es meet Al - - - le - lu - ia!
"Christ is ris'n," to - day we cry; Al - - - le - lu - la!
While in strange and aw - ful strife Al - - - le - lu - ia!
"Christ is ris'n," to - day we cry; Al - - - le - lu - ia!

At the Pas - chal Vic - tim's feet. Al - - le - lu - ia!
Now He lives no more to die. Al - - le - lu - ia!
Met to - geth - er death and Life: Al - - le - lu - ia!
Now He lives no more to die. Al - - le - lu - ia! A - MEN

5 Christ, Who once for sinners bled,
Now the first-born from the dead,
Throned in endless might and power,
Lives and reigns for evermore.

6 Hail, Eternal Hope on high!
Hail, Thou King of victory!
Hail, Thou Prince of Life adored!
Help and save us, Gracious Lord.

Jesus Christ is Risen Today

WORGAN. 7 7, 7 7. With Alleluia.

From the Latin, XIII Century
Tr. in *Lyra Davidica*, 1708
Arnold's *Compleat Psalmodist*, 1749, a

Lyra Davidica, 1708

1. Je - sus Christ is ris'n to - day, Al - le - lu - ia!
2. Hymns of praise then let us sing, Al - le - lu - ia!
3. But the pains which He en - dured, Al - le - lu - ia!

Our tri - umph - ant ho - ly day, Al - le - lu - ia!
Un - to Christ, our heaven - ly King, Al - le - lu - ia!
Our sal - va - tion have pro - cured, Al - le - lu - ia!

Who did once, up - on the Cross, Al - le - lu - ia!
Who en - dured the Cross and grave, Al - le - lu - ia!
Now a - bove the sky He's King, Al - le - lu - ia!

Suf - fer to re - deem our loss. Al - le - lu - ia!
Sin - ners to re - deem and save. Al - le - lu - ia!
Where the an - gels ev - er sing. Al - le - lu - ia! A-MEN.

85 Welcome, Happy Morning

FORTUNATUS. 11 11, 11 11, 11.

From FORTUNATUS, VI Century
Tr. JOHN ELLERTON, 1868, a

ARTHUR S. SULLIVAN, 1872

1. Wel-come, hap-py morn-ing! age to age shall say: Hell to-day is
2. Ma-ker and Re-deem-er, Life and Health of all, Thou from heaven be-
3. Thou, of life the Au-thor, death didst un-der-go, Tread the path of
4. Loose the souls long pris-oned, bound with Sa-tan's chain; All that now is

van-quished; heaven is won to-day! Lo! the Dead is liv-ing,
hold-ing hu-man na-ture's fall, Thou of God the Fa-ther,
dark-ness, sav-ing strength to show; Come then, True and Faith-ful,
fal-len raise to life a-gain; Show Thy face in bright-ness,

God for ev-er-more! Him, their true Cre-a-tor, all His works a-dore.
true and on-ly Son, Man-hood to de-liv-er, man-hood didst put on.
now ful-fill Thy word; 'Tis Thine own third morn-ing: rise, O bur-ied Lord!
bid the na-tions see; Bring a-gain our day-light; day re-turns with Thee;

Hell to-day is van-quished; heaven is won to-day! A-MEN.

O Joyous Easter Morning

UNISON

1. O joy - ous East - er morn - ing, That saw the Lord a - rise!
2. O glad - some East - er morn - ing! Our hearts re - joice to - day,
3. O bless - ed East - er morn - ing! What day so bright as this,

O bright and hap - py morn - ing! The clouds have left the skies.
The grave and death are con - quered, He is of Life, the Way.
When, through His might-y tri - umph, He won the courts of bliss!

The night of grief is end - ed, The day has come a - gain;
The hosts of sin are van - quished, He is the Vic - tor King!
The doors of Heaven are o - pen, The grave no more has dread;

rit.

And Christ has won the vic - t'ry For all the sons of men.
Then let us all with glad - ness Our thank - ful prais - es sing.
For ris - en is our Sav - iour, The first fruits of the dead.

87 Christ is Risen! Alleluia!

JOHN S. B. MONSELL, 1863

FREDERICK C. MAKER, 1876

1. Christ is ris - en! Al - le - lu - ia! Ris - en our vic - tor-ious Head!
2. Christ is ris - en! all the sad-ness Of our Lent-en fast is o'er;
3. Christ is ris - en! all the sor-row That last even-ing round Him lay,
4. Christ is ris - en! hence-forth nev - er Death or hell shall us en-thrall;

Sing His prais - es! Al - le - lu - ia! Christ is ris - en from the dead!
Through the o - pen gates of glad-ness He re-turns to life once more;
Now hath found a glo - rious mor-row In the ris - ing of to - day;
Be we Christ's, in Him for ev - er We have tri-umphed o - ver all;

Grate - ful - ly our hearts a - dore Him As His light once more ap-pears;
Death and hell be - fore Him bend-ing, He doth rise, the Vic - tor now,
And the grave its first-fruits giv - eth, Spring-ing up from ho - ly ground;
All the doubt-ing and de - jec - tion Of our tremb-ling hearts have ceased

Bow - ing down in joy be - fore Him, Ris - ing up from griefs and tears.
An - gels on His steps at - tend-ing, Glo - ry round His wound-ed brow.
He was dead, but now He liv - eth; He was lost, but He is found:
'Tis His day of Res - ur - rec-tion! Let us rise and keep the Feast.

CHORUS, *a tempo*
Unison   Harmony

Christ is ris - en! Al - le - lu - ia! Ris - en our vic - tor-ious Head!

ff

Unison   Harmony

Sing His prais-es! Al - le - lu - ia! Christ is ris - en from the dead. A-MEN.

Angels, Roll the Rock Away   88

THOMAS SCOTT, 1769   J. F. OHL, 1886

1. An - gels, roll the rock a - way; Death, yield up thy might - y prey;
2. 'Tis the Sav - iour; an - gels raise Fame's e - ter - nal trump of praise;
3. Praise Him, all ye heav-enly choirs, Strike and sweep your gold - en lyres;

See, He ris - es from the tomb, Glow - ing with im - mor - tal bloom.
Let the earth's re - mot - est bound Hear the joy - in - spir - ing sound.
Shout, O earth, in raptur-ous song, Let the strains be sweet and strong.

ff   *p*   *f*

Al - le - lu - ia! Al - le - lu - ia! Christ the Lord is risen to - day.

89   Come, Ye Faithful, Raise the Strain

JOHN OF DAMASCUS, VIII Century
Tr. JOHN MASON NEALE, 1859

ARTHUR S. SULLIVAN, 1872

1. Come, ye faith-ful, raise the strain Of tri-um-phant glad-ness;
2. All the win-ter of our sins, Long and dark, is fly-ing
3. But to-day a-midst the Twelve Thou didst stand, be-stow-ing

God hath brought His Is-ra-el In-to joy from sad-ness;
From His light, to Whom we give Laud and praise un-dy-ing.
That Thy peace, which ev-er-more Pass-eth hu-man know-ing.

'Tis the spring of souls to-day: Christ hath burst His pris-on,
Nei-ther might the gates of death, Nor the tomb's dark por-tal,
Come, ye faith-ful, raise the strain Of tri-umph-ant glad-ness;

And from three days' sleep in death, As a sun hath ris-en,
Nor the watch-ers, nor the seal, Hold Thee as a mor-tal.
God hath brought His Is-ra-el In-to joy from sad-ness.

God Hath Sent His Angels to the Earth Again 90

PHILLIPS BROOKS, 1877   JAMES C. D. PARKER (1820–1916)

1. God hath sent His an-gels to the earth a-gain, Bring-ing joy-ful ti-dings
2. In the dread-ful des-ert, where the Lord was tried, There the faith-ful an-gels
3. Yet the Christ they hon-or is the same Christ still, Who, in light and dark-ness,
4. God has still His an-gels, help-ing, at His word, All His faith-ful chil-dren,

to the sons of men; They who first, at Christ-mas, thronged the heavenly way,
gath-ered at His side; And when in the gar-den, grief and pain and care
did His Fa-ther's will; And the tomb de-sert-ed shin-eth like the sky,
like their faithful Lord; Sooth-ing them in sor-row, arm-ing them in strife,

REFRAIN

Now be-side the tomb-door, sit on Eas-ter Day.
Bowed Him down with an-guish, they were with Him there.   An-gels sing His
Since He passed out from it in-to vic-to-ry.
Op-'ning wide the tomb-doors, lead-ing in-to life.

tri-umph, as you sang His birth, "Christ, the Lord, is ris-en, Peace, good-will on earth."

91 The World Itself Keeps Easter Day

JOHN MASON NEALE, 1853   EMANUEL SCHMAUK, 1907

1. The world it-self keeps Eas-ter Day, And Eas-ter larks are sing-ing;
2. There stood three Ma-rys by the tomb, On Eas-ter morn-ing ear-ly,
3. But ear-lier still the an-gel sped, The news of com-fort giv-ing;
4. The world it-self keeps Eas-ter Day, And Eas-ter larks are sing-ing;

And Eas-ter flow'rs are bloom-ing gay, And Eas-ter buds are spring-ing.
When day had scarce-ly chased the gloom, And dew was white and pearl-y.
And "Why," he said, "a-mong the dead, Thus seek ye for the Liv-ing?"
And Eas-ter flow'rs are bloom-ing gay, And Eas-ter buds are spring-ing.

The Lord of all things lives a-new, And all His works are ris-ing too;
With lov-ing, but with err-ing mind, They come, the Prince of Life to find:
"Go, tell them all, and make them blest; Tell Pe-ter first, and then the rest."
The Lord hath ris'n, as all things tell, Good Christians, see ye rise as well.

Al-le-lu-ia! Al-le-lu-ia! Al-le-lu----ia!

Ye Happy Bells of Easter Day

Anonymous

John S. B. Hodges (1830–1915)

1. Ye hap-py bells of Eas-ter-Day!
2. Ye glo-ry-bells of Eas-ter-Day!
3. Ye mer-cy-bells of Eas-ter-Day!
4. Ye vic-tor-bells of Eas-ter-Day!

Ring, ring your joy   Thro' earth and sky,   Ye ring a glo-rious word.
The hills that rise   A - gainst the skies,   Re-ech-o with the word—
His ten - der side   Was riv-en wide,   Where floods of mer-cy poured:
The thorn-y crown   He lay-eth down: Ring! ring! with strong ac-cord—

The notes that swell in glad-ness tell   The ris-ing of the Lord!
The vic-tor-breath that con-quers death—   The ris-ing of the Lord!
Re-deem-ed clay doth sing to-day   The ris-ing of the Lord!
The might-y strain of love and pain,   The ris-ing of the Lord!

93   Let the Merry Church Bells Ring

Anonymous   GEORGE W. WARREN (1828–1902)

All things rise to-geth-er.   Let the mer-ry church-bells ring,
Is the strain they ut-ter.   Let the mer-ry church-bells ring,
"He's not here, He's ris-en."   Let the mer-ry church-bells ring,

ring, ring, ring!   Let the mer-ry church-bells ring, ring, ring, ring!

Easter Flowers Are Blooming Bright   94

MARY A. NICHOLSON, 1875   FREDERICK A. G. OUSELEY, 1881

1. Eas-ter flow'rs are bloom-ing bright,   Eas-ter skies pour ra-diant light;
2. An-gels car-oled this sweet lay,   When in man-ger rude He lay;
3. He, then born to grief and pain,   Now to glo-ry born a-gain,
4. As He ris-eth, rise we too,   Tune we heart and voice a-new,

Christ our Lord is risen in might,   Glo-ry in the high-est!
Now once more cast grief a-way,   Glo-ry in the high-est!
Call-eth forth our glad-dest strain,   Glo-ry in the high-est!
Off-'ring hom-age glad and true,   Glo-ry in the high-est!

95   Now All the Bells Are Ringing

Anonymous

JOHN B. DYKES (1823–1876)

Al - le - lu - ia!   Al - le - lu - ia!   Al - le - lu - ia!

1. Now all the bells are ring - ing, To wel - come Eas-ter Day, And we with
2. O hast - en we to meet Him With our com-pan-ions dear, With love and
3. Still, Je - sus! we a - dore Thee With faith which may not fail; Still, as we

joy are sing - ing Our car - ols sweet and gay; For Je - sus hath a-
awe to greet Him, As He is draw-ing near; Of old His friends were
kneel be - fore Thee, We hear Thee say "All hail"! Thou, Who art now de-

ris - en From Jos-eph's rock-y cave, Hath burst His three days' pris - on,
bid - den To haste to Gal - i - lee: Still in His Church all glo - rious,
scend - ing To raise us up to Thee, An Eas - ter-tide un - end - ing

And triumphed o'er the grave. Al - le - lu - ia! Al - le - lu - ia! Al - le - lu - ia!
Our ris - en Lord will be. Al - le - lu - ia! Al - le - lu - ia! Al - le - lu - ia!
Grant us in heaven to see. Al - le - lu - ia! Al - le - lu - ia! Al - le - lu - ia!

Golden Harps Are Sounding

HERMAS. 6 5, 6 5. D. With Refrain.

FRANCES R. HAVERGAL, 1871

FRANCES R. HAVERGAL, 1871

1. Gold - en harps are sound - ing, An - gels' voi - ces ring,
2. He Who came to save us, He Who bled and died,
3. Pray - ing for His chil - dren In that bless - ed place,

Pearl - y gates are o - pened, O - pened for the King.
Now is crowned with glo - ry At His Fa - ther's side.
Call - ing them to glo - ry, Send - ing them His grace;

Je - sus, King of Glo - ry, Je - sus, King of Love, Is gone up in
Nev - er more to suf - fer, Nev - er more to die, Je - sus, King of
His bright home pre-par - ing, Faith-ful ones, for you, Je - sus ev - er

REFRAIN

tri - umph To His throne a - bove.
Glo - ry, Has gone up on high. All His suff - 'ring end - ed,
liv - eth, Ev - er lov - eth, too.

Joy - ful - ly we sing: "Je-sus hath as-cend - ed; Glo-ry to our King!" A-MEN.

97 See the Conqueror Mounts in Triumph

REX GLORIAE. 87, 87. D.

CHRISTOPHER WORDSWORTH, 1862

HENRY SMART, 1868

1. See the Conqueror mounts in triumph! See the King, in roy-al state,
2. Who is this that comes in glo-ry With the trump of ju-bi-lee?
3. Now our heavenly Aa-ron en-ters With His Blood with-in the veil;

Rid-ing on the clouds, His char-iot, To His heaven-ly pal-ace gate!
Lord of bat-tles, God of ar-mies, He has gained the vic-to-ry!
Josh-ua now is come to Ca-naan. And the kings be-fore Him quail;

Hark! the choir of an-gel voi-ces, Joy-ful al-le-lu-ias sing,
He Who on the Cross did suf-fer, He Who from the grave a-rose,
Now He plants the tribes of Is-rael In their prom-ised rest-ing-place;

And the port-als high are lift-ed To re-ceive their heaven-ly King.
He has vanquished sin and Sa-tan, He by death has spoiled His foes.
Now our great E-li-jah of-fers Doub-le por-tion of His grace. A-MEN.

4 Thou hast raised our human nature
   On the clouds to God's right hand;
There we sit in heavenly places,
   There with Thee in glory stand;
Jesus reigns, adored by angels;
   Man with God is on the throne;
Mighty Lord, in Thine Ascension
   We by faith behold our own.

5 Glory be to God the Father;
   Glory be to God the Son,
Dying, risen, ascending for us,
   Who the heavenly realm has won;
Glory to the Holy Spirit;
   To One God in Persons Three;
Glory both in earth and heaven,
   Glory, endless glory, be.

Look, Ye Saints! the Sight is Glorious   98

CORONAE. 8 7, 8 7, 4 7.

Thomas Kelly, 1899   William H. Monk, 1871

1. Look, ye saints! the sight is glo - rious, See the Man of Sor - rows now;
2. Crown the Sav - iour! an - gels crown Him! Rich the tro - phies Je - sus brings;
3. Sin - ners in de - ri - sion crowned Him, Mock - ing thus the Sav - iour's claim;
4. Hark, those bursts of ac - cla - ma - tion! Hark, those loud tri - umph - ant chords!

From the fight re - turned vic - to - rious, Ev - 'ry knee to Him shall bow;
In the seat of pow'r en - throne Him, While the vault of heav - en rings;
Saints and an - gels crowd a - round Him, Own His Ti - tle, praise His Name;
Je - sus takes the high - est sta - tion; O what joy the sight af - fords!

Crown Him! Crown Him! Crowns be - come the Vic - tor's brow.
Crown Him! Crown Him! Crown the Sav - iour King of kings.
Crown Him! Crown Him! Spread a - broad the Vic - tor's fame.
Crown Him! Crown Him! King of kings, and Lord of lords. A - men.

99 Let Songs of Praises Fill the Sky

MEIRINGEN. 8 6, 8 6, 8 8.

THOMAS COTTERILL, 1819

CHRISTIAN G. NEEFE, 1777

1. Let songs of prais - es fill the sky: Christ our as - cend - ed Lord,
2. The Spir - it by His heaven - ly breath Cre - ates new life with - in;
3. The things of Christ the Spir - it takes, And to our hearts re - veals;
4. Come, Ho - ly Spir - it, from a - bove, With Thy ce - les - tial fire;

Sends down His Spir - it from on high, Ac - cord - ing to His word.
He quick - ens sin - ners from the death Of tres - pass - es and sin.
Our bod - y He His tem - ple makes, And our re - demp - tion seals.
Come, and with flames of zeal and love Our hearts and tongues in - spire.

All hail the day of Pen - te - cost, The com - ing of the Ho - ly Ghost! A-MEN.

100 Holy Spirit, Truth Divine

HAVEN. 77, 77.

SAMUEL LONGFELLOW, 1864

EDWIN H. LEMARE, 1889

1. Ho - ly Spir - it, Truth di - vine, Dawn up - on this soul of mine;
2. Ho - ly Spir - it, Love di - vine, Glow with - in this heart of mine;
3. Ho - ly Spir - it, Pow'r di - vine, Fill and nerve this will of mine;
4. Ho - ly Spir - it, Joy di - vine, Glad - den Thou this heart of mine;

Word of God, and in-ward Light, Wake my spir - it, clear my sight.
Kin - dle ev - 'ry high de - sire; Per - ish self in thy pure fire.
By Thee may I strong - ly live, Brave - ly bear, and no - bly strive.
In the des - ert ways I sing, "Spring, O Well, for - ev - er spring!" A-MEN.

Holy Spirit, Hear Us 101

ST. LUCIAN. 65, 65.

WM. HENRY PARKER, 1880   JOHANN C. H. RINCK (1770–1846)

1. Ho - ly Spir - it, hear us, Help us while we sing;
2. Ho - ly Spir - it, prompt us When we kneel to pray;
3. Ho - ly Spir - it, shine Thou On the Book we read;

Breathe in - to the mu - sic Of the praise we bring.
Near - er come, and teach us What we ought to say.
Gild its ho - ly pa - ges With the light we need. A-MEN.

4 Holy Spirit, give us
    Each a lowly mind;
  Make us more like Jesus,
    Gentle, pure, and kind.

5 Holy Spirit, brighten
    Little deeds of toil;
  And our playful pastimes
    Let no folly spoil.

6 Holy Spirit, keep us
    Safe from sins which lie
  Hidden by some pleasure
    From our youthful eye.

7 Holy Spirit, help us
    Daily by Thy might
  What is wrong to conquer,
    And to choose the right.

102 Come, Holy Spirit, God and Lord

GERMANY. L M.

Martin Luther, 1524
Tr. Catherine Winkworth, 1855, a

Melody adapted from Beethoven (?)
William Gardiner's *Sacred Melodies*, 1815

1. Come, Ho-ly Spir-it, God and Lord! Be all Thy gra-ces now out-poured
2. Lord, by the brightness of Thy light, Thou in the faith dost men u-nite
3. Thou strong Defence, Thou ho-ly Light, Teach us to know our God a-right,
4. That we may love not doctrines strange, Nor e'er to oth-er teach-ers range,

On the be-liev-er's mind and soul, To strengthen, save, and make us whole.
Of ev-'ry land and ev-'ry tongue: This to Thy praise, O Lord, be sung.
And call Him Fa-ther from the heart; The Word of life and truth im-part,
But Je-sus for our Mas-ter own, And put our trust in Him a-lone. A-MEN.

5 Thou sacred Ardor, Comfort sweet,
Help us to wait with ready feet
And willing heart at Thy command,
Nor trial fright us from Thy band.

6 Lord, make us ready with Thy powers:
Strengthen the flesh in weaker hours,
That as good warriors we may force
Through life and death to Thee our course

103 Holy Ghost, With Light Divine

WEBER. 77,77.

Andrew Reed, 1817, a

Arr. from Carl M. von Weber, 1826

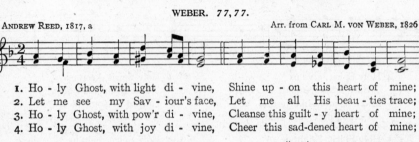

1. Ho-ly Ghost, with light di-vine, Shine up-on this heart of mine;
2. Let me see my Sav-iour's face, Let me all His beau-ties trace;
3. Ho-ly Ghost, with pow'r di-vine, Cleanse this guilt-y heart of mine;
4. Ho-ly Ghost, with joy di-vine, Cheer this sad-dened heart of mine;

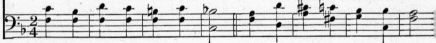

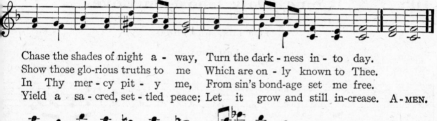

Chase the shades of night a - way, Turn the dark - ness in - to day.
Show those glo-rious truths to me Which are on - ly known to Thee.
In Thy mer - cy pit - y me, From sin's bond-age set me free.
Yield a sa - cred, set - tled peace; Let it grow and still in-crease. A - MEN.

5 Holy Spirit, all divine,
  Dwell within this heart of mine;
  Cast down every idol throne,
  Reign supreme, and reign alone.

6 See, to Thee I yield my heart;
  Shed Thy life through every part:
  A pure temple I would be,
  Wholly dedicate to Thee.

Come, Gracious Spirit, Heavenly Dove 104

WAREHAM. L. M.

SIMON BROWNE, 1720
Bristol *Collection*, 1769

WILLIAM KNAPP, 1837

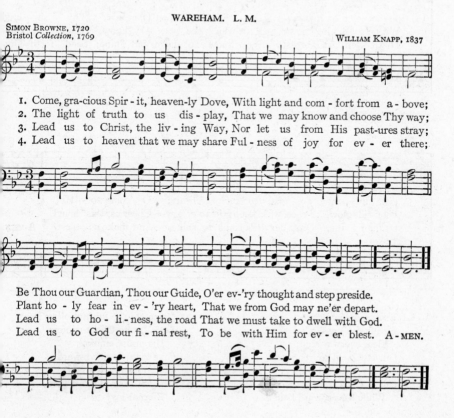

1. Come, gra-cious Spir - it, heaven-ly Dove, With light and com - fort from a - bove;
2. The light of truth to us dis - play, That we may know and choose Thy way;
3. Lead us to Christ, the liv - ing Way, Nor let us from His past-ures stray;
4. Lead us to heaven that we may share Ful - ness of joy for ev - er there;

Be Thou our Guardian, Thou our Guide, O'er ev-'ry thought and step preside.
Plant ho - ly fear in ev - 'ry heart, That we from God may ne'er depart.
Lead us to ho - li - ness, the road That we must take to dwell with God.
Lead us to God our fi - nal rest, To be with Him for ev - er blest. A - MEN.

105 Come, Holy Ghost, in Love

FIAT LUX. 664, 6664.

First Tune

From the Latin
Tr. RAY PALMER, 1858

HENRY HILES (1826–1904)

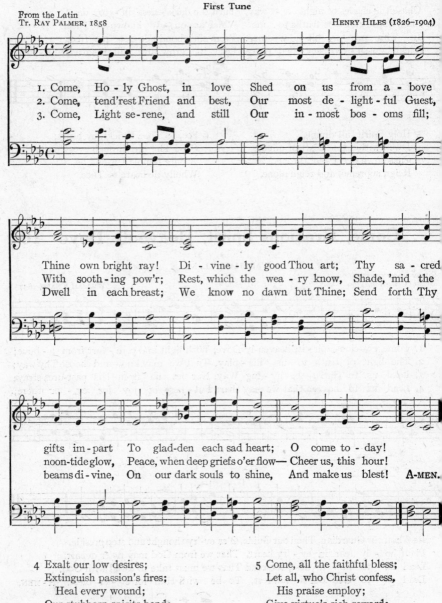

1. Come, Ho-ly Ghost, in love Shed on us from a-bove
2. Come, tend'rest Friend and best, Our most de-light-ful Guest,
3. Come, Light se-rene, and still Our in-most bos-oms fill;

Thine own bright ray! Di-vine-ly good Thou art; Thy sa-cred
With sooth-ing pow'r; Rest, which the wea-ry know, Shade, 'mid the
Dwell in each breast; We know no dawn but Thine; Send forth Thy

gifts im-part To glad-den each sad heart; O come to-day!
noon-tide glow, Peace, when deep griefs o'er flow— Cheer us, this hour!
beams di-vine, On our dark souls to shine, And make us blest! A-MEN.

4 Exalt our low desires;
  Extinguish passion's fires;
    Heal every wound;
  Our stubborn spirits bend;
  Our icy coldness end;
  Our devious steps attend,
    While heavenward bound.

5 Come, all the faithful bless;
  Let all, who Christ confess,
    His praise employ;
  Give virtue's rich reward;
  Victorious death accord,
  And with our glorious Lord,
    Eternal joy!

Come, Holy Ghost, in Love

OLIVET. 664, 6664.

Second Tune

From the Latin
Tr. RAY PALMER, 1858

LOWELL MASON, 1832

1. Come, Ho - ly Ghost, in love Shed on us from a - bove
2. Come, tend'r - est Friend and best, Our most de - light - ful Guest,
3. Come, Light se - rene, and still Our in - most bo - soms fill;

Thine own bright ray! Di - vine - ly good Thou art; Thy sa - cred
With sooth - ing pow'r; Rest, which the wea - ry know, Shade, 'mid the
Dwell in each breast; We know no dawn but Thine; Send forth Thy

gifts im - part To glad - den each sad heart; O come to - day!
noon-tide glow, Peace, when deep griefs o'erflow—Cheer us, this hour!
beams di - vine, On our dark souls to shine, And make us blest! A - MEN.

4 Exalt our low desires;
  Extinguish passion's fires;
    Heal every wound;
  Our stubborn spirits bend;
  Our icy coldness end;
  Our devious steps attend,
    While heavenward bound.

5 Come, all the faithful bless;
  Let all, who Christ confess,
    His praise employ;
  Give virtue's rich reward;
  Victorious death accord,
  And with our glorious Lord,
    Eternal joy!

106 Come, Holy Ghost, Our Souls Inspire

MENDON. L. M.

From the Latin
Tr. JOHN COSIN, 1627, a

German Melody
Arranged by SAMUEL DYER, 1882

1. Come, Ho - ly Ghost, our souls in - spire And light - en with ce - les - tial fire;
2. Thy bless - ed unc - tion from a - bove Is com - fort, life, and fire of love.
3. A - noint our heart and cheer our face With the a - bund - ance of Thy grace.
4. Teach us to know the Fa - ther, Son, And Thee, of Both, to be but One;

Thou the a - noint - ing Spir - it art Who dost Thy seven-fold gifts im - part.
En - able with per - pet - u - al light The dull-ness of our blind-ed sight.
Keep far our foes; give peace at home; Where Thou art Guide, no ill can come.
That, thro' the a - ges all a - long, Thy praise may be our end - less song! A-MEN.

107 Blest Spirit, One With God Above

ROCKINGHAM. L. M.

From the Latin
Tr. JOHN CHANDLER, 1837

EDWARD MILLER'S Psalms of David, 1790

1. Blest Spir - it, one with God a - bove, Thou Source of life and ho - ly love,
2. O may our lips con-fess Thy Name, Our ho - ly lives Thy praise pro-claim;
3. O Ho - ly Fa - ther, Ho - ly Son, And Ho - ly Spir - it, Three in One,

O cheer us with Thy sa-cred beams, Re-fresh us with Thy plen-teous streams.
With love di-vine our hearts in-spire, And fill us with Thy ho - ly fire.
Thy grace de-vout-ly we im-plore, Thy Name be praised for ev-er-more. A-MEN.

Holy, Holy, Holy! Lord God Almighty 108

NICÆA. Irregular.

REGINALD HEBER, 1826

JOHN B. DYKES, 1861

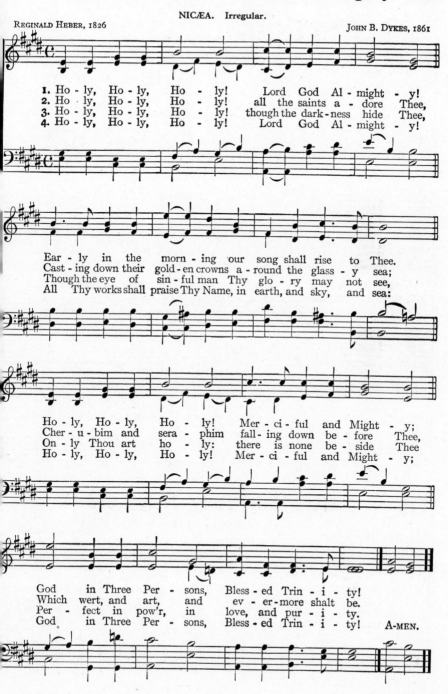

1. Ho - ly, Ho - ly, Ho - ly! Lord God Al - might - y!
2. Ho - ly, Ho - ly, Ho - ly! all the saints a - dore Thee,
3. Ho - ly, Ho - ly, Ho - ly! though the dark - ness hide Thee,
4. Ho - ly, Ho - ly, Ho - ly! Lord God Al - might - y!

Ear - ly in the morn - ing our song shall rise to Thee.
Cast - ing down their gold - en crowns a - round the glass - y sea;
Though the eye of sin - ful man Thy glo - ry may not see,
All Thy works shall praise Thy Name, in earth, and sky, and sea:

Ho - ly, Ho - ly, Ho - ly! Mer - ci - ful and Might - y;
Cher - u - bim and sera - phim fall - ing down be - fore Thee,
On - ly Thou art ho - ly: there is none be - side Thee
Ho - ly, Ho - ly, Ho - ly! Mer - ci - ful and Might - y;

God in Three Per - sons, Bless - ed Trin - i - ty!
Which wert, and art, and ev - er - more shalt be.
Per - fect in pow'r, in love, and pur - i - ty.
God in Three Per - sons, Bless - ed Trin - i - ty! A - MEN.

109   Holy, Holy, Holy Lord

ST. ATHANASIUS. 77, 77, 77.

CHRISTOPHER WORDSWORTH, 1862   EDWARD J. HOPKINS, 1872

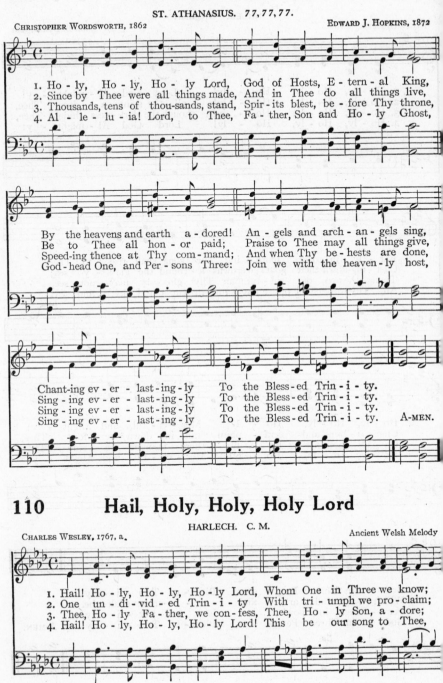

1. Ho - ly, Ho - ly, Ho - ly Lord, God of Hosts, E - tern - al King,
2. Since by Thee were all things made, And in Thee do all things live,
3. Thousands, tens of thou-sands, stand, Spir - its blest, be - fore Thy throne,
4. Al - le - lu - ia! Lord, to Thee, Fa - ther, Son and Ho - ly Ghost,

By the heavens and earth a - dored! An - gels and arch - an - gels sing,
Be to Thee all hon - or paid; Praise to Thee may all things give,
Speed-ing thence at Thy com - mand; And when Thy be - hests are done,
God - head One, and Per - sons Three: Join we with the heaven - ly host,

Chant-ing ev - er - last-ing-ly To the Bless - ed Trin - i - ty.
Sing - ing ev - er - last-ing-ly To the Bless - ed Trin - i - ty.
Sing - ing ev - er - last-ing-ly To the Bless - ed Trin - i - ty.
Sing - ing ev - er - last-ing-ly To the Bless - ed Trin - i - ty. A - MEN.

110   Hail, Holy, Holy, Holy Lord

HARLECH. C. M.

CHARLES WESLEY, 1767, a.   Ancient Welsh Melody

1. Hail! Ho - ly, Ho - ly, Ho - ly Lord, Whom One in Three we know;
2. One un - di - vid - ed Trin - i - ty With tri - umph we pro - claim;
3. Thee, Ho - ly Fa - ther, we con - fess, Thee, Ho - ly Son, a - dore;
4. Hail! Ho - ly, Ho - ly, Ho - ly Lord! This be our song to Thee,

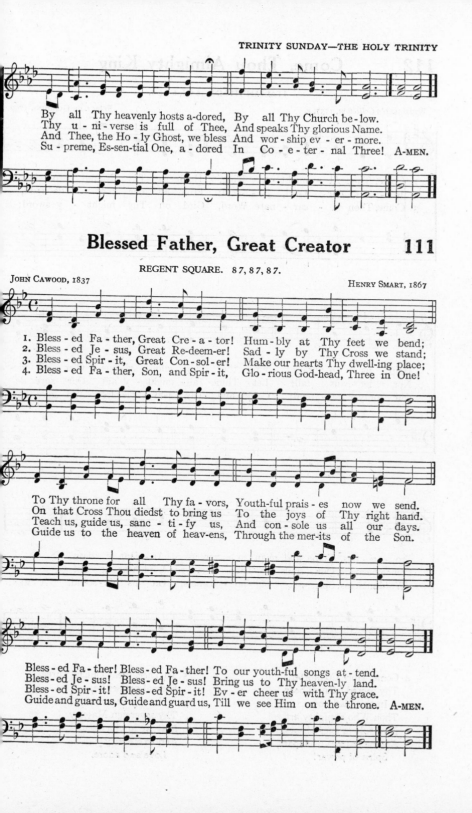

By all Thy heavenly hosts a-dored, By all Thy Church be - low.
Thy u - ni - verse is full of Thee, And speaks Thy glorious Name.
And Thee, the Ho - ly Ghost, we bless And wor - ship ev - er - more.
Su - preme, Es-sen-tial One, a-dored In Co - e - ter - nal Three! A-MEN.

Blessed Father, Great Creator   111

REGENT SQUARE.   8 7, 8 7, 8 7.

JOHN CAWOOD, 1837

HENRY SMART, 1867

1. Bless - ed Fa - ther, Great Cre - a - tor! Hum - bly at Thy feet we bend;
2. Bless - ed Je - sus, Great Re-deem-er! Sad - ly by Thy Cross we stand;
3. Bless - ed Spir - it, Great Con - sol - er! Make our hearts Thy dwell-ing place;
4. Bless - ed Fa - ther, Son, and Spir - it, Glo - rious God-head, Three in One!

To Thy throne for all Thy fa - vors, Youth-ful prais - es now we send.
On that Cross Thou diedst to bring us To the joys of Thy right hand.
Teach us, guide us, sanc - ti - fy us, And con - sole us all our days.
Guide us to the heaven of heav-ens, Through the mer-its of the Son.

Bless - ed Fa - ther! Bless - ed Fa - ther! To our youth-ful songs at - tend.
Bless - ed Je - sus! Bless - ed Je - sus! Bring us to Thy heaven-ly land.
Bless - ed Spir - it! Bless - ed Spir - it! Ev - er cheer us with Thy grace.
Guide and guard us, Guide and guard us, Till we see Him on the throne. A-MEN.

112 Come, Thou Almighty King

ITALIAN HYMN. 664, 6664.

WHITFIELD'S *Collection*, 1757, a

FELICE DE GIARDINI, 1769

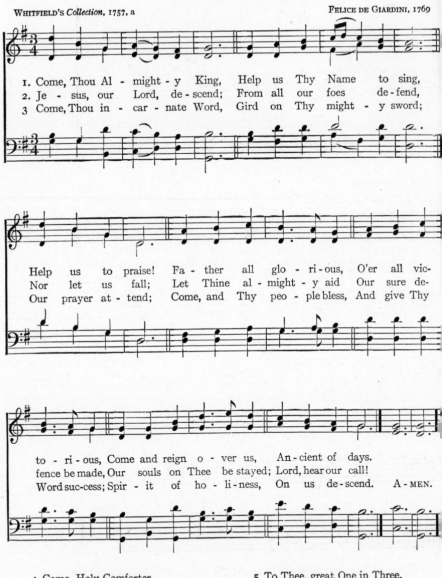

1. Come, Thou Al - might - y King, Help us Thy Name to sing,
2. Je - sus, our Lord, de - scend; From all our foes de - fend,
3 Come, Thou in - car - nate Word, Gird on Thy might - y sword;

Help us to praise! Fa - ther all glo - ri - ous, O'er all vic -
Nor let us fall; Let Thine al - might - y aid Our sure de -
Our prayer at - tend; Come, and Thy peo - ple bless, And give Thy

to - ri - ous, Come and reign o - ver us, An - cient of days.
fence be made, Our souls on Thee be stayed; Lord, hear our call!
Word suc - cess; Spir - it of ho - li - ness, On us de - scend. A - MEN.

4 Come, Holy Comforter,
  Thy sacred witness bear
    In this glad hour:
  Thou Who almighty art,
  Now rule in every heart,
  And ne'er from us depart,
    Spirit of power!

5 To Thee, great One in Three,
  Eternal praises be,
    Hence, evermore!
  Thy sovereign Majesty
  May we in glory see,
  And to eternity
    Love and adore.

Ancient of Days, Who Sittest Throned in Glory   113

ANCIENT OF DAYS. 11 10, 11 10.

WILLIAM C. DOANE, 1886

J. ALBERT JEFFERY, 1886

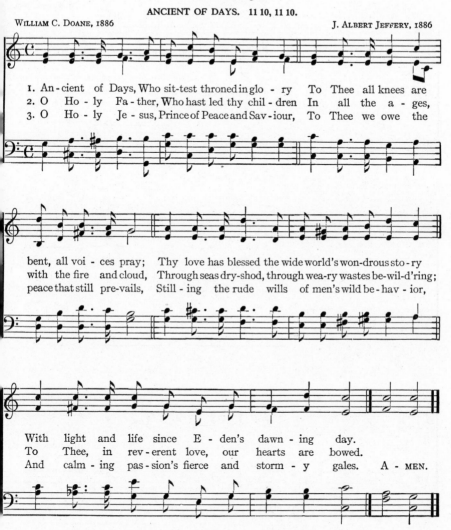

1. An-cient of Days, Who sit-test throned in glo - ry   To Thee all knees are
2. O Ho - ly Fa - ther, Who hast led thy chil - dren In all the a - ges,
3. O Ho - ly Je - sus, Prince of Peace and Sav-iour, To Thee we owe the

bent, all voi - ces pray;   Thy love has blessed the wide world's won-drous sto - ry
with the fire and cloud, Through seas dry-shod, through wea-ry wastes be-wil-d'ring;
peace that still pre-vails, Still - ing the rude wills of men's wild be - hav - ior,

With light and life since E - den's dawn - ing day.
To Thee, in rev - erent love, our hearts are bowed.
And calm - ing pas - sion's fierce and storm - y gales. A - MEN.

4 O Holy Ghost, the Lord and the Life-giver,
   Thine is the quickening power that gives increase;
   From Thee have flowed, as from a pleasant river,
   Our plenty, wealth, prosperity and peace.

5 O Triune God, with heart and voice adoring,
   Praise we the goodness that doth crown our days;
   Pray we that Thou wilt hear us, still imploring
   Thy love and favor kept to us always.

114 Round the Lord in Glory Seated

URBS BEATA. 87, 87. D.

RICHARD MANT, 1837

J. F. OHL, 1886

UNISON

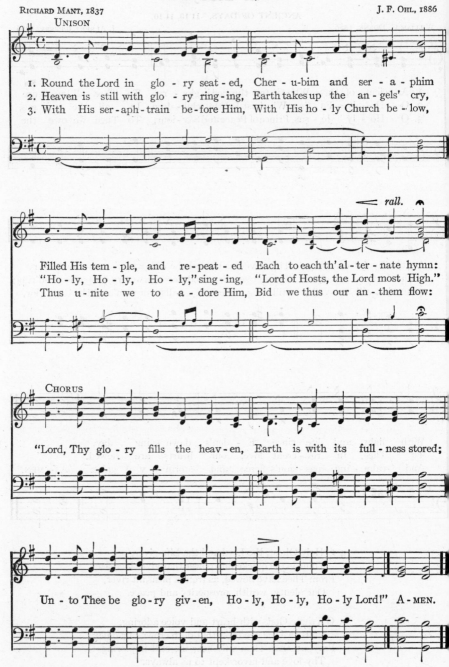

1. Round the Lord in glo - ry seat - ed, Cher - u-bim and ser - a - phim
2. Heaven is still with glo - ry ring - ing, Earth takes up the an - gels' cry,
3. With His ser-aph-train be-fore Him, With His ho - ly Church be - low,

Filled His tem - ple, and re - peat - ed Each to each th' al - ter - nate hymn:
"Ho - ly, Ho - ly, Ho - ly," sing - ing, "Lord of Hosts, the Lord most High."
Thus u - nite we to a - dore Him, Bid we thus our an - them flow:

CHORUS

"Lord, Thy glo - ry fills the heav - en, Earth is with its full - ness stored;

Un - to Thee be glo - ry giv - en, Ho - ly, Ho - ly, Ho - ly Lord!" A - MEN.

Lead Us, Heavenly Father, Lead Us 115

SICILIAN MARINERS' HYMN. 8 7, 8 7, 4 4 7.

Sicilian Folksong

JAMES EDMESTON, 1821, a

J. MERRICK and W. D. TATTERSALL'S *Psalms*, 1794

1. Lead us, heaven-ly Fa - ther, lead us O'er the world's tem-pest-uous sea;
2. Sav-iour, breathe for - give - ness o'er us; All our weak-ness Thou dost know;
3. Spir - it of our God, de - scend - ing, Fill our hearts with heaven-ly joy,

Guard us, guide us, keep us, feed us, For we have no help but Thee;
Thou didst tread this earth be - fore us, Thou didst feel its keen - est woe;
Love all oth - er love tran - scend - ing, Pleas-ure that can nev - er cloy;

Yet pos - sess-ing Ev - 'ry bless-ing, If our God our Fa - ther be.
Lone and dreary, Faint and weary, Thro' the des - ert Thou didst go.
Thus pro-vid-ed, Pardoned, guided, Noth-ing can our peace de-stroy. A-MEN.

THE WORD

116 Thy Word, O Lord, Like Gentle Dews

ST. LEONARD. C. M. D.

CARL BERNHARD GARVE, 1825
Tr. CATHERINE WINKWORTH, 1855, a

HENRY HILES, 1867

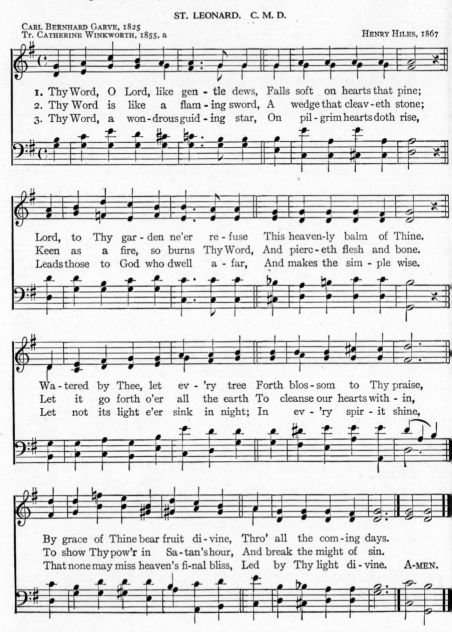

1. Thy Word, O Lord, like gen - tle dews, Falls soft on hearts that pine;
2. Thy Word is like a flam - ing sword, A wedge that cleav - eth stone;
3. Thy Word, a won - drous guid - ing star, On pil - grim hearts doth rise,

Lord, to Thy gar - den ne'er re - fuse This heaven-ly balm of Thine.
Keen as a fire, so burns Thy Word, And pierc - eth flesh and bone.
Leads those to God who dwell a - far, And makes the sim - ple wise.

Wa - tered by Thee, let ev - 'ry tree Forth blos - som to Thy praise,
Let it go forth o'er all the earth To cleanse our hearts with - in,
Let not its light e'er sink in night; In ev - 'ry spir - it shine,

By grace of Thine bear fruit di - vine, Thro' all the com - ing days.
To show Thy pow'r in Sa - tan's hour, And break the might of sin.
That none may miss heaven's fi - nal bliss, Led by Thy light di - vine. A-MEN.

O Word of God Incarnate

EVERTS. 7 6, 7 6. D.

WM. WALSHAM HOW, 1867

German

1. O   Word of God In - car - nate,   O   Wis - dom from   on   high,
2. The Church from Thee, her Mas - ter   Re - ceived the   gift   di - vine,
3. It   float - eth like   a   ban - ner   Be - fore God's host   un - furled;
4. O   make Thy Church, dear Sav - iour,   A   lamp   of   burn - ished gold,

O   Truth un-changed, un - chang - ing,   O   Light   of   our   dark sky!
And   still   that light she   lift - eth   O'er   all   the earth   to   shine.
It   shin - eth like   a   bea - con   A - bove the dark - ling world;
To   bear   be - fore   the   na - tions   Thy   true light   as   of   old:

We   praise Thee for the   ra - diance   That from   the   hal - lowed page,
It   is   the gold - en   cask - et   Where gems of   truth are stored;
It   is   the chart and com - pass   That o'er   life's surg - ing sea,
O   teach Thy wan-d'ring pil - grims   By   this   their path   to trace,

A   lan - tern to   our foot - steps,   Shines on from age   to age.
It   is   the heaven-drawn pic-ture   Of   Thee, th' In-car-nate Word.
'Mid mists, and rocks, and quick-sands Still guides, O   Christ, to Thee.
Till, clouds and dark-ness end - ed,   They see Thee face   to   face.   A-MEN.

118 Father of Mercies, in Thy Word

ST. AGNES. C. M.

ANNA STEELE, 1760

JOHN B. DYKES, 1866

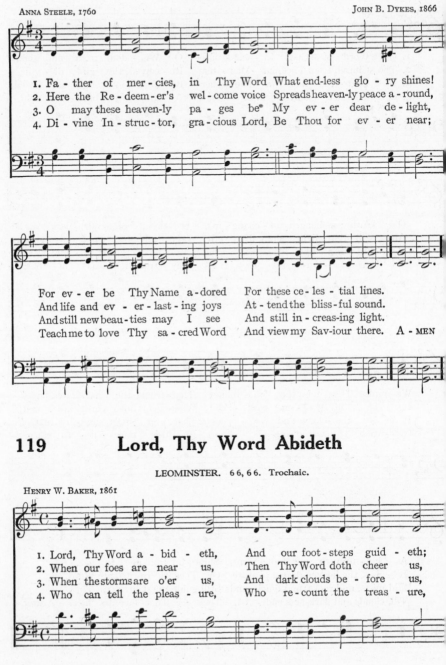

1. Fa - ther of mer - cies, in Thy Word What end-less glo - ry shines!
2. Here the Re - deem - er's wel - come voice Spreads heaven-ly peace a - round,
3. O may these heaven-ly pa - ges be My ev - er dear de - light,
4. Di - vine In - struc - tor, gra - cious Lord, Be Thou for ev - er near;

For ev - er be Thy Name a - dored For these ce - les - tial lines.
And life and ev - er - last - ing joys At - tend the bliss - ful sound.
And still new beau - ties may I see And still in - creas-ing light.
Teach me to love Thy sa - cred Word And view my Sav-iour there. A - MEN

119 Lord, Thy Word Abideth

LEOMINSTER. 6 6, 6 6. Trochaic.

HENRY W. BAKER, 1861

1. Lord, Thy Word a - bid - eth, And our foot - steps guid - eth;
2. When our foes are near us, Then Thy Word doth cheer us,
3. When the storms are o'er us, And dark clouds be - fore us,
4. Who can tell the pleas - ure, Who re - count the treas - ure,

Who its truth be - liev - eth   Light and joy re - ceiv - eth.
Word of con - so - la - tion,   Mes - sage of sal - va - tion.
Then its light di - rect - eth,   And our way pro - tect - eth.
By Thy Word im - part - ed   To the sim - ple - heart - ed?   A-MEN.

5 Word of mercy, giving
Succor to the living;
Word of life, supplying
Comfort to the dying!

6 O that we, discerning
Its most holy learning,
Lord, may love and fear Thee,
Evermore be near Thee!

Spread, O Spread, Thou Mighty Word 120

GOTT SEI DANK DURCH ALLE WELT. 77,77.

JONATHAN F. BAHNMEIER, 1827
Tr. CATHARINE WINKWORTH, 1858

FREYLINGHAUSEN's *Gesangbuch*, Halle, 1704

1. Spread, O spread, thou might - y Word, Spread the king-dom of the Lord
2. Tell them how the Fath - er's will Made the world, and keeps it still;
3. Tell of our Re - deem - er's love, Who for - ev - er doth re - move,
4. Tell them of the Spir - it given Now to guide us up to heaven,

Where - so - e'er His breath has given   Life to be - ings meant for heaven.
How His on - ly Son He gave,   Man from sin and death to save.
By His ho - ly sac - ri - fice,   All the guilt that on us lies.
Strong and ho - ly, just and true,   Work-ing both to will and do.   A-MEN.

5 Word of life, most pure and strong,
Lo, for Thee the nations long;
Spread, till from its dreary night
All the world awakes to light.

6 Lord of harvest, let there be
Joy and strength to work for Thee;
Let the nations far and near,
See Thy light, and learn Thy fear.

121 Lord, Keep Us Steadfast in Thy Word

ERHALT UNS, HERR, BEI DEINEM WORT. L. M.

MARTIN LUTHER, 1541
Tr. CATHERINE WINKWORTH, 1863

First Tune

JOSEPH KLUG'S *Geistliche Lieder*, 1543

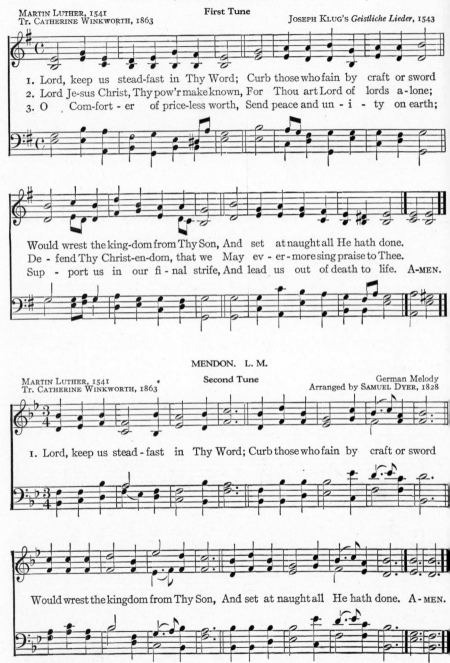

1. Lord, keep us stead-fast in Thy Word; Curb those who fain by craft or sword
2. Lord Je-sus Christ, Thy pow'r make known, For Thou art Lord of lords a-lone;
3. O Com-fort - er of price-less worth, Send peace and un - i - ty on earth;

Would wrest the king-dom from Thy Son, And set at naught all He hath done.
De - fend Thy Christ-en-dom, that we May ev - er-more sing praise to Thee.
Sup - port us in our fi - nal strife, And lead us out of death to life. A-MEN.

MENDON. L. M.

MARTIN LUTHER, 1541
Tr. CATHERINE WINKWORTH, 1863

Second Tune

German Melody
Arranged by SAMUEL DYER, 1828

1. Lord, keep us stead - fast in Thy Word; Curb those who fain by craft or sword

Would wrest the kingdom from Thy Son, And set at naught all He hath done. A - MEN.

Lo, On a Mount a Tree Doth Stand   122

AUF EINEM BERG. C. M. D.

CHR. G. BARTH (1809–1862)
Tr. HARRIET R. SPAETH, 1884

German

1. Lo, on a mount a tree doth stand; It bends with weight of gold;
2. Yet ev - er full the tree is found, Its rich - es all re - main;

And ev - 'ry one throughout the land Its glo - ry may be - hold.
How - ev - er much falls to the ground, The fruit still grows a - gain.

Ear - ly and late, come count - less bands In search of treas - ure rare;
What is its name, and can you tell Where it on earth may be?

They shake the tree with ea - ger hands, To gath - er fruit so fair.
Who knows it? Who can ans - wer well?—The Bi - ble is the Tree.

123 Thy Word is Like a Garden, Lord

ELLACOMBE. C. M. D.

EDWIN HODDER, 1863   *Gesangbuch der Herzogl. Wirtemb. Kath. Hofkapelle, 1784*

1. Thy Word is like a gar - den, Lord, With flow-ers bright and fair;
2. Thy Word is like a star - ry host: A thou-sand rays of light
3. O, may I love Thy pre-cious Word, May I ex - plore the mine,

And ev - 'ry one who seeks may pluck A love - ly clus - ter there.
Are seen to guide the trav - el - er, And make his path-way bright.
May I its fra - grant bow - ers glean, May light up - on me shine!

Thy Word is like a deep, deep mine, And jew - els rich and rare
Thy Word is like an arm - o - ry, Where sol-diers may re - pair,
O, may I find my ar - mor there, Thy Word my trust - y sword,

Are hid - den in its might - y depths For ev - 'ry search-er there.
And find, for life's long bat - tle day, All need - ful wea-pons there.
I'll learn to fight with ev - 'ry foe, The bat - tle of the Lord. A - MEN.

God of Eternal Love   124

THATCHER. S. M.

Seaton's *Church H. B.*, 1855

Arranged from GEORG F. HÄNDEL, 1732

1. God of e - ter - nal Love, Our Fa - ther and our Friend, We lift our hearts to Thee a - bove: Do Thou our prayer at - tend.
2. Bap-tized in - to Thy Name, We all have Christ put on: O may Thy love our hearts in - flame, The course of truth to run.
3. May earth-ly feel - ings die, And fruits of faith in - crease; And Ad - am's na - ture pros - trate lie Be - fore the Prince of Peace.
4. En - due us, Lord, with strength To tri - umph o - ver sin: That we may with Thy saints at length E - ter - nal glo - ry win. A-MEN.

Lamb of God, For Sinners Slain   125

PLEYEL'S HYMN. 77,77.

JAMES R. WOODFORD, 1852

Arranged from IGNAZ J. PLEYEL, 1790

1. Lamb of God, for sin - ners slain; By Thy mer - cy born a - gain, For Thy guid-ance still we pray, Lest from grace we fall a - way.
2. By the mys - tic, cleans-ing flood, By the Wa - ter and the Blood, Washed and sanc-ti - fied to Thee, Ho - ly may we ev - er be.
3. Aid us with Thy dai - ly grace Stead-fast-ly to run our race: Grant us vic - t'ry in the strife, And the prize of end - less life.
4. Praise to Thee, from all on earth, God, who gav est us new birth; Praise from all the heaven-ly host; Fa-ther, Son, and Ho - ly Ghost. A-MEN.

126 I Was Made a Christian

LYNDHURST. 65, 65. D.

JOHN SAMUEL JONES, c. 1880

Harmonized by GEORGE H. LOUD, 1883

1. I was made a Chris - tian When my name was given, One of God's dear
2. I must, like a Chris - tian, Shun all e - vil ways, Keep the faith of
3. All a Christian's bless - ings I will claim for mine: Ho - ly work and

chil - dren And an heir of heaven. In the name of Chris - tian,
Je - sus, Serve Him all my days. Called to be a Chris - tian,
wor - ship, Fel - low - ship di - vine. Fa - ther, Son, and Spir - it,

I will glo - ry now, Ev - er-more re-mem - ber My bap-tis-mal vow.
I will praise the Lord Seek for His as - sist - ance So to keep my word.
Give me grace, that I Still may live a Chris-tian, And a Chris-tian die. A-MEN.

127 Saviour, Who Thy Flock Art Feeding

BROCKLESBY. 87, 87.

WM. AUGUSTUS MUHLENBERG, 1826

CHARLOTTE A. BARNARD, 1868

1. Sav-iour, Who Thy flock art feed - ing With the Shep-herd's kind - est care,
2. Now, these lit - tle ones re - ceiv - ing, Fold them in Thy gra - cious arm;
3. Nev - er, from Thy past-ure rov - ing, Let them be the li - on's prey;
4. Then with-in Thy fold e - ter - nal Let them find a rest - ing - place,

All the fee - ble gent - ly lead - ing, While the lambs Thy bos - om share;
There, we know, Thy Word be - liev - ing, On - ly there se - cure from harm.
Let Thy ten - der - ness, so lov - ing, Keep them thro' life's dan - g'rous way.
Feed in past - ures ev - er ver - nal, Drink the riv - ers of Thy grace. A - MEN.

Baptized into Thy Name 128

ST. GODRIC. 6 6, 6 6, 8 8.

CHARLES WESLEY, 1767

JOHN B. DYKES, 1826

1. Bap - tized in - to Thy Name, Mys - te - rious One in Three, Our souls and
2. O that our light may shine, And all our lives ex - press The char - ac-

bod - ies claim A sac - ri - fice to Thee; And let us live our
ter di - vine, The re - al ho - li - ness; And then re - ceive us

faith to prove, The faith which works by hum - ble love.
up to a - dore The Tri - une God for ev - er - more. A - MEN.

THE HOLY COMMUNION

129 **Let Thy Blood in Mercy Poured**

AMNOS. 7 8, 7 8, 7 7.

JOHN BROWNLIE, 1907
Based on the Greek

WILLIAM BENBOW, 1914

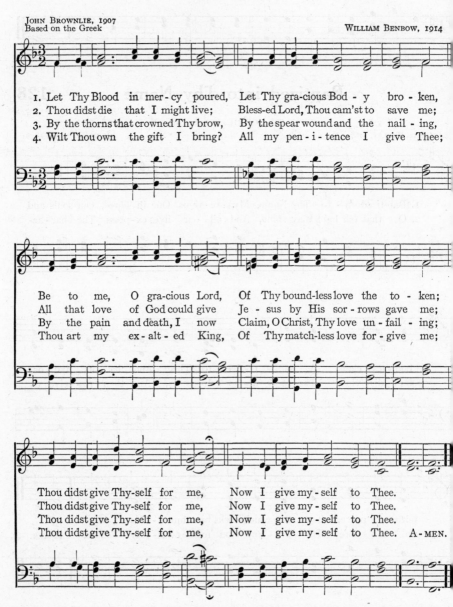

1. Let Thy Blood in mer-cy poured, Let Thy gra-cious Bod - y bro - ken,
2. Thou didst die that I might live; Bless-ed Lord, Thou cam'st to save me;
3. By the thorns that crowned Thy brow, By the spear wound and the nail - ing,
4. Wilt Thou own the gift I bring? All my pen - i - tence I give Thee;

Be to me, O gra-cious Lord, Of Thy bound-less love the to - ken,
All that love of God could give Je - sus by His sor - rows gave me;
By the pain and death, I now Claim, O Christ, Thy love un - fail - ing;
Thou art my ex - alt - ed King, Of Thy match-less love for - give me;

Thou didst give Thy-self for me, Now I give my-self to Thee.
Thou didst give Thy-self for me, Now I give my-self to Thee.
Thou didst give Thy-self for me, Now I give my-self to Thee.
Thou didst give Thy-self for me, Now I give my-self to Thee. A-MEN.

Lord, When Before Thy Throne We Meet 130

REED. 8 6, 8 6, 8 8.

TRESSILIAN G. NICHOLAS, 1838   J. F. OHL, 1926

1. Lord, when be - fore Thy throne we meet, Thy good - ness to a - dore, From heaven, th'e - ter - nal mer - cy - seat, On us Thy bles - sings pour! And make our in - most souls to be A ho - ly tem - ple meet for Thee.

2. Thy Bod - y for our ran - som given, Thy Blood in mer - cy shed; With this im - mor - tal food from heaven, Lord, let our souls be fed; And as we at Thine al - tar kneel, Grant us Thy quick'ning grace to feel.

3. Be Thou, O Ho - ly Spir - it, nigh! Ac - cept the hum - ble prayer, The con - trite soul's re - pent - ant sigh, The sin - ner's heart - felt tear; And let our ad - o - ra - tion rise. As fra - grant in - cense to the skies. A - MEN.

THE CHURCH

FOUNDATION AND REFORMATION

131

I Love Thy Zion, Lord

ST. THOMAS. S. M.

TIMOTHY DWIGHT, 1800, a

AARON WILLIAMS, c. 1770

1. I love Thy Zi - on, Lord, The house of Thine a - bode,
2. I love Thy Church, O God! Her walls be - fore Thee stand,
3. For her my tears shall fall, For her my prayers as - cend;
4. Be - yond my high - est joy I prize her heaven - ly ways,

The Church our blest Re - deem - er saved With His own pre - cious Blood.
Dear as the ap - ple of Thine eye, And grav - en on Thy hand.
To her my cares and toils be given, Till toils and cares shall end.
Her sweet com - mun - ion, sol - emn vows, Her hymns of love and praise. A - MEN.

5 Jesus, Thou Friend divine,
　Our Saviour and our King,
Thy hand from every snare and foe
　Shall great deliverance bring.

6 Sure as Thy truth shall last,
　To Zion shall be given
The brightest glories earth can yield,
　And brighter bliss of heaven.

132 O Where Are Kings and Empires Now

ST. ANNE. C. M.

ARTHUR CLEVELAND COXE, 1839

WILLIAM CROFT, 1708

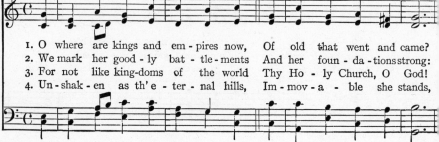

1. O where are kings and em - pires now, Of old that went and came?
2. We mark her good - ly bat - tle - ments And her foun - da - tions strong;
3. For not like king - doms of the world Thy Ho - ly Church, O God!
4. Un - shak - en as th' e - ter - nal hills, Im - mov - a - ble she stands,

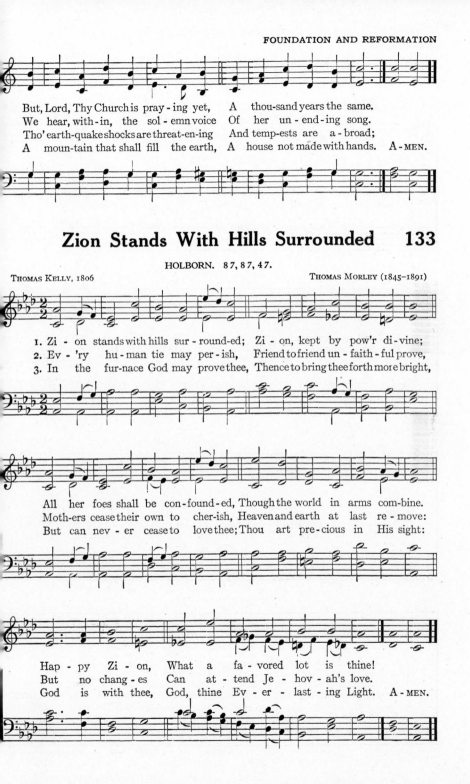

But, Lord, Thy Church is pray-ing yet, A thou-sand years the same.
We hear, with-in, the sol-emn voice Of her un-end-ing song.
Tho' earth-quake shocks are threat-en-ing And temp-ests are a-broad;
A moun-tain that shall fill the earth, A house not made with hands. A-MEN.

Zion Stands With Hills Surrounded   133

HOLBORN. 8 7, 8 7, 4 7.

THOMAS KELLY, 1806

THOMAS MORLEY (1845–1891)

1. Zi - on stands with hills sur - round-ed; Zi - on, kept by pow'r di-vine;
2. Ev - 'ry hu - man tie may per-ish, Friend to friend un - faith-ful prove,
3. In the fur-nace God may prove thee, Thence to bring thee forth more bright,

All her foes shall be con-found-ed, Though the world in arms com-bine.
Moth-ers cease their own to cher-ish, Heaven and earth at last re - move:
But can nev - er cease to love thee; Thou art pre-cious in His sight:

Hap - py Zi - on, What a fa - vored lot is thine!
But no chang - es Can at - tend Je - hov - ah's love.
God is with thee, God, thine Ev - er - last - ing Light. A - MEN.

134   A Mighty Fortress is Our God

EIN' FESTE BURG.   8 7, 8 7, 5 5 5 6, 7.

MARTIN LUTHER, 1529
Tr. COMPOSITE, 1866

MARTIN LUTHER, 1529

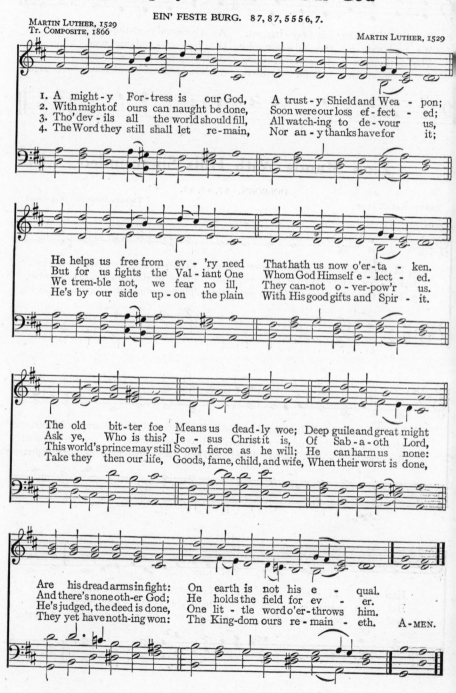

1. A might-y For-tress is our God, A trust-y Shield and Wea - pon;
2. With might of ours can naught be done, Soon were our loss ef-fect - ed;
3. Tho' dev-ils all the world should fill, All watch-ing to de-vour us,
4. The Word they still shall let re-main, Nor an-y thanks have for it;

He helps us free from ev - 'ry need That hath us now o'er-ta - ken.
But for us fights the Val - iant One Whom God Himself e - lect - ed.
We trem-ble not, we fear no ill, They can-not o - ver-pow'r us.
He's by our side up - on the plain With His good gifts and Spir - it.

The old bit-ter foe Means us dead-ly woe; Deep guile and great might
Ask ye, Who is this? Je - sus Christ it is, Of Sab-a-oth Lord,
This world's prince may still Scowl fierce as he will; He can harm us none:
Take they then our life, Goods, fame, child, and wife, When their worst is done,

Are his dread arms in fight: On earth is not his e - qual.
And there's none oth-er God; He holds the field for ev - er.
He's judged, the deed is done, One lit - tle word o'er-throws him.
They yet have noth-ing won: The King-dom ours re-main - eth. A-MEN.

The Church's One Foundation   135

AURELIA. 76, 76. D.

SAMUEL J. STONE, 1866   SAMUEL S. WESLEY, 1864

1. The Church's one foun-da-tion   Is Je-sus Christ, her Lord;
2. E-lect from ev-'ry na-tion,   Yet one o'er all the earth,
3. Though, with a scorn-ful won-der,   Men see her sore op-pressed,
4. 'Mid toil and trib-u-la-tion,   And tu-mult of her war,

She is His new cre-a-tion   By wa-ter and the Word;
Her char-ter of sal-va-tion   One Lord, one Faith, one Birth;
By schisms rent a-sun-der,   By her-e-sies dis-tressed;
She waits the con-sum-ma-tion   Of peace for ev-er-more;

From heaven He came and sought her   To be His ho-ly Bride,
One ho-ly Name she bless-es,   Par-takes one ho-ly Food,
Yet saints their watch are keep-ing,   Their cry goes up, "How long?"
Till, with the vis-ion glo-rious,   Her long-ing eyes are blest,

With His own Blood He bought her,   And for her life He died.
And to one hope she press-es,   With ev-'ry grace en-dued.
And soon the night of weep-ing   Shall be the morn of song.
And the great Church vic-to-rious   Shall be the Church at rest.   A-MEN.

THE CHURCH

136 Glorious Things of Thee Are Spoken

AUSTRIAN HYMN. 87, 87. D.

JOHN NEWTON, 1779

JOSEPH HAYDN, 1797

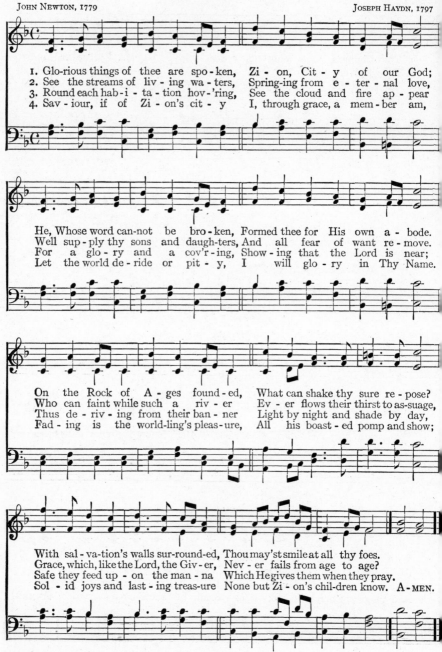

1. Glo-rious things of thee are spo-ken, Zi - on, Cit - y of our God;
2. See the streams of liv - ing wa - ters, Spring-ing from e - ter - nal love,
3. Round each hab-i - ta - tion hov-'ring, See the cloud and fire ap - pear
4. Sav - iour, if of Zi - on's cit - y I, through grace, a mem - ber am,

He, Whose word can-not be bro-ken, Formed thee for His own a - bode.
Well sup-ply thy sons and daugh-ters, And all fear of want re - move.
For a glo - ry and a cov'r-ing, Show-ing that the Lord is near;
Let the world de - ride or pit - y, I will glo - ry in Thy Name.

On the Rock of A - ges found-ed, What can shake thy sure re - pose?
Who can faint while such a riv - er Ev - er flows their thirst to as-suage,
Thus de - riv - ing from their ban - ner Light by night and shade by day,
Fad - ing is the world-ling's pleas-ure, All his boast - ed pomp and show;

With sal - va-tion's walls sur-round-ed, Thou may'st smile at all thy foes.
Grace, which, like the Lord, the Giv - er, Nev - er fails from age to age?
Safe they feed up - on the man - na Which He gives them when they pray.
Sol - id joys and last - ing treas-ure None but Zi - on's chil-dren know. A-MEN.

The tune ST. ASAPH *on the opposite page may also be used.*

Through the Night of Doubt and Sorrow 137

ST. ASAPH. 87, 87. D.

Bernhardt S. Ingemann, 1825
Tr. S. Baring-Gould, 1867, a

William S. Bambridge, 1872

1. Through the night of doubt and sor-row On - ward goes the pil - grim band,
2. One the light of God's own pres-ence, O'er His ran-somed peo - ple shed,
3. One the strain that lips of thou-sands Lift as from the heart of one;
4. On - ward, there-fore, pil - grim broth-ers, On - ward, with the Cross our aid!

Sing - ing songs of ex - pec - ta - tion, March-ing to the prom - ised land.
Chas - ing far the gloom and ter - ror, Bright'ning all the path we tread;
One the con - flict, one the per - il, One the march in God be - gun;
Bear its shame, and fight its bat - tle, Till we rest be - neath its shade!

Clear be - fore us through the dark - ness Gleams and burns the guid-ing light;
One the ob - ject of our jour - ney, One the faith which nev - er tires,
One the glad - ness of re - joic - ing On the far e - ter - nal shore,
Soon shall come the great a - wak - ing. Soon the rend - ing of the tomb;

Broth-er clasps the hand of broth-er, Step-ping fear-less through the night.
One the ear - nest look-ing for-ward, One the hope our God in - spires;
Where the one Al-might-y Fa - ther Reigns in love for ev - er - more.
Then the scat-t'ring of all shad-ows, And the end of toil and gloom. A-MEN.

138 My Church, My Church, My Dear Old Church

ATHENS. C. M. D.

Anonymous

F. GIARDINI

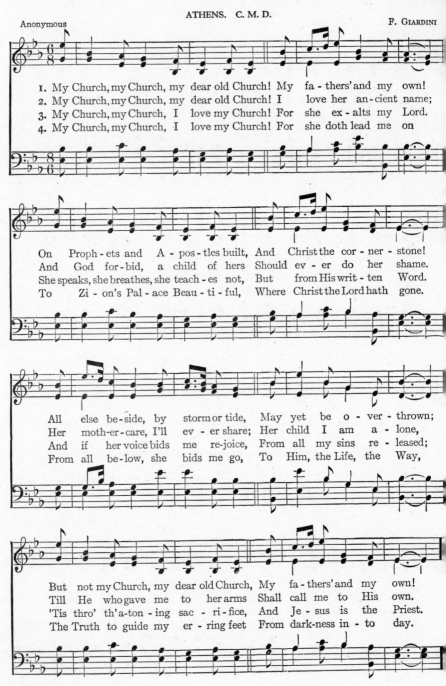

1. My Church, my Church, my dear old Church! My fa-thers' and my own!
2. My Church, my Church, my dear old Church! I love her an-cient name;
3. My Church, my Church, I love my Church! For she ex-alts my Lord.
4. My Church, my Church, I love my Church! For she doth lead me on

On Proph-ets and A-pos-tles built, And Christ the cor-ner-stone!
And God for-bid, a child of hers Should ev-er do her shame.
She speaks, she breathes, she teach-es not, But from His writ-ten Word.
To Zi-on's Pal-ace Beau-ti-ful, Where Christ the Lord hath gone.

All else be-side, by storm or tide, May yet be o-ver-thrown;
Her moth-er-care, I'll ev-er share; Her child I am a-lone,
And if her voice bids me re-joice, From all my sins re-leased;
From all be-low, she bids me go, To Him, the Life, the Way,

But not my Church, my dear old Church, My fa-thers' and my own!
Till He who gave me to her arms Shall call me to His own.
'Tis thro' th'a-ton-ing sac-ri-fice, And Je-sus is the Priest.
The Truth to guide my er-ring feet From dark-ness in-to day.

Faith of Our Fathers, Living Still   139

ST. CATHERINE.   8 8, 8 8, 8 8.   With Refrain

FREDERICK W. FABER, 1849

HENRI F. HEMY, 1865
Altered by JAMES G. WALTON, 1871

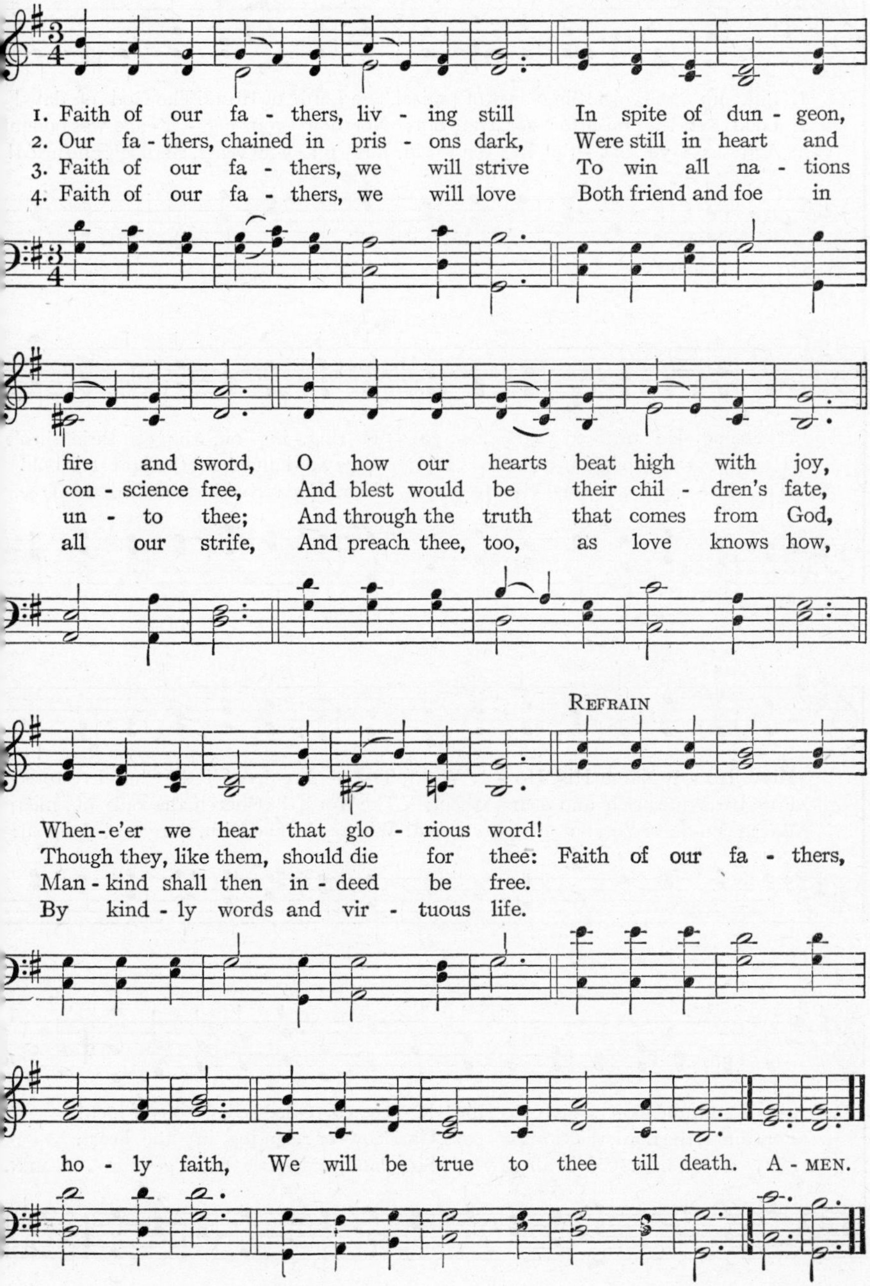

1. Faith of our fa - thers, liv - ing still   In spite of dun - geon,
2. Our fa - thers, chained in pris - ons dark,   Were still in heart and
3. Faith of our fa - thers, we will strive   To win all na - tions
4. Faith of our fa - thers, we will love   Both friend and foe in

fire and sword,   O how our hearts beat high with joy,
con - science free,   And blest would be their chil - dren's fate,
un - to thee;   And through the truth that comes from God,
all our strife,   And preach thee, too, as love knows how,

REFRAIN

When - e'er we hear that glo - rious word!
Though they, like them, should die for thee: Faith of our fa - thers,
Man - kind shall then in - deed be free.
By kind - ly words and vir - tuous life.

ho - ly faith, We will be true to thee till death. A - MEN.

140 Lift Up the Voice! Sing Songs of Praise!

ZELLER. L. M. D.

PAUL ZELLER STRODACH, 1917

J. F. OHL, 1917

1. Lift up the voice! Sing songs of praise! The Lord of Hosts! The God of days!
2. Loud swell the praise; for-get Him not; Nor how your her - it - age was bought
3. And as ye bat - tle in the world, Lift up your heart, His flag's un-furled!

The song He start - ed years a - go Is ring - ing on, the cen-turies thro':
How Spir - it wrought in hearts of gold; How val - iant fought the fight-ers bold
The En - sign heart-'ning vic - to - ry In all that strive, blessed thro' the Tree.

His Ho - ly Name: His Ho - ly Word; The soul re-deemed: the Church restored-
For treas - ures rich and dear to them:— The Word, the Church, the souls of men;
World con-quer? Yes, but first your soul! Win out! The faith, the grace, the goal:

Sing! Laud, and glo - ry give to Him! Re-deemed, re-deemed, ye sons of men!
For Christ, the Lord, the vic - tor's part, Christ ev - er reign - ing in the heart.
All yours in Christ! Christ all in you! Sing, laud, and praise the a - ges thro'. A-MEN.

Lord of the Living Harvest

HOLY CHURCH. 7 6, 7 6. D.

JOHN S. B. MONSELL, 1866

ARTHUR H. BROWN, 1862

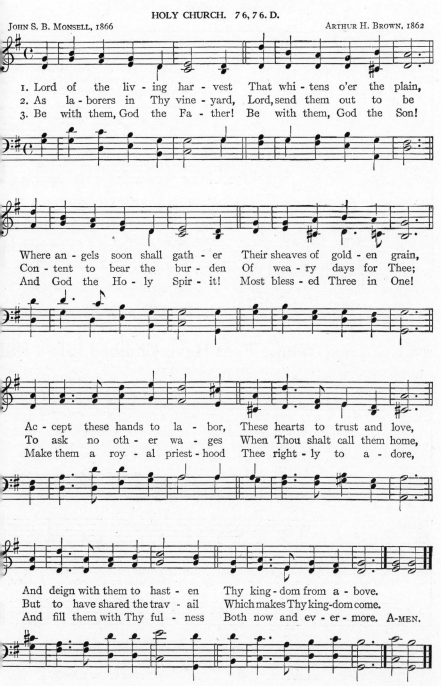

1. Lord of the liv - ing har - vest That whi - tens o'er the plain,
2. As la - borers in Thy vine - yard, Lord, send them out to be
3. Be with them, God the Fa - ther! Be with them, God the Son!

Where an - gels soon shall gath - er Their sheaves of gold - en grain,
Con - tent to bear the bur - den Of wea - ry days for Thee;
And God the Ho - ly Spir - it! Most bless - ed Three in One!

Ac - cept these hands to la - bor, These hearts to trust and love,
To ask no oth - er wa - ges When Thou shalt call them home,
Make them a roy - al priest - hood Thee right - ly to a - dore,

And deign with them to hast - en Thy king - dom from a - bove.
But to have shared the trav - ail Which makes Thy king-dom come.
And fill them with Thy ful - ness Both now and ev - er - more. A-MEN.

142 Lord, Pour Thy Spirit from on High

FEDERAL STREET. L. M.

JAMES MONTGOMERY, 1833   HENRY K. OLIVER, 1832

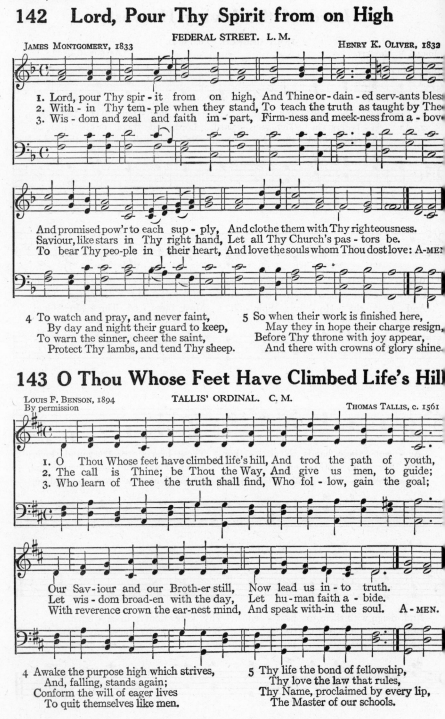

1. Lord, pour Thy spir - it from on high, And Thine or - dain - ed serv-ants bless;
2. With - in Thy tem - ple when they stand, To teach the truth as taught by Thee;
3. Wis - dom and zeal and faith im - part, Firm-ness and meek-ness from a - bove,

And promised pow'r to each sup - ply, And clothe them with Thy righteousness.
Saviour, like stars in Thy right hand, Let all Thy Church's pas - tors be.
To bear Thy peo - ple in their heart, And love the souls whom Thou dost love: A-MEN.

4 To watch and pray, and never faint,
By day and night their guard to keep,
To warn the sinner, cheer the saint,
Protect Thy lambs, and tend Thy sheep.

5 So when their work is finished here,
May they in hope their charge resign,
Before Thy throne with joy appear,
And there with crowns of glory shine.

143 O Thou Whose Feet Have Climbed Life's Hill

LOUIS F. BENSON, 1894   TALLIS' ORDINAL. C. M.
By permission   THOMAS TALLIS, c. 1561

1. O Thou Whose feet have climbed life's hill, And trod the path of youth,
2. The call is Thine; be Thou the Way, And give us men, to guide;
3. Who learn of Thee the truth shall find, Who fol - low, gain the goal;

Our Sav - iour and our Broth-er still, Now lead us in - to truth.
Let wis - dom broad-en with the day, Let hu - man faith a - bide.
With reverence crown the ear-nest mind, And speak with - in the soul. A - MEN.

4 Awake the purpose high which strives,
And, falling, stands again;
Conform the will of eager lives
To quit themselves like men.

5 Thy life the bond of fellowship,
Thy love the law that rules,
Thy Name, proclaimed by every lip,
The Master of our schools.

O Lord, Thy Benediction Give   144

ABENDS. L. M.

JOHN ARMSTRONG, 1847   HERBERT S. OAKELEY, 1874

1. O Lord, thy ben - e - dic - tion give   On all who teach, on all who learn,
2. Give those that teach pure hearts and wise,   Faith, hope, and love, all warmed by prayer:
3. Give those that learn the will - ing ear,   The spir - it meek, the guile - less mind;
4. O bless the shep-herd, bless the sheep,   That guide and guid-ed both be one,

That so Thy Church may ho-lier live, And ev'ry lamp more brightly burn.
Themselves first training for the skies,   They best will raise their people there.
Such gifts will make the low-liest here Far bet-ter than a king-dom find.
One in the faith-ful watch they keep,   One in the joy of work well done. A - MEN.

Org.

Teach Me, O Teach Me, Lord, Thy Way 145

ST. CATHERINE. L. M.

JAMES MERRICK, 1765, a   R. F. SMITH

1. Teach me, O teach me, Lord, Thy way,   That, to my life's re - mo - test day,
2. In-formed by Thee, with sa - cred awe   My heart shall med - i - tate Thy law;
3. Give me to know Thy will a - right,   Thy will, my glo - ry and de - light;
4. O turn from van - i - ty my eye;   To me Thy quickening strength sup-ply;

By Thine un-err - ing pre - cepts led,   My feet Thy heavenly paths may tread.
And, with ce-les - tial wis-dom filled,   To Thee its full o - be - dience yield.
That, raised above the world, my mind In Thee its high-est good may find.
And with Thy promised mer-cy cheer A heart de-vo - ted to Thy fear. A - MEN.

146 Saviour, Teach Me, Day By Day

FERRIER. 77,77.

JANE ELIZA LEESON, 1842

JOHN B. DYKES, 1862

1. Sav-iour, teach me, day by day, Love's sweet les-son to o-bey;
2. With a child's glad heart of love At Thy bid-ding may I move;
3. Teach me thus Thy steps to trace, Strong to fol-low in Thy grace;
4. Love in lov-ing finds em-ploy, In o-be-dience all her joy;

Sweet-er les-son can-not be: Lov-ing Him Who first loved me.
Prompt to serve and fol-low Thee, Lov-ing Him Who first loved me.
Learn-ing how to love from Thee, Lov-ing Him Who first loved me.
Ev-er new that joy will be, Lov-ing Him Who first loved me. A-MEN.

147 My God, Accept My Heart This Day

ST. PETER. C. M.

MATTHEW BRIDGES, 1848

ALEXANDER R. REINAGLE, 1830

1. My God, ac-cept my heart this day, And make it al-ways Thine,
2. Be-fore the Cross of Him Who died, Be-hold, I pros-trate fall;
3. A-noint me with Thy heaven-ly grace, A-dopt me for Thine own,
4. Let ev-'ry thought, and work, and word To Thee be ev-er given;

That I from Thee no more may stray, No more from Thee de-cline.
Let ev-'ry sin be cru-ci-fied, Let Christ be all in all!
That I may see Thy glo-rious face, And wor-ship at Thy throne.
Then life shall be Thy ser-vice, Lord, And death the gate of heaven. A-MEN.

Father, Son, and Holy Spirit

148

HOLYWOOD. 8 7, 8 7, 4 7.

JOHANN J. RAMBACH, 1734
Tr. CHARLES W. SCHAEFFER, 1860

J. F. WADE's *Cantus Diversi*, 1751

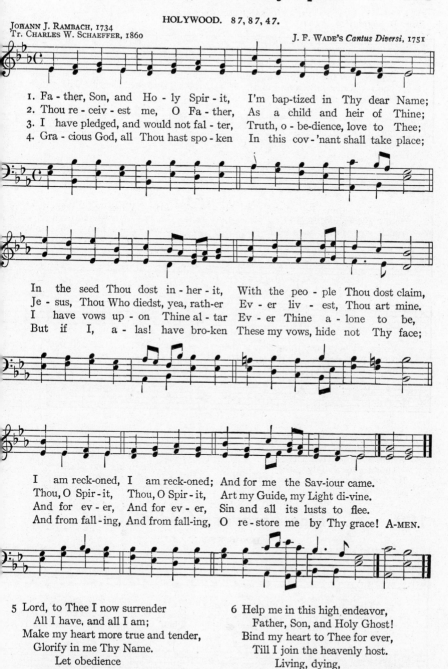

1. Fa - ther, Son, and Ho - ly Spir - it,   I'm bap-tized in Thy dear Name;
2. Thou re - ceiv - est me,   O Fa - ther,   As a child and heir of Thine;
3. I have pledged, and would not fal - ter,   Truth, o - be-dience, love to Thee;
4. Gra - cious God, all Thou hast spo - ken   In this cov-'nant shall take place;

In the seed Thou dost in - her - it,   With the peo - ple Thou dost claim,
Je - sus, Thou Who diedst, yea, rath-er   Ev - er liv - est, Thou art mine.
I have vows up - on Thine al - tar   Ev - er Thine a - lone to be,
But if I, a - las! have bro-ken   These my vows, hide not Thy face;

I am reck-oned, I am reck-oned; And for me the Sav-iour came.
Thou, O Spir - it, Thou, O Spir - it,   Art my Guide, my Light di-vine.
And for ev - er, And for ev - er,   Sin and all its lusts to flee.
And from fall-ing, And from fall-ing,   O re - store me by Thy grace! A-MEN.

5 Lord, to Thee I now surrender
   All I have, and all I am;
  Make my heart more true and tender,
   Glorify in me Thy Name.
       Let obedience
   To Thy will be all my aim.

6 Help me in this high endeavor,
   Father, Son, and Holy Ghost!
  Bind my heart to Thee for ever,
   Till I join the heavenly host.
       Living, dying,
   Let me make in Thee my boast.

149 Hushed Was the Evening Hymn

SAMUEL. 6 6, 6 6, 8 8.

JAMES D. BURNS, 1856

ARTHUR S. SULLIVAN, 1874

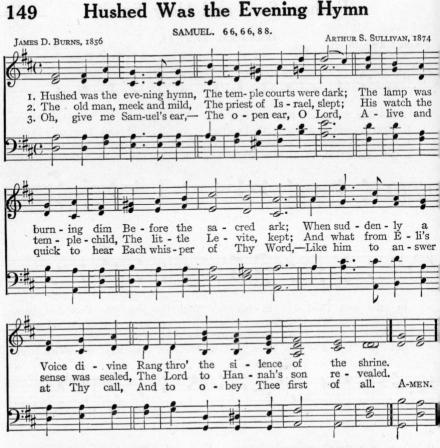

1. Hushed was the eve-ning hymn, The tem-ple courts were dark; The lamp was
2. The old man, meek and mild, The priest of Is-rael, slept; His watch the
3. Oh, give me Sam-uel's ear,— The o-pen ear, O Lord, A-live and

burn-ing dim Be-fore the sa-cred ark; When sud-den-ly a
tem-ple-child, The lit-tle Le-vite, kept; And what from E-li's
quick to hear Each whis-per of Thy Word,—Like him to an-swer

Voice di-vine Rang thro' the si-lence of the shrine.
sense was sealed, The Lord to Han-nah's son re-vealed.
at Thy call, And to o-bey Thee first of all. A-MEN.

4 Oh, give me Samuel's heart,—
  A lowly heart, that waits
Where in Thy house Thou art,
  Or watches at Thy gates
By day and night;—a heart that still
Moves at the breathing of Thy will.

5 Oh, give me Samuel's mind—
  A sweet unmurmuring faith,
Obedient and resigned
  To Thee in life and death;—
That I may read with childlike eyes
Truths that are hidden from the wise.

150 Thine Forever! God of Love

INNOCENTS. 7 7, 7 7.

MARY FOWLER MAUDE, 1847

The Parish Choir, London, 1850

1. Thine for-ev-er! God of Love, Hear us from Thy throne a-bove;
2. Thine for-ev-er! Lord of Life, Shield us through our earth-ly strife;
3. Thine for-ev-er! O how blest They who find in Thee their rest!

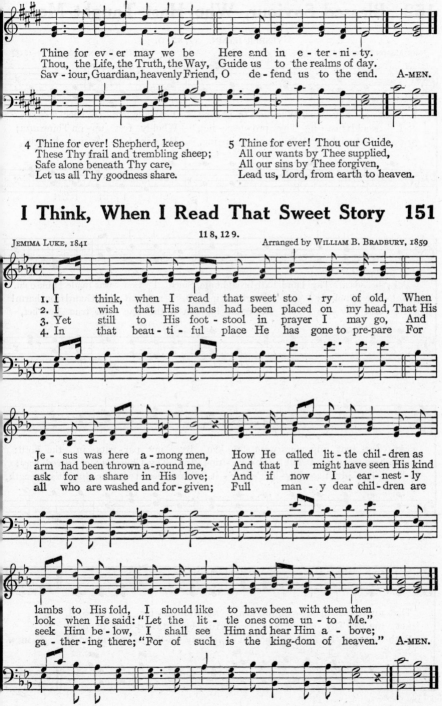

Thine for ev - er may we be Here and in e - ter - ni - ty.
Thou, the Life, the Truth, the Way, Guide us to the realms of day.
Sav - iour, Guardian, heavenly Friend, O de - fend us to the end. A-MEN.

4 Thine for ever! Shepherd, keep
These Thy frail and trembling sheep;
Safe alone beneath Thy care,
Let us all Thy goodness share.

5 Thine for ever! Thou our Guide,
All our wants by Thee supplied,
All our sins by Thee forgiven,
Lead us, Lord, from earth to heaven.

I Think, When I Read That Sweet Story 151

118, 129.

JEMIMA LUKE, 1841   Arranged by WILLIAM B. BRADBURY, 1859

1. I think, when I read that sweet sto - ry of old, When
2. I wish that His hands had been placed on my head, That His
3. Yet still to His foot - stool in prayer I may go, And
4. In that beau - ti - ful place He has gone to pre-pare For

Je - sus was here a - mong men, How He called lit - tle chil - dren as
arm had been thrown a - round me, And that I might have seen His kind
ask for a share in His love; And if now I ear - nest - ly
all who are washed and for - given; Full man - y dear chil - dren are

lambs to His fold, I should like to have been with them then
look when He said: "Let the lit - tle ones come un - to Me."
seek Him be - low, I shall see Him and hear Him a - bove;
ga - ther-ing there; "For of such is the king-dom of heaven." A-MEN.

152 Blessed Saviour, Who Hast Taught Me

VESPER HYMN. 8 7, 8 7. D.

John Mason Neale, 1842, a

Dimitri Bortniansky (1751–1815)

1. Bless - ed Sav - iour, Who hast taught me   I should live to Thee a - lone,
2. I would trust in Thy pro - tect - ing,   Whol-ly rest up - on Thine arm;
3. So that might and firm - ness gain - ing,   Hope in dan - ger, joy in grief,

All these years Thy hand hath brought me, Since I first was made Thine own.
Fol - low whol - ly Thy di - rect - ing O my on - ly Guard from harm!
Now and ev - er - more re - main - ing In the one and true be - lief,

At the font my vows were spo - ken By my par - ents in the Lord:
Meet me now with Thy sal - va - tion In Thy Church's or - dered way;
Rest - ing in my Sav - iour's mer - it, Strengthened with the Spir - it's strength,

That my vows shall be un - bro - ken, At the al - tar I re - cord.
Let me feel Thy con - firm - a - tion In Thy truth and fear to - day;
With Thy saints I may in - her - it All my Fa - ther's joy at length. A - MEN.

Shine Thou Upon Us, Lord   **153**

BEULAH. 66, 66. D.

John Ellerton, 1889

Henri F. Hemy (1818–1889)

1. Shine Thou up-on us, Lord, True Light of men, to-day,
2. Breathe Thou up-on us, Lord, Thy Spir-it's liv-ing flame,
3. Speak Thou for us, O Lord, In all we say of Thee;
4. Live Thou with-in us, Lord; Thy mind and will be ours;

And thro' the writ-ten Word Thy ver-y self dis-play;
That so with one ac-cord Our lips may tell Thy Name;
Ac-cord-ing to Thy Word Let all our teach-ing be;
Be Thou be-loved, a-dored, And served with all our pow'rs;

That so from hearts which burn With gaz-ing on Thy face,
Give Thou the hear-ing ear, Fix Thou the wan-d'ring thought,
That so Thy lambs may know Their own true Shep-herd's voice,
That so our lives may teach Thy chil-dren what Thou art,

Thy lit-tle ones may learn The won-ders of Thy grace.
That those we teach may hear The great things Thou hast wrought.
Wher-e'er He leads them go, And in His love re-joice.
And plead, by more than speech, For Thee with ev-'ry heart. A-MEN.

154 Sing Them Over Again to Me

WORDS OF LIFE. 8 6, 8 6, 6 6. With Refrain.

PHILIP P. BLISS

PHILIP P. BLISS (1838–1876)

1. Sing them o - ver a - gain to me, Won-der-ful words of life,
2. Christ, the bless-ed One, gives to all Won-der-ful words of life,
3. Sweet-ly ech-o the gos-pel call, Won-der-ful words of life,

Let me more of their beau-ty see, Won-der-ful words of life.
Sin - ner, list to the lov-ing call, Won-der-ful words of life.
Of - fer par-don and peace to all, Won-der-ful words of life.

Words of life and beau-ty, Teach me faith and du-ty;
All so free-ly giv-en, Woo-ing us to heav-en,
Je - sus, on-ly Sav-iour, Sanc-ti-fy for-ev-er,

REFRAIN

Beau-ti-ful words, won-der-ful words, Won-der-ful words of life,

Beau-ti-ful words, won-der-ful words, Won-der-ful words of life. A-MEN.

O Jesus, I Have Promised

CHENIES. 7 6, 7 6. D.

JOHN E. BODE, 1869

TIMOTHY R. MATTHEWS, 1855

155

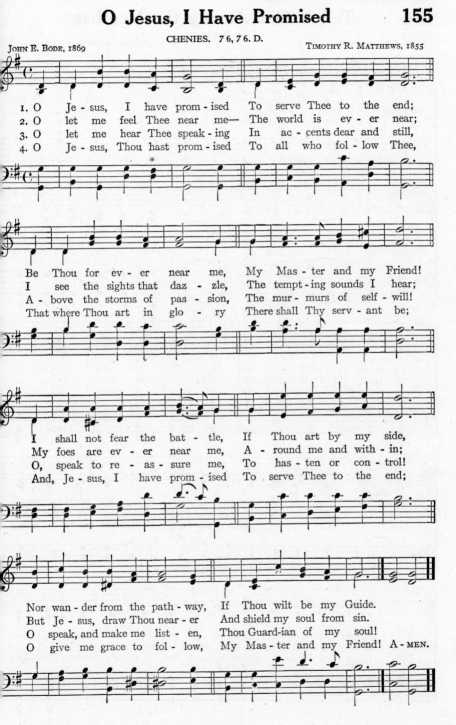

1. O Je - sus, I have prom - ised To serve Thee to the end;
2. O let me feel Thee near me— The world is ev - er near;
3. O let me hear Thee speak - ing In ac - cents dear and still,
4. O Je - sus, Thou hast prom - ised To all who fol - low Thee,

Be Thou for ev - er near me, My Mas - ter and my Friend!
I see the sights that daz - zle, The tempt - ing sounds I hear;
A - bove the storms of pas - sion, The mur - murs of self - will!
That where Thou art in glo - ry There shall Thy serv - ant be;

I shall not fear the bat - tle, If Thou art by my side,
My foes are ev - er near me, A - round me and with - in;
O, speak to re - as - sure me, To has - ten or con - trol!
And, Je - sus, I have prom - ised To serve Thee to the end;

Nor wan - der from the path - way, If Thou wilt be my Guide.
But Je - sus, draw Thou near - er And shield my soul from sin.
O speak, and make me list - en, Thou Guard-ian of my soul!
O give me grace to fol - low, My Mas - ter and my Friend! A - MEN.

156 Tell it Out Among the Heathen

P. M.

Frances R. Havergal, 1872

Frederick Stevenson (1845-1925)

1. Tell it out a-mong the heath-en that the Lord is King!
2. Tell it out a-mong the heath-en that the Sav-iour reigns;
3. Tell it out a-mong the heath-en, Je-sus reigns a-bove;

Tell it out! Tell it out! Tell it out a-mong the
Tell it out! Tell it out! Tell it out a-mong the
Tell it out! Tell it out! Tell it out a-mong the

na-tions; bid them shout and sing! Tell it out! Tell it
na-tions; bid them burst their chains; Tell it out! Tell it
na-tions that His reign is love; Tell it out! Tell it

out! Tell it out with ad-o-ra-tion that He shall in-crease,
out! Tell it out a-mong the weep-ing ones that Je-sus lives,
out! Tell it out a-mong the high-ways and the lanes at home;

That the might-y King of Glo-ry is the King of Peace; Tell it
Tell it out a-mong the wea-ry what sweet rest He gives; Tell it
Let it ring a-cross the moun-tains and the o-cean foam; Like the

out with ju - bi - la - tion, tho' the waves may roar, That He sit - teth on the
out a - mong the sin - ners that He came to save; Tell it out a - mong the
sound of ma - ny wa - ters let the glad shout be, Till it ech - o and re-

wa - ter-floods, our King for ev - er-more! Tell it out! Tell it out!
dy - ing that He tri - umphed o'er the grave. Tell it out! Tell it out!
ech - o from the is - lands of the sea. Tell it out! Tell it out!

Hasten, Lord, the Glorious Time 157

INNOCENTS. 7 7, 7 7.

HARRIET AUBER, 1829   *The Parish Choir*, London, 1850

1. Hast - en, Lord, the glor - ious time, When be-neath Mes - si - ah's sway,
2. Might-iest kings His pow'r shall own, Heath - en tribes His Name a - dore;
3. Then shall war and tu - mults cease, Then be ban - ished grief and pain;
4. Bless we, then, our gra - cious Lord; Ev - er praise His glo - rious Name;

Ev - 'ry na - tion, ev - 'ry clime Shall the gos - pel call o - bey.
Sa - tan and his host o'er-thrown, Bound in chains, shall hurt no more.
Right-eous-ness and joy and peace Un - dis-turbed shall ev - er reign.
All His might - y acts re - cord; All His won-drous love pro-claim. A-MEN.

158 From Greenland's Icy Mountains

MISSIONARY HYMN. 7 6, 7 6. D.

REGINALD HEBER, 1819   LOWELL MASON, 1824

1. From Green-land's i - cy moun-tains, From In - dia's cor - al strand,
2. What tho' the spi - cy breez - es Blow soft o'er Cey-lon's isle,
3. Can we whose souls are light - ed With wis - dom from on high,
4. Waft, waft, ye winds, His sto - ry, And you, ye wa - ters, roll,

Where Af - ric's sun - ny foun - tains Roll down their gold - en sand,
Though ev - 'ry pros-pect pleas - es, And on - ly man is vile;
Can we to men be - night - ed The lamp of life de - ny?
Till, like a sea of glo - ry, It spreads from pole to pole;

From many an an - cient riv - er, From many a palm - y plain,
In vain with lav - ish kind - ness The gifts of God are strown;
Sal - va - tion! O sal - va - tion! The joy - ful sound pro - claim,
Till o'er our ran-somed na - ture The Lamb for sin - ners slain,

They call us to de - liv - er Their land from er - ror's chain.
The heath - en in his blind - ness Bows down to wood and stone.
Till each re - mot - est na - tion Has learned Mes - si - ah's Name.
Re - deem - er, King, Cre - a - tor, In bliss re - turns to reign.

Who is On the Lord's Side?

SUMUS TIBI. 6 5. 12 lines.

FRANCES R. HAVERGAL, 1877

H. ELLIOT BUTTON

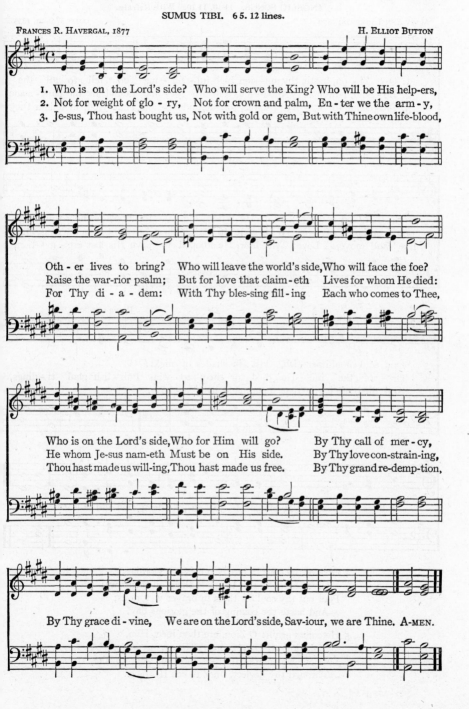

1. Who is on the Lord's side? Who will serve the King? Who will be His help-ers,
2. Not for weight of glo - ry, Not for crown and palm, En - ter we the arm - y,
3. Je-sus, Thou hast bought us, Not with gold or gem, But with Thine own life-blood,

Oth - er lives to bring? Who will leave the world's side, Who will face the foe?
Raise the war-rior psalm; But for love that claim - eth Lives for whom He died:
For Thy di - a - dem: With Thy bles-sing fill - ing Each who comes to Thee,

Who is on the Lord's side, Who for Him will go? By Thy call of mer - cy,
He whom Je-sus nam-eth Must be on His side. By Thy love con-strain-ing,
Thou hast made us will-ing, Thou hast made us free. By Thy grand re-demp-tion,

By Thy grace di - vine, We are on the Lord's side, Sav-iour, we are Thine. A-MEN.

160 O Zion, Haste

ANGELIC SONGS. 11 10, 11 10. With Refrain.

MARY ANN THOMPSON, 1870

JAMES WALCH, 1875

1. O Zi - on, haste, thy mis-sion high ful - fill - ing To tell to all the
2. Be - hold, how man - y thou-sands still are ly - ing Bound in the dark - some
3. Pro - claim to ev - 'ry peo-ple, tongue, and na - tion That God, in Whom they

world that God is light; That He Who made all na - tions is not will - ing
pris - on-house of sin, With none to tell them of the Saviour's dy - ing,
live and move, is Love: Tell how He stooped to save His lost cre - a - tion,

REFRAIN

One soul should per - ish, lost in shades of night:
Or of the life He died for them to win. Pub - lish glad ti - dings,
And died on earth that man might live a - bove.

ti-dings of peace; Ti - dings of Je - sus, Re-demp-tion and re-lease. A - MEN.

4 Give of thy sons to bear the message glorious,
Give of thy wealth to speed them on their way;
Pour out thy soul for them in prayer victorious;
And haste the coming of the glorious day.

5 He comes again: O Zion, ere thou meet Him,
Make known to every heart His saving grace;
Let none whom He hath ransomed fail to greet Him,
Through thy neglect, unfit to see His face.

Saviour, Sprinkle Many Nations

O DU LIEBE MEINER LIEBE. 87, 87. D.

Arthur Cleveland Coxe, 1851   Thommen's *Christenschatz*, Basel, 1745

1. Sav-iour, sprin - kle ma - ny na - tions; Fruit-ful let Thy sor - rows be;
2. Far and wide, though all un-know - ing, Pants for Thee each mor - tal breast;
3. Sav-iour, lo! the isles are wait - ing, Stretched the hand, and strained the sight,

By Thy pains and con - so - la - tions Draw the Gen-tiles un - to Thee.
Hu - man tears for Thee are flow - ing; Hu - man hearts in Thee would rest;
For Thy Spir - it new - cre - a - ting, Love's pure flame, and wis-dom's light.

Of Thy Cross the won-drous sto - ry Be it to the na - tions told;
Thirst-ing as for dews of ev - en, As the new - mown grass for rain,
Give the word, and of the preach-er Speed the foot, and touch the tongue,

Let them see Thee in Thy glo - ry And Thy mer-cy man - i - fold!
Thee they seek, as God of heav - en, Thee, as Man for sin - ners slain.
Till on earth, by ev-'ry crea-ture, Glo - ry to the Lamb be sung! A - MEN.

162 Thou, Whose Almighty Word

DORT. 664,6664.

JOHN MARRIOTT, 1813
Revised by THOMAS RAFFLES

LOWELL MASON, 1832

1. Thou, Whose al - might - y Word Cha - os and dark - ness heard,
2. Thou, Who didst come to bring On Thy re - deem - ing wing
3. Spir - it of truth and love, Life - giv - ing, ho - ly Dove,
4. Ho - ly and bless - ed Three, Glo - ri - ous Trin - i - ty,

And took their flight, Hear us, we hum - bly pray, And where the
Heal - ing and sight, Health to the sick in mind, Sight to the
Speed forth Thy flight! Move on the wa - ters' face, Bear - ing the
Wis - dom, Love, Might, Bound-less as o - cean's tide Roll - ing in

gos - pel day Sheds not its glo-rious ray, Let there be light!
in - ly blind, O, now to all man-kind Let there be light!
lamp of grace, And in earth's dark-est place Let there be light!
full - est pride, Through the earth, far and wide, Let there be light! A - MEN.

163 Arm of the Lord, Awake

TRURO. L. M.

WM. SHRUBSOLE, 1795

WILLIAMS' *Psalmodia Evangelica*, 1790

1. Arm of the Lord, a - wake! a - wake! Put on Thy strength! the na-tions shake!
2. Say to the heath-en from Thy throne, I am Je - ho - vah, God a - lone:
3. Let Si - on's time of fa - vor come; O bring the tribes of Is - rael home:
4. Al - might - y God, Thy grace pro-claim In ev - 'ry clime, of ev - 'ry name;

And let the world a - dor - ing see Tri-umphs of mer - cy wrought by Thee.
Thy voice their i - dols shall confound, And cast their al - tars to the ground.
And let our wondering eyes be-hold Gen-tiles and Jews in Je - sus' Fold.
Let ad-verse pow'rs be-fore Thee fall, And crown the Sav-iour Lord of all. A-MEN.

Christ For the World We Sing   164

DYB AF KJÆRLIGHED. 664, 6664.

SAMUEL WOLCOTT, 1869

J. P. E. HARTMAN

1. Christ for the world we sing; The world to Christ we bring,
2. Christ for the world we sing; The world to Christ we bring,
3. Christ for the world we sing; The world to Christ we bring,
4. Christ for the world we sing; The world to Christ we bring,

With lov - ing zeal, The poor and them that mourn, The faint and
With fer - vent prayer; The way-ward and the lost, By rest - less
With one ac - cord; With us the work to share, With us re-
With joy - ful song; The new-born souls, whose days, Re - claimed from

o - ver-borne, Sin - sick and sor - row-worn, Whom Christ doth heal.
pas-sions tossed, Re-deemed at count-less cost, From dark de - spair.
proach to dare, With us the cross to bear, For Christ our Lord.
er - ror's ways, In - spired with hope and praise, To Christ be - long.

165 Heralds of Christ Who Bear the King's Commands

PRO PATRIA. 10 10, 10 10.

LAURA S. COPENHAVER   HORATIO W. PARKER, 1894

1. Her - alds of Christ who bear the King's com-mands, Im - mor - tal ti - dings
2. Thro' des - ert ways, dark fen and deep mo - rass, Thro' jun-gles, slug - gish
3. Where once the twist - ing trail in dark - ness wound Let march-ing feet and
4. Lord, give us faith and strength the road to build, To see the prom - ise

in your mor - tal hands, Pass on and car - ry swift the news ye
seas, and moun-tain pass, Build ye the road, and fal - ter not, nor
joy - ous song re - sound, Where burn the fun - eral pyres and cen - sers
of the day ful - filled, When war shall be no more and strife shall

bring, Make straight, make straight the high - way of the King.
stay, Pre - pare a - cross the earth the King's high - way.
swing, Make straight, make straight the high - way of the King.
cease Up - on the high - way of the Prince of Peace. A-MEN.

Words by permission of the Women's Missionary Society.

166   Fling Out the Banner

WALTHAM. L. M.

GEORGE W. DOANE, 1848   JOHN B. CALKIN, 1872

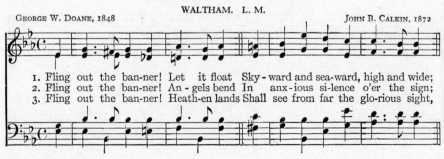

1. Fling out the ban-ner! Let it float Sky - ward and sea - ward, high and wide;
2. Fling out the ban-ner! An - gels bend In anx - ious si - lence o'er the sign;
3. Fling out the ban-ner! Heath-en lands Shall see from far the glo-rious sight,

The sun, that lights its shin-ing folds, The Cross, on which the Sav-iour died.
And vain-ly seek to com-pre-hend The won-der of the love di-vine.
And na-tions, crowding to be born, Bap-tize their spir-its in its light. A-MEN.

4 Fling out the banner! Sin-sick souls
  That sink and perish in the strife,
  Shall touch in faith its radiant hem,
  And spring immortal into life.

5 Fling out the banner! Let it float
  Skyward and seaward, high and wide;
  Our glory, only in the Cross;
  Our only hope, the Crucified!

Look From Thy Sphere of Endless Day 167

MELCOMBE. L. M.

WM. CULLEN BRYANT, 1840, a

SAMUEL WEBBE, 1782

1. Look from Thy sphere of end-less day, O God of mer-cy and of might!
2. In peo-pled vale, in lone-ly glen, In crowd-ed mart, by stream or sea,
3. Send forth Thy her-alds, Lord, to call The thought-less young, the hard-ened old,

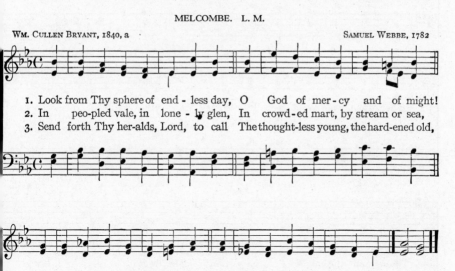

In pi-ty look on those who stray, Be-night-ed in this land of light.
How ma-ny of the sons of men Hear not the mes-sage sent from Thee!
A scat-tered, home-less flock, till all Be gath-ered to Thy peace-ful fold. A-MEN.

4 Send them Thy mighty Word, to speak
  Till faith shall dawn, and doubt depart,
  To awe the bold, to stay the weak,
  And bind and heal the broken heart.

5 Then all these wastes,—a dreary scene,
  That fills with sadness as we gaze,—
  Shall grow with living waters green,
  And lift to heaven the voice of praise.

168 The Whole Wide World for Jesus

THE WHOLE WIDE WORLD. 7 6, 7 6. D. With Refrain.

J. Dempster Hammond, 1880

John H. Maunder, 1894

1. The whole wide world for Je - sus! This shall our watch-word be;
2. The whole wide world for Je - sus! In - spires us with the thought
3. The whole wide world for Je - sus! The march - ing or - der sound:

Up - on the high - est moun - tain, Down by the wid - est sea;
That all God's wan - dering chil - dren Have by His love been sought.
Go ye and preach the Gos - pel Wher - ev - er man is found.

The whole wide world for Je - sus! To Him shall all men bow,
The whole wide world for Je - sus! O faint not by the way!
The whole wide world for Je - sus! Ride forth, O con-quering King,

In cit - y or in prai - rie— The world for Je - sus now!
The Cross shall sure - ly con - quer In this our glo - rious day.
Through all the might - y na - tions The world to glo - ry bring!

REFRAIN

The whole wide world, The whole wide world—Pro-claim the gos-pel tidings through

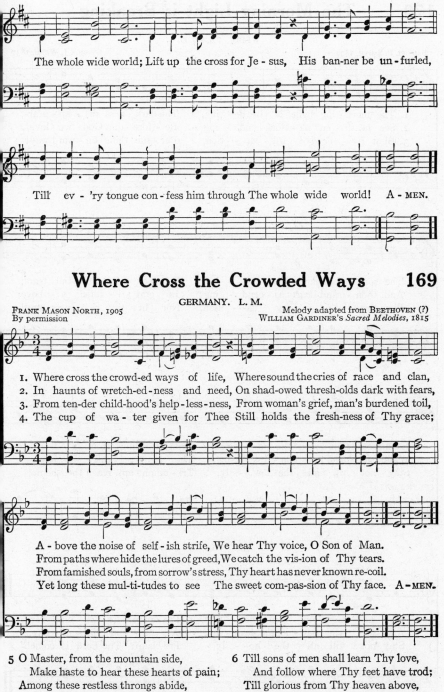

The whole wide world; Lift up the cross for Je - sus, His ban-ner be un-furled,

Till ev - 'ry tongue con-fess him through The whole wide world! A - MEN.

Where Cross the Crowded Ways 169

GERMANY. L. M.

FRANK MASON NORTH, 1905
By permission

Melody adapted from BEETHOVEN (?)
WILLIAM GARDINER'S *Sacred Melodies*, 1815

1. Where cross the crowd-ed ways of life, Where sound the cries of race and clan,
2. In haunts of wretch-ed-ness and need, On shad-owed thresh-olds dark with fears,
3. From ten-der child-hood's help-less-ness, From woman's grief, man's burdened toil,
4. The cup of wa - ter given for Thee Still holds the fresh-ness of Thy grace;

A - bove the noise of self - ish strife, We hear Thy voice, O Son of Man.
From paths where hide the lures of greed, We catch the vis-ion of Thy tears.
From famished souls, from sorrow's stress, Thy heart has never known re-coil.
Yet long these mul-ti-tudes to see The sweet com-pas-sion of Thy face. A - MEN.

5 O Master, from the mountain side,
 Make haste to hear these hearts of pain;
 Among these restless throngs abide,
 O tread the city's streets again;

6 Till sons of men shall learn Thy love,
 And follow where Thy feet have trod;
 Till glorious from Thy heaven above,
 Shall come the City of our God.

170 The Morning Light is Breaking

WEBB. 7 6, 7 6. D.

SAMUEL F. SMITH, 1832

GEORGE J. WEBB, 1837

1. The morn - ing light is break - ing, The dark - ness dis - ap - pears;
2. See heath - en na - tions bend - ing Be - fore the God we love,
3. Blest riv - er of sal - va - tion, Pur - sue thine on - ward way!

The sons of earth are wak - ing To pen - i - ten - tial tears;
And thou - sand hearts as - cend - ing In grat - i - tude a - bove;
Flow thou to ev - 'ry na - tion, Nor in thy rich - ness stay!

Each breeze that sweeps the o - cean Brings ti - dings from a - far
While sin - ners, now con - fess - ing, The gos - pel call o - bey,
Stay not till all the low - ly, Tri - umph - ant, reach their home;

Of na - tions in com - mo - tion, Pre - pared for Zi - on's war.
And seek the Sav - iour's bless - ing, A na - tion in a day.
Stay not till all the ho - ly Pro - claim: "The Lord is come!"

Angel Voices Ever Singing

ANGEL VOICES. 8 5, 8 5, 8 4 3.

FRANCIS POTT, 1861

ARTHUR S. SULLIVAN, 1872

1. An - gel voi - ces ev - er sing - ing   Round Thy throne of light,
2. Thou, Who art be - yond the farth - est   Mor - tal eye can scan,
3. Yea, we know that Thou re - joic - est   O'er each work of Thine;

An - gel-harps, for ev - er ring-ing,   Rest not day nor night; Thou-sands on-ly
Can it be that Thou re-gard-est   Songs of sin - ful man? Can we know that
Thou didst ears and hands and voi-ces   For Thy praise com-bine; Craftsman's art and

live to bless Thee, And con - fess Thee,   Lord   of Might!
Thou art near us, And wilt hear us?   Yes,   we can!
mu - sic's meas-ure For Thy pleas-ure   Didst de - sign.   A - MEN.

4 Here, great God, to-day we offer
   Of Thine own to Thee,
   And for Thine acceptance proffer,
   All unworthily,
   Hearts and minds and hands and voices,
   In our choicest
   Melody.

5 Honor, glory, might and merit
   Thine shall ever be,
   Father, Son, and Holy Spirit,
   Blessèd Trinity!
   Of the best that Thou hast given,
   Earth and heaven
   Render Thee.

172 Lord of the Worlds Above

DARWALL'S 148th. 6 6, 6 6, 4 4, 4 4.

ISAAC WATTS, 1719

JOHN DARWALL, 1770

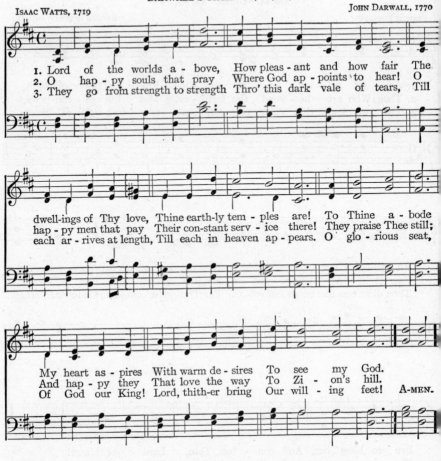

1. Lord of the worlds a - bove, How pleas - ant and how fair The
2. O hap - py souls that pray Where God ap - points to hear! O
3. They go from strength to strength Thro' this dark vale of tears, Till

dwell-ings of Thy love, Thine earth-ly tem - ples are! To Thine a - bode
hap - py men that pay Their con-stant serv - ice there! They praise Thee still;
each ar - rives at length, Till each in heaven ap - pears. O glo - rious seat,

My heart as - pires With warm de - sires To see my God.
And hap - py they That love the way To Zi - on's hill.
Of God our King! Lord, thith-er bring Our will - ing feet! A-MEN.

173 We Love the Place, O God

QUAM DILECTA. 6 6, 6 6.

WM. BULLOCK, 1854, a

HENRY L. JENNER, 1861

1. We love the place, O God, Where - in Thine hon - or dwells;
2. We love the house of prayer, Where - in Thy serv - ants meet;
3. We love the sa - cred font, Where - in the ho - ly Dove
4. We love Thine al - tar, Lord, Its mys - ter - ies re - vere;

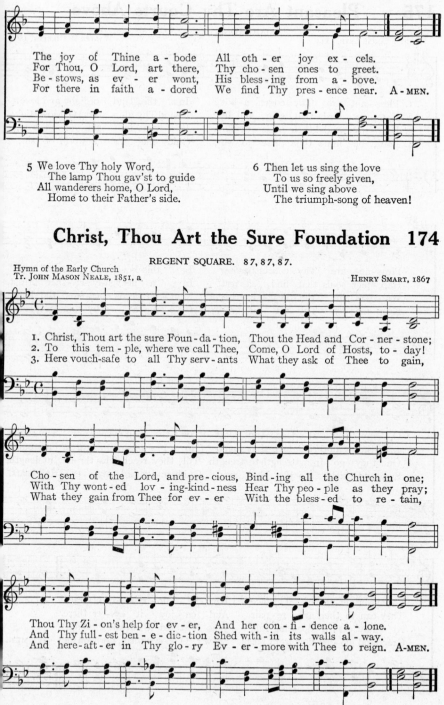

The joy of Thine a - bode   All oth - er joy ex - cels.
For Thou, O Lord, art there,   Thy cho - sen ones to greet.
Be - stows, as ev - er wont,   His bless - ing from a - bove.
For there in faith a - dored   We find Thy pres - ence near. A - MEN.

5 We love Thy holy Word,
    The lamp Thou gav'st to guide
All wanderers home, O Lord,
    Home to their Father's side.

6 Then let us sing the love
    To us so freely given,
Until we sing above
    The triumph-song of heaven!

Christ, Thou Art the Sure Foundation 174

REGENT SQUARE. 8 7, 8 7, 8 7.

Hymn of the Early Church
Tr. JOHN MASON NEALE, 1851, a

HENRY SMART, 1867

1. Christ, Thou art the sure Foun - da - tion,   Thou the Head and Cor - ner - stone;
2. To this tem - ple, where we call Thee,   Come, O Lord of Hosts, to - day!
3. Here vouch-safe to all Thy serv - ants   What they ask of Thee to gain,

Cho - sen of the Lord, and pre - cious,   Bind - ing all the Church in one;
With Thy wont - ed lov - ing-kind-ness   Hear Thy peo - ple as they pray;
What they gain from Thee for ev - er   With the bless - ed to re - tain,

Thou Thy Zi - on's help for ev - er,   And her con - fi - dence a - lone.
And Thy full - est ben - e - dic - tion   Shed with - in its walls al - way.
And here-aft - er in Thy glo - ry   Ev - er - more with Thee to reign. A - MEN.

175 Pleasant Are Thy Courts Above

MAIDSTONE. 77, 77. D.

HENRY FRANCIS LYTE, 1834

WALTER B. GILBERT, 1862

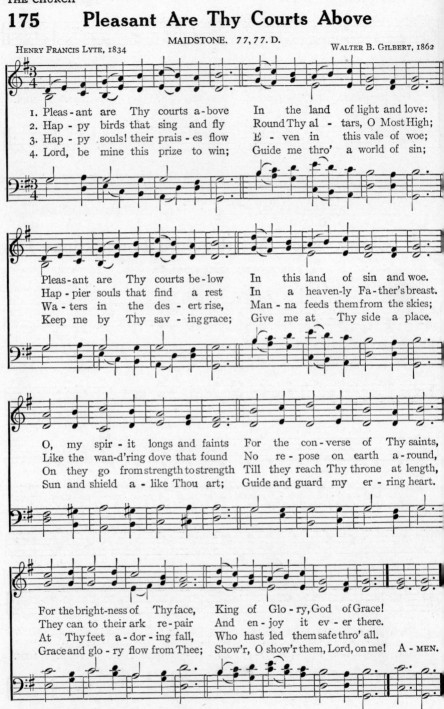

1. Pleas - ant are Thy courts a - bove   In   the land   of light and love:
2. Hap - py birds that sing and fly   Round Thy al - tars, O Most High;
3. Hap - py souls! their prais - es flow   E - ven in   this vale of woe;
4. Lord, be mine this prize to win;   Guide me thro' a world of sin;

Pleas - ant are Thy courts be - low   In   this land of sin and woe.
Hap - pier souls that find a rest   In   a heaven-ly Fa-ther's breast.
Wa - ters in the des - ert rise,   Man - na feeds them from the skies;
Keep me by Thy sav - ing grace;   Give me at Thy side a place.

O, my spir - it longs and faints   For the con - verse of Thy saints,
Like the wan-d'ring dove that found   No re - pose on earth a - round,
On they go from strength to strength   Till they reach Thy throne at length,
Sun and shield a - like Thou art;   Guide and guard my er - ring heart.

For the bright-ness of Thy face,   King of Glo - ry, God of Grace!
They can to their ark re - pair   And en - joy it ev - er there.
At Thy feet a - dor - ing fall,   Who hast led them safe thro' all.
Grace and glo - ry flow from Thee;   Show'r, O show'r them, Lord, on me! A - MEN.

Jerusalem the Golden

EWING. 7 6, 7 6. D.

BERNARD OF CLUNY, c. 1145
TR. JOHN MASON NEALE, 1851

ALEXANDER EWING, 1853

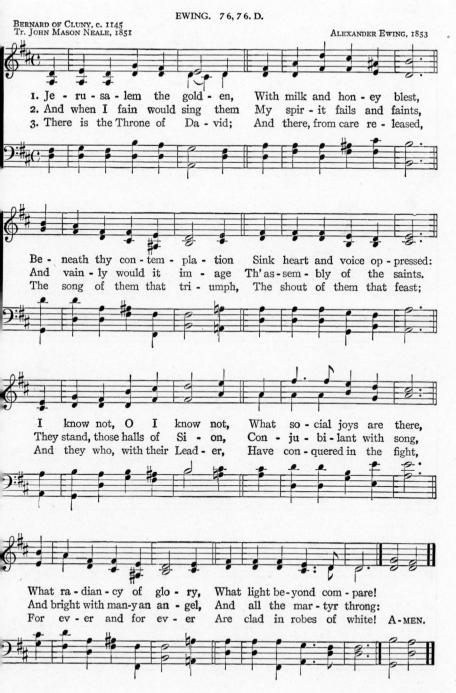

1. Je - ru - sa - lem the gold - en, With milk and hon - ey blest,
2. And when I fain would sing them My spir - it fails and faints,
3. There is the Throne of Da - vid; And there, from care re - leased,

Be - neath thy con - tem - pla - tion Sink heart and voice op - pressed:
And vain - ly would it im - age Th' as - sem - bly of the saints.
The song of them that tri - umph, The shout of them that feast;

I know not, O I know not, What so - cial joys are there,
They stand, those halls of Si - on, Con - ju - bi - lant with song,
And they who, with their Lead - er, Have con - quered in the fight,

What ra - dian - cy of glo - ry, What light be - yond com - pare!
And bright with man-y an an - gel, And all the mar - tyr throng:
For ev - er and for ev - er Are clad in robes of white! A - MEN.

177 Hark! the Sound of Holy Voices

SANCTUARY. 87, 87. D.

Christopher Wordsworth, 1862

John B. Dykes, 1871

1. Hark! the sound of ho - ly voi - ces Chant-ing at the crys - tal sea:
2. They have come from trib - u - la - tion, And have washed their robes in blood,
3. March-ing with Thy Cross, their ban - ner, They have tri-umphed fol - low - ing
4. Now they reign in heaven-ly glo - ry, Now they walk in gold - en light,

Al - le - lu - ia! Al - le - lu - ia! Al - le - lu - ia! Lord, to Thee.
Washed them in the Blood of Je - sus; Tried they were, and firm they stood;
Thee, the Cap-tain of Sal - va - tion, Thee, their Sav-iour, and their King;
Now they drink, as from a riv - er, Ho - ly bliss and in - fi - nite;

Mul - ti - tudes, which none can num-ber, Like the stars in glo - ry stand,
Mocked, im-pris-oned, stoned, tor-ment-ed, Sawn a - sun - der, slain with sword,
Glad - ly, Lord, with Thee they suf-fered; Glad - ly, Lord, with Thee they died;
Love and peace they taste for ev - er And all truth and knowl-edge see

Clothed in white ap - par - el, hold-ing Palms of vic - t'ry in their hand.
They have con-quered death and Sa-tan By the might of Christ the Lord.
And by death to life im - mor-tal They were born and glo - ri - fied.
In the be - a - tif - ic vis-ion Of the Bless-ed Trin - i - ty. A-MEN.

For All the Saints Who From Their Labors Rest 178

PRO OMNIBUS SANCTIS. 10 10 10, 4.

WM. WALSHAM HOW, 1864   JOSEPH BARNBY, 1869

1. For all the saints who from their la - bors rest,
2. Thou wast their Rock, their Fort - ress and their Might;
3. O may Thy sol - diers, faith - ful, true and bold,

Who Thee by
Thou, Lord, their
Fight as the

faith be - fore the world con - fessed, Thy Name, O Je - sus,
Cap - tain in their well - fought fight; Thou, in the dark - ness
saints who no - bly fought of old, And win, with them, the

be for ev - er blest. Al - le - lu - ia! Al - le - lu - ia!
drear, their one true Light. Al - le - lu - ia! Al - le - lu - ia!
vic - tor's crown of gold. Al - le - lu - ia! Al - le - lu - ia! A-MEN.

4 O blest communion, fellowship divine!
We feebly struggle, they in glory shine;
Yet all are one in Thee, for all are Thine.
Alleluia!

5 The golden evening brightens in the west;
Soon, soon to faithful warriors cometh rest;
Sweet is the calm of Paradise the blest.
Alleluia!

6 But lo! there breaks a yet more glorious day:
The saints triumphant rise in bright array;
The King of Glory passes on His way.
Alleluia!

7 From earth's wide bounds, from ocean's farthest coast,
Through gates of pearl streams in the countless host,
Singing to Father, Son and Holy Ghost:
Alleluia!

179 A Pilgrim and a Stranger

LLANGLOFFAN. 7 6, 7 6. D.

Paul Gerhardt, 1666
Tr. Jane Borthwick, 1858

Welsh Hymn Melody

1. A pil-grim and a stran-ger, I jour-ney here be-low;
2. There still my thoughts are dwell-ing, 'Tis there I long to be;
3. There I shall dwell for ev-er, No more a strang-er guest,

Far dis-tant is my coun-try, The home to which I go.
Come, Lord, and call Thy serv-ant To bless-ed-ness with Thee.
With all Thy blood-bought chil-dren In ev-er-last-ing rest,—

Here I must toil and trav-ail, Oft wea-ry and op-pressed,
Come, bid my toils be end-ed, Let all my wan-d'rings cease;
The pil-grim toils for-got-ten, The pil-grim con-flicts o'er,

But there my God shall lead me To ev-er-last-ing rest.
Call from the way-side lodg-ing To the sweet home of peace.
All earth-ly griefs be-hind us, E-ter-nal joys be-fore! A-men.

Hark! Hark, My Soul!

180

ANGELS OF JESUS. 11 10, 11 10. With Refrain.

FREDERICK W. FABER, 1854

JOSEPH BARNBY, 1868

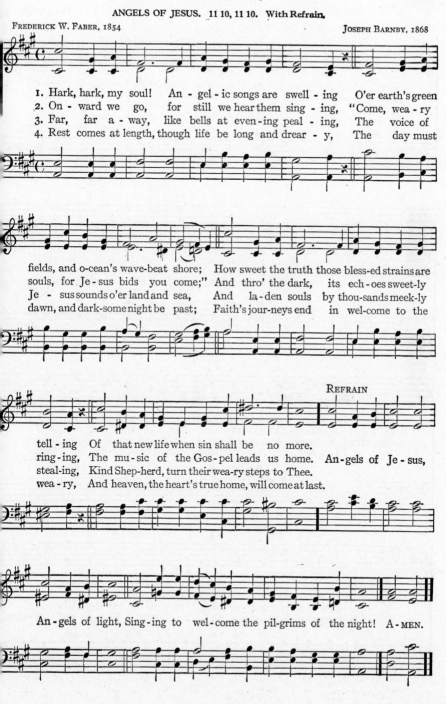

1. Hark, hark, my soul! An - gel - ic songs are swell - ing O'er earth's green fields, and o-cean's wave-beat shore; How sweet the truth those bless-ed strains are tell - ing Of that new life when sin shall be no more.

2. On - ward we go, for still we hear them sing - ing, "Come, wea - ry souls, for Je - sus bids you come;" And thro' the dark, its ech - oes sweet-ly ring-ing, The mu - sic of the Gos-pel leads us home.

3. Far, far a - way, like bells at even-ing peal - ing, The voice of Je - sus sounds o'er land and sea, And la - den souls by thou-sands meek-ly steal-ing, Kind Shep-herd, turn their wea-ry steps to Thee.

4. Rest comes at length, though life be long and drear - y, The day must dawn, and dark-some night be past; Faith's jour-neys end in wel-come to the wea - ry, And heaven, the heart's true home, will come at last.

REFRAIN

An - gels of Je - sus, An - gels of light, Sing-ing to wel-come the pil-grims of the night! A - MEN.

181 O Mother Dear, Jerusalem!

MATERNA. C. M. D.

Adapted from two hymns of the 16th and 17th Century

SAMUEL A. WARD, 1882

1. O moth - er dear, Je - ru - sa - lem! When shall I come to thee?
2. No murk - y cloud o'er-shad - ows thee, No cold nor dark-some night;
3. Thy gar - dens and thy gal - lant walks Con - tin - ual - ly are green,
4. There trees for ev - er - more bear fruit, And ev - er - more do spring;

When shall my sor - rows have an end? Thy joys when shall I see?
There ev - 'ry soul shines as the sun, For God Him - self gives light.
There grow such sweet and pleas-ant flow'rs As no - where else are seen.
There ev - er - more the an - gels are, And ev - er - more do sing.

O hap - py har - bor of God's saints! O sweet and pleas - ant soil!
O my sweet home Je - ru - sa - lem, Thy joys when shall I see?
Quite thro' thy streets, with sil - ver sound, The flood of life doth flow,
Je - ru - sa - lem, my hap - py home, Would God I were in thee;

In thee no sor - row can be found, No grief, no care, no toil.
The King that sit - teth on thy throne In His fe - lic - i - ty?
Up - on whose banks, on eith - er side, The wood of life doth grow.
Would God my woes were at an end, Thy joys that I might see! A - MEN.

Around the Throne of God in Heaven 182

CHILDREN'S PRAISES. C. M. With Refrain.

ANNA H. SHEPHERD, 1836   Arranged by HENRY E. MATTHEWS, c. 1841

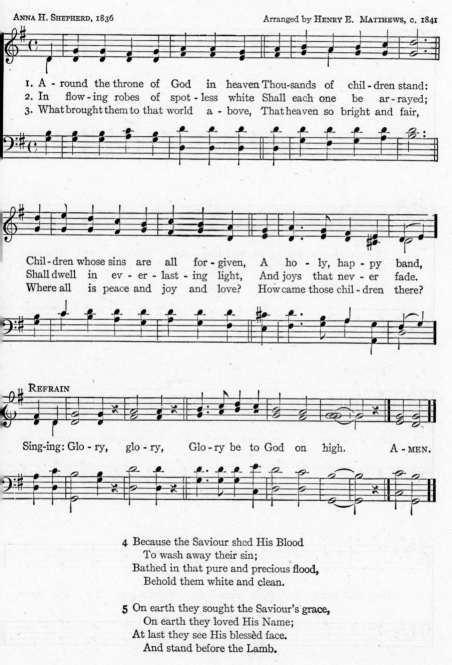

1. A - round the throne of God in heaven Thou-sands of chil - dren stand:
2. In flow - ing robes of spot - less white Shall each one be ar - rayed;
3. What brought them to that world a - bove, That heaven so bright and fair,

Chil - dren whose sins are all for - given, A ho - ly, hap - py band,
Shall dwell in ev - er - last - ing light, And joys that nev - er fade.
Where all is peace and joy and love? How came those chil - dren there?

REFRAIN

Sing-ing: Glo - ry, glo - ry, Glo - ry be to God on high. A - MEN.

4 Because the Saviour shed His Blood
    To wash away their sin;
    Bathed in that pure and precious flood,
    Behold them white and clean.

5 On earth they sought the Saviour's grace,
    On earth they loved His Name;
    At last they see His blessèd face,
    And stand before the Lamb.

183

When He Cometh

JEWELS. 8 6, 8 5. With Refrain.

WILLIAM O. CUSHING

GEORGE F. ROOT

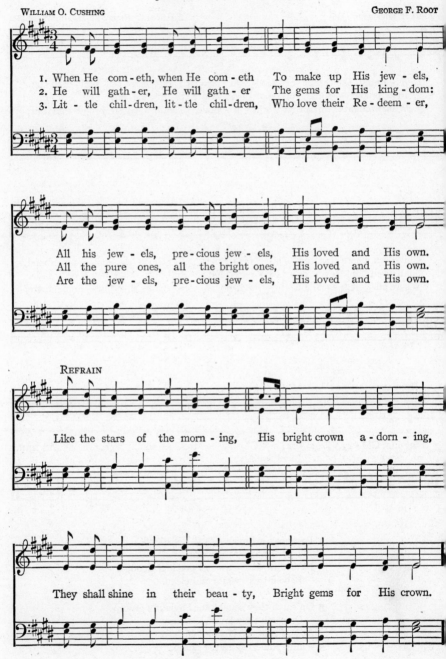

1. When He com-eth, when He com-eth To make up His jew-els,
2. He will gath-er, He will gath-er The gems for His king-dom:
3. Lit-tle chil-dren, lit-tle chil-dren, Who love their Re-deem-er,

All his jew-els, pre-cious jew-els, His loved and His own.
All the pure ones, all the bright ones, His loved and His own.
Are the jew-els, pre-cious jew-els, His loved and His own.

REFRAIN

Like the stars of the morn-ing, His bright crown a-dorn-ing,

They shall shine in their beau-ty, Bright gems for His crown.

THE KINGDOM AND GLORY OF CHRIST

Beautiful Saviour 184

SCHÖNSTER HERR JESU. 5 5 7. D.

Münster Gesangbuch, 1677
Tr. JOSEPH A. SEISS, 1873

Silesian Folk-Song
HOFFMANN VON FALLERSLEBEN'S *Volkslieder*, 1842

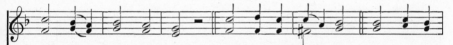

1. Beau - ti - ful Sav - iour! King of Cre - a - tion! Son of
2. Fair are the mead - ows, Fair are the wood-lands, Robed in
3. Fair is the sun - shine, Fair is the moon-light, Bright the
4. Beau - ti - ful Sav - iour! Lord of the na - tions! Son of

God and Son of Man! Tru - ly I'd love Thee, Tru - ly I'd
flow'rs of bloom - ing spring; Je - sus is fair - er, Je - sus is
spark - ling stars on high; Je - sus shines bright-er, Je - sus shines
God and Son of Man! Glo - ry and hon - or, Praise, ad - o -

serve Thee, Light of my soul, my Joy, my Crown.
pur - er; He makes our sor - rowing spir - it sing.
pur - er, Than all the an - gels in the sky.
ra - tion, Now and for ev - er - more be Thine! A-MEN.

185 All Hail the Power of Jesus' Name!

MILES' LANE. C. M.

4 Let every kindred, every tribe,
On this terrestrial ball,
To Him all majesty ascribe,
And crown Him Lord of all.

5 O that with yonder sacred throng
We at His feet may fall;
We'll join the everlasting song
And crown Him Lord of all.

Second Tune

LAUD. C. M.

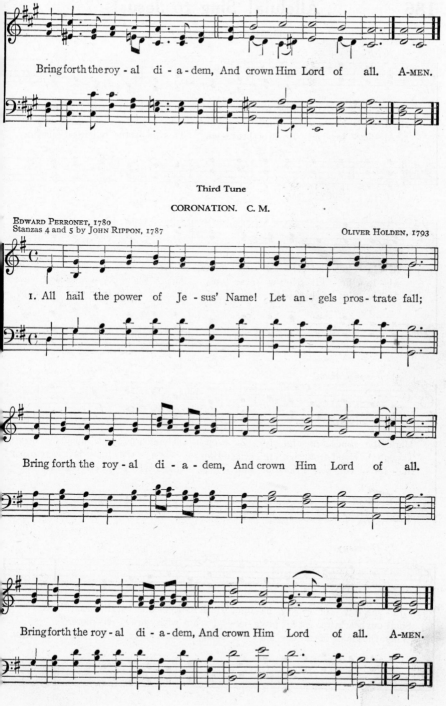

Bring forth the roy - al di - a - dem, And crown Him Lord of all. A-MEN.

Third Tune

CORONATION. C. M.

EDWARD PERRONET, 1780
Stanzas 4 and 5 by JOHN RIPPON, 1787

OLIVER HOLDEN, 1793

1. All hail the power of Je - sus' Name! Let an - gels pros - trate fall;

Bring forth the roy - al di - a - dem, And crown Him Lord of all.

Bring forth the roy - al di - a - dem, And crown Him Lord of all. A-MEN.

186   Alleluia! Sing to Jesus!

EUCHARISTICA. 87, 87. D.

WM. CHATTERTON DIX, 1866   JAMES WM. ELLIOTT

Brisk

1. Al - le - lu - ia! sing to Je - sus! His the scep - tre, His the throne;
2. Al - le - lu - ia! Not as or - phans Are we left in sor-row now;
3. Al - le - lu - ia! Bread of heav - en, Thou on earth our Food, our Stay,

Al - le - lu - ia! His the tri - umph, His the vic - to - ry a - lone;
Al - le - lu - ia! He is near us, Faith be - lieves, nor ques-tions how:
Al - le - lu - ia! here the sin - ful Flee to Thee from day to day;

Voices in Unison

Hark the songs of ho - ly Zi - on Thunder like a might-y flood:
Though the cloud from sight re - ceived Him When the forty days were o'er,
In - ter - ces - sor, Friend of sin - ners, Earth's Re-deem-er, plead for me,

In Harmony   *poco rall.*

"Je - sus, out of ev - 'ry na - tion, Hath re-deemed us by His blood!"
Shall our hearts for - get his prom-ise—"I am with you ev - er-more?"
Where the songs of all the sin - less Sweep a-cross the crys - tal sea.   A - MEN.

Come, Let Us Join Our Cheerful Songs 187

NUN DANKET ALL' UND BRINGET EHR. C. M.

First Tune

ISAAC WATTS, 1707

JOHANN CRÜGER, 1656

1. Come, let us join our cheer-ful songs With an-gels round the throne;
2. "Wor-thy the Lamb that died," they cry, "To be ex-alt-ed thus."
3. Je-sus is wor-thy to re-ceive Hon-or and power di-vine;

Ten thou-sand thou-sand are their tongues, But all their joys are one.
"Wor-thy the Lamb," our lips re-ply, "For He was slain for us."
And bless-ings more than we can give, Be, Lord, for ev-er Thine. A-MEN.

4 Let all that dwell above the sky,
   And air, and earth, and seas,
Conspire to lift Thy glories high,
   And speak Thine endless praise!

5 The whole creation join in one
   To bless the sacred Name
Of Him that sits upon the throne,
   And to adore the Lamb.

Second Tune

CHRISTMAS. C. M.

ISAAC WATTS, 1707

Arranged from GEORG F. HÄNDEL, 1728

1. Come, let us join our cheerful songs With angels round the throne; Ten thousand thousand

are their tongues, But all their joys are one, But all their joys are one. A-MEN.

188 Crown Him With Many Crowns

DIADEMATA. S. M. D.

Stanza 1, MATTHEW BRIDGES, 1851
Stanzas 2-4, GODFREY THRING, 1882

GEORGE J. ELVEY, 1868

1. Crown Him with man - y crowns, The Lamb up - on His throne;
2. Crown Him the Son of God Be - fore the worlds be - gan;
3. Crown Him the Lord of life, Who tri-umphed o'er the grave,
4. Crown Him the Lord of heaven, En - throned in worlds a - bove,

Hark! how the heaven-ly an - them drowns All mu - sic but its own!
And ye, who tread where He hath trod, Crown Him the Son of Man,
And rose vic - to - rious in the strife For those He came to save;
Crown Him the King to Whom is given The won-drous name of Love.

A - wake, my soul, and sing Of Him Who died for thee,
Who ev - 'ry grief hath known That wrings the hu - man breast,
His glo - ries now we sing, Who died, and rose on high,
Crown Him with man - y crowns As thrones be - fore Him fall,

And hail Him as thy cho-sen King Thro' all e - ter - ni - ty.
And takes and bears them for His own That all in Him may rest.
Who died, e - ter - nal life to bring, And lives, that death may die.
Crown Him, ye kings, with man-y crowns, For He is King of all. A-MEN.

O for a Thousand Tongues to Sing **189**

BEATITUDO. C. M.

First Tune

CHARLES WESLEY, 1738, a

JOHN B. DYKES, 1874

1. O for a thou-sand tongues to sing My great Re-deem-er's praise,
2. My gra-cious Mas-ter and my God, As-sist me to pro-claim,
3. Je-sus, the Name that charms our fears, That bids our sor-rows cease;

The glo-ries of my God and King, The tri-umphs of His grace!
To spread thro' all the earth a-broad The hon-ors of Thy Name.
'Tis mu-sic in the sin-ner's ears, 'Tis life, and health, and peace. A-MEN.

4 He breaks the power of cancelled sin,
  He sets the prisoner free;
  His blood can make the foulest clean;
  His blood avails for me.

5 Look unto Him, ye nations; own
  Your God, ye fallen race;
  Look, and be saved through faith alone,
  Be justified by grace.

6 See all your sins on Jesus laid;
  The Lamb of God was slain:
  His soul was once an offering made
  For every soul of man.

7 Glory to God, and praise, and love,
  Be ever, ever given,
  By saints below and saints above,
  The Church in earth and heaven.

Second Tune

AZMON. C. M.

CHARLES WESLEY, 1738, a

Arranged from CARL G. GLÄSER, by LOWELL MASON, 1839

1. O for a thou-sand tongues to sing My great Re-deem-er's praise,

The glo-ries of my God and King, The tri-umphs of His grace! A-MEN

190 Saviour, Blessed Saviour

FIDES. 6 5, 6 5. D.

GODFREY THRING, 1862

MARCHEL DAVIS, cir. 1848

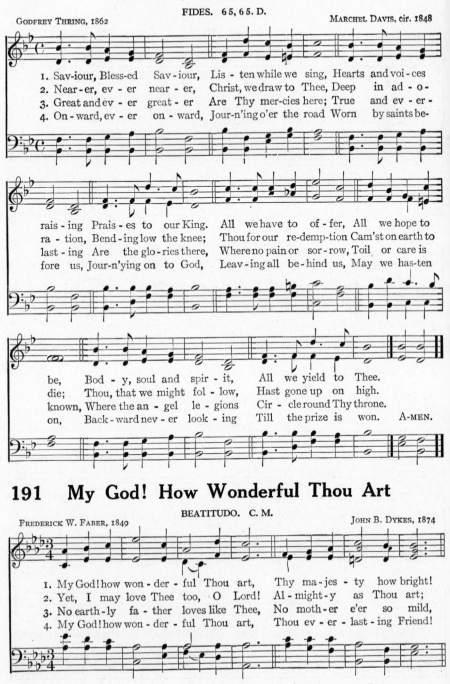

1. Sav-iour, Bless-ed Sav-iour, Lis - ten while we sing, Hearts and voi - ces rais - ing Prais - es to our King. All we have to of - fer, All we hope to be, Bod - y, soul and spir - it, All we yield to Thee.

2. Near - er, ev - er near - er, Christ, we draw to Thee, Deep in ad - o - ra - tion, Bend-ing low the knee; Thou for our re-demp-tion Cam'st on earth to die; Thou, that we might fol - low, Hast gone up on high.

3. Great and ev - er great - er Are Thy mer-cies here; True and ev - er - last - ing Are the glo-ries there, Where no pain or sor - row, Toil or care is known, Where the an - gel le - gions Cir - cle round Thy throne.

4. On - ward, ev - er on - ward, Jour-n'ing o'er the road Worn by saints be - fore us, Jour-n'ying on to God, Leav-ing all be-hind us, May we has-ten on, Back-ward nev - er look - ing Till the prize is won. A-MEN.

191 My God! How Wonderful Thou Art

BEATITUDO. C. M.

FREDERICK W. FABER, 1849

JOHN B. DYKES, 1874

1. My God! how won - der - ful Thou art, Thy ma - jes - ty how bright!

2. Yet, I may love Thee too, O Lord! Al - might - y as Thou art;

3. No earth - ly fa - ther loves like Thee, No moth - er e'er so mild,

4. My God! how won - der - ful Thou art, Thou ev - er - last - ing Friend!

How beau-ti-ful Thy Mer-cy-seat   In depths of burn-ing light!
For Thou hast stooped to ask of me   The love of my poor heart.
Bears and for-bears, as Thou hast done   With me, Thy sin-ful child.
On Thee I stay my trust-ing heart   Till faith in vis-ion end.   A-MEN.

Rejoice, the Lord is King!   192

LAUS REGIS.   6 6, 6 6, 8 8.

CHARLES WESLEY, 1744   WILLIAM E. FISCHER, 1887

1. Re - joice, the Lord is King!   Your Lord and King a - dore;   Mor-
2. Je - sus, the Sav-iour, reigns,   The God of truth and love;   When
3. His king-dom can-not fail,   He rules o'er earth and heaven,   The
4. He sits at God's right hand   Till all His foes sub-mit,   And

tals, give thanks and sing, And tri-umph ev - er - more;   Lift up your heart, lift
He had purged our stains He took His seat a - bove;   Lift up your heart, lift
keys of death and hell Are to our Je - sus given;   Lift up your heart, lift
bow to His com-mand, And fall be - neath His feet;   Lift up your heart, lift

up your voice; Re - joice, a - gain I say, re - joice.   A - MEN.

193   I Know That My Redeemer Lives!

DUKE STREET. L. M.

SAMUEL MEDLEY, 1775, a

JOHN HATTON, 1793

1. I know that my Re-deem-er lives! What comfort this sweet sen-tence gives!
2. He lives to bless me with His love, He lives to plead for me a-bove,
3. He lives to grant me rich sup-ply, He lives to guide me with His eye,

He lives, He lives, Who once was dead, He lives, my ev-er-liv-ing Head.
He lives my hun-gry soul to feed, He lives to help in time of need.
He lives to com-fort me when faint, He lives to hear my soul's complaint. A-MEN.

4 He lives to silence all my fears,
He lives to wipe away my tears,
He lives to calm my troubled heart,
He lives all blessings to impart.

5 He lives, all glory to His Name!
He lives, my Jesus still the same;
O the sweet joy this sentence gives;
I know that my Redeemer lives!

194   Hail, Holy, Holy, Holy Lord!

HARLECH. C. M.

EDWARD PERRONET, 1785, a

Ancient Welsh Melody

1. Hail, Ho-ly, Ho-ly, Ho-ly Lord! Let pow'rs im-mor-tal sing,
2. To Thee all an-gels cry a-loud, Thy Name ho-san-nas ring;
3. Hail Him, they cry, ye sons of light, Of joy th'e-ter-nal Spring;
4. Hail Him, ye saints, Whose love for you Has drawn the mon-ster's sting;

A-dore the co-e-ter-nal Word, Re-joice, the Lord is King!
A-round Thy throne their myriads crowd, And shout,"The Lord is King!"
Praise Him Who formed you by His might, Re-joice, the Lord is King!
O ren-der to the Lord His due; Re-joice, the Lord is King! A-MEN.

5 Cry out and shout, fair Zion's land!
Ye priests, your offerings bring;
Watchmen, that on her ramparts stand,
O shout, "The Lord is King!"

6 Let worlds above and worlds below,
In songs united sing;
And, while eternal ages flow,
Rejoice, the Lord is King!

Hark! Ten Thousand Harps and Voices 195

HARWELL. 87, 87, 77. With Refrain.

THOMAS KELLY, 1806, a

LOWELL MASON, 1840

1. Hark! ten thou-sand harps and voi-ces | Sound the note of praise a-bove:
2. Je - sus, hail! Whose glo-ry bright-ens | All a-bove, and makes it fair;
3. King of glo-ry, reign for ev-er; | Thine an ev-er-last-ing crown;
4. Sav-iour, hast-en Thine ap-pear-ing; | Bring, O bring the glo-rious day,

Je - sus reigns, and heav'n re-joic-es; | Je-sus reigns, the God of love.
Lord of life, Thy smile en-light-ens, | Cheers, and charms Thy peo-ple here.
Noth-ing from Thy love shall sev-er | Those whom Thou hast made Thine own;
When, the aw-ful sum-mons hear-ing, | Heaven and earth shall pass a-way;

See, He sits on yon-der throne; | Je-sus rules the world a-lone.
When we think of love like Thine, | Lord, we own it love di-vine.
Hap-py ob-jects of Thy grace, | Des-tined to be-hold Thy face.
Then, with golden harps, we'll sing: | "Glo-ry, glo-ry, to our King."

1. See, He sits on yon-der throne; Je-sus rules the world a-lone.

REFRAIN

Al - le-lu-ia! Al-le-lu-ia! Al-le-lu-ia! A-men.

196 Stand Up, Stand Up for Jesus

GEORGE DUFFIELD, JR., 1858; Abridged

HERBERT S. IRONS, 1875

1. Stand up! Stand up for Je - sus! Ye sol - diers of the Cross;
2. Stand up! Stand up for Je - sus! The trum - pet call o - bey;
3. Stand up! Stand up for Je - sus! Stand in His strength a - lone;

Lift high His roy - al ban - ner, It must not suf - fer loss.
Forth to the might - y con - flict, In this His glo - rious day.
The arm of flesh will fail you, Ye dare not trust your own.

From vic - t'ry un - to vic - t'ry His arm - y He shall lead,
Ye that are men now serve Him, A - gainst un - num-bered foes;
Put on the Gos - pel ar - mor, Each piece put on with prayer;

Till ev - 'ry foe is van - quished, And Christ is Lord in - deed.
Let cour - age rise with dan - ger, And strength to strength op - pose.
Where du - ty calls or dan - ger, Be nev - er want - ing there.

Stand up! Stand up for Je - sus! Ye sol - diers of the Cross;

Lift up His roy - al ban - ner, It must not suf - fer loss. A-MEN.

4 Stand up! Stand up for Jesus!
    The strife will not be long;
  This day the noise of battle,
    The next the victor's song.
  To him that overcometh,
    A crown of life shall be;
  He with the King of Glory
    Shall reign eternally!

197 We March, We March to Victory

GERARD MOULTRIE, 1867; Abridged

JOSEPH BARNBY, 1869

1. We march, we march to vic-to-ry, With the Cross of the Lord be-fore us, With His lov-ing eye look-ing down from the sky, And His ho-ly arm spread o'er us, His ho-ly arm spread o'er us. o'er us.

|All st. except last | Last st. only

His arm

His arm

1. We come in the might of the Lord of Light, In joy-ous train to
2. The bands of the a-lien flee a-way, When our chant goes up as
3. Our sword is the Spir-it of God on high, Our hel-met His sal-
4. We tread in the might of the Lord of hosts, And fear not man nor

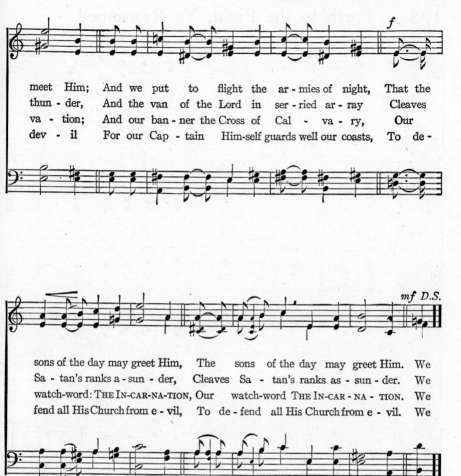

meet Him;   And we put   to   flight the   ar - mies of night,   That the
thun - der,   And the van   of the Lord in   ser - ried ar - ray   Cleaves
va - tion;   And our ban - ner the Cross of   Cal - va - ry,   Our
dev - il   For our Cap - tain   Him-self guards well our coasts,   To de-

sons of the day may greet Him,   The   sons   of the day   may greet Him.   We
Sa - tan's ranks a - sun - der,   Cleaves Sa - tan's ranks as - sun - der.   We
watch-word: THE IN-CAR-NA-TION, Our   watch-word THE IN-CAR - NA - TION.   We
fend all His Church from e - vil,   To de - fend all His Church from e - vil.   We

5 He marches in front of His banner unfurled,
    Which He raised that His own might find Him;
    And the holy Church throughout all the world
    ‖:Falls in rank and marches behind Him.:‖
        We march, we march, etc.

6 And the angel choir with its song awaits
    Our march to the Golden Sion;
    For our Captain has broken the brazen gates,
    ‖:And burst the bars of iron.:‖
        We march, we march, etc.

198 Forth to the Fight, Ye Ransomed

W. H. KIRBY, 1882   JOHN HEYWOOD

1. Forth to the fight, ye ran - somed, Might - y in God's own might,
2. Fear not the din of bat - tle, Fol - low where He has trod,
3. An - gels a - round us hov - er, Suc - cor in time of need,

Stem - ming the tide of bat - tle, Rout - ing the hosts of night.
Per - fect - ing strength in weak - ness— Je - sus, In - car - nate God.
Ev - er at hand to strength - en, Guar - dians they in - deed.

FULL.

Lift ye the blood-red Ban - ner, Wield ye the vic - tor's sword,

Raise ye the Chris-tian's war-cry—"The Cross of Christ the Lord." A - MEN.

Full Swell.   *Large notes on Great Organ reed.*

Sw. *to* PED. *dopp.*

4 Arm ye against the battle,
  Watch ye, and fast, and pray,
Peace shall succeed the warfare,
  Night shall be changed to day.
    Lift ye, etc.

5 Fight, for the Lord is o'er you,
  Fight, for He bids you fight;
There where the fray is thickest
  Close with the hosts of night.
    Lift ye, etc.

With Happy Voices Singing

199

TOURS. 7 6, 7 6. D.

WILLIAM G. TARRANT, 1888

BERTHOLD TOURS, 1872

1. With hap - py voi - ces sing - ing, Thy chil - dren, Lord, ap - pear;
2. For though no eye be - holds Thee, No hand Thy touch may feel,
3. And shall we not a - dore Thee With more than joy - ous song,

Their joy - ous prais - es bring - ing In an - thems sweet and clear.
Thy u - ni - verse un - folds Thee, Thy star - ry heavens re - veal;
And live in truth be - fore Thee, All beau - ti - ful and strong?

For skies of gold - en splen - dor, For az - ure roll - ing sea,
The earth and all its glo - ry, Our homes and all we love,
Lord, bless our weak en - deav - or Thy serv - ants true to be,

For blos-soms sweet and ten - der, O Lord, we wor - ship Thee.
Tell forth the won-drous sto - ry Of One who reigns a - bove.
And through all life, for - ev - er, To live our praise to Thee. A - MEN.

200   Brightly Gleams Our Banner

ST. THERESA.   6 5, 6 5. D.   With Refrain.

THOMAS J. POTTER, 1867   ARTHUR S. SULLIVAN, 1874

1. Bright-ly gleams our ban-ner, Point-ing to the sky, Wav-ing wan-d'rers
2. Je - sus, Lord and Mas - ter, At Thy sa - cred feet, Here, with hearts re-
3. Pat - tern of our child-hood, Once Thy-self a child, Make our child-hood

on - ward To their home on high. March-ing thro' the des - ert,
joic - ing, See Thy chil - dren meet. Oft - en have we left Thee,
ho - ly, Pure, and meek, and mild. In the hour of dan - ger

Glad-ly thus we pray, Still, with hearts u-ni - ted, Sing-ing on our way.
Oft - en gone a - stray, Keep us, might-y Sav-iour, In the nar-row way.
Whith-er can we flee, Save to Thee, our Sav-iour, On - ly un - to Thee?

Chorus

Bright-ly gleams our ban - ner, Point-ing to the sky,

Wav - ing wan-d'rers on - ward To their home on high. A - MEN.

4 All our days direct us
   In the way we go,
Lead us on victorious
   Over every foe;
Bid Thine angels shield us
   When the storm-clouds lower;
Pardon Thou and save us
   In the last dread hour.

5 Then with saints and angels
   May we join above,
Offering prayers and praises
   At Thy throne of love.
When the march is over
   Then come rest and peace,
Jesus in His beauty!
   Songs that never cease!

201 All the Happy Children

HERMAS. 6 5, 6 5. D. With Refrain.

FRANCES BENT DILLINGHAM

FRANCES R. HAVERGAL, 1871

1. All the hap-py chil-dren Glad-ly join our song, Ris-ing to the
2. See the sky a-bove us, Spread so warm and blue; So God's love is
3. All the hap-py chil-dren Thank Thee, Fa-ther dear, For this day for

Fa - ther, In a cho - rus strong. Birds are bright-ly sing-ing,
reach-ing O - ver me and you. Fa-ther dear, we thank Thee
chil-dren Out of all the year. We will still re-mem-ber

Leaves are open-ing wide, Flow-er bells are ring-ing Forth on ev-'ry side.
For long sum-mer days, For the birds and flow-ers, For the grass-y ways.
We are Thine a-lone; He Who made the sum-mer Made us ev-'ry one.

REFRAIN

All the hap - py chil - dren Glad - ly join our song,

Ris - ing to the Fa - ther In a cho - rus strong.

Far O'er Yon Horizon

202

BONIFACE. 6 5. 12 lines.

HENRY ALFORD, 1871

HENRY GADSBY, 1842–1907

1. Far o'er yon ho - ri - zon   Rise the cit - y towers, Where our God a - bid - eth;
2. In - to God's high tem-ple   On - ward as we press, Beauty spreads a-round us,
3. Naught that cit-y need - eth   Of these aisles of stone; Where the God-head dwelleth,
4. To th' e-ter - nal Fa - ther   Loudest an-thems raise; To the Son and Spir - it,

That fair home is ours.   Flash the streets with jas - per, Shine the gates with gold,
Born of ho - li - ness;   Arch, and vault, and carv-ing, Lights of var - ied tone,
Tem - ple there is none;   All the saints, that ev - er In these courts have stood,
Ech - o songs of praise;   To the Lord of glo - ry, Bless - ed Three in One,

Flows the gladdening riv-er, Shed-ding joys un - told. Thith - er, on-ward thith-er,
Soft-ened words and ho - ly, Prayer and praise a-lone: Ev-'ry thought up- rais-ing
Are but babes, and feed-ing On the chil-dren's food. On through sign and to-ken,
Be   by men and an-gels   End - less hon - ors done.   Weak are earth-ly prais-es;

In the Spir-it's might,   Pil - grims to your coun-try, For-ward in - to light.
To our cit - y bright,   Where the tribes as-sem-ble Round the throne of light.
Stars a-mid the night,   Forward thro' the dark-ness, For-ward in - to light.
Dull the songs of night;   For-ward in - to tri - umph, For-ward in - to light! A-MEN.

CALLING, REPENTANCE AND FAITH

203   ## O Jesus, Thou Art Standing

ST. EDITH. 7 6, 7 6. D.

WM. WALSHAM HOW, 1867

JUSTIN HEINRICH KNECHT, 1799
Adapted by EDWARD HUSBAND, 1871

1. O Je - sus, Thou art stand - ing   Out - side the fast-closed door,
2. O Je - sus, Thou art knock - ing;   And lo! that hand is scarred,
3. O Je - sus, Thou art plead - ing   In ac - cents meek and low,

In   low - ly   pa - tience wait - ing   To   pass the thresh - old o'er:
And thorns Thy brow en - cir - cle,   And tears Thy face have marred.
"I   died   for   you, My chil - dren,   And will ye treat Me so?"

Shame on us, Chris - tian breth - ren,   His Name and sign who bear,
O   love that pass - eth knowl - edge,   So pa - tient - ly   to wait!
O   Lord, with shame and sor - row   We o - pen now the door;

Oh shame, thrice shame up - on us   To keep Him stand-ing there!
O sin that hath no e - qual,   So fast to bar the gate!
Dear Sav-iour, en - ter, en - ter,   And leave us nev - er - more. A-MEN.

Jesus Calls Us; O'er the Tumult 204

GALILEE. 8 7, 8 7.

C. F. ALEXANDER, 1852

W. H. JUDE, 1886

1. Je - sus calls us; o'er the tu - mult Of our life's wild, rest - less sea;
2. Je - sus calls us—from the wor - ship Of the vain world's gold-en store;
3. In our joys and in our sor - rows, Days of toil and hours of ease,
4. Je - sus calls us; by Thy mer - cies, Sav-iour, may we hear Thy call;

Day by day His sweet voice soundeth, Say-ing, "Chris-tian, fol-low Me,"
From each i - dol that would keep us, Say-ing, "Chris-tian, love Me more,"
Still He calls, in cares and pleas-ures, "Christian, love Me more than these,"
Give our hearts to Thy o - be - dience, Serve and love Thee best of all! A - MEN.

Who, O Lord, when Life is O'er 205

REDHEAD No. 48. 7 7, 7 7.

HARRIET AUBER, 1829
From JAMES MERRICK, 1765

RICHARD REDHEAD, 1853

1. Who, O Lord, when life is o'er Shall to heaven's blest man-sions soar?
2. He whose heart Thy love has warmed; He whose will, to Thine con-formed,
3. He who shuns the sin - ner's road, Lov - ing those who love their God;
4. He who trusts in Christ a - lone, Not in aught him - self has done;

Who, an ev - er - wel - come guest, In Thy ho - ly place shall rest?
Bids his life un - sul - lied run; He whose word and thought are one:
Who, with hope and faith un-feigned, Treads the path by Thee or - dained;
He, great God, shall be Thy care, And Thy choic-est bless-ings share. A - MEN.

206   I Heard the Voice of Jesus Say

VOX DILECTI. C. M. D.

HORATIO BONAR, 1846

JOHN B. DYKES, 1868

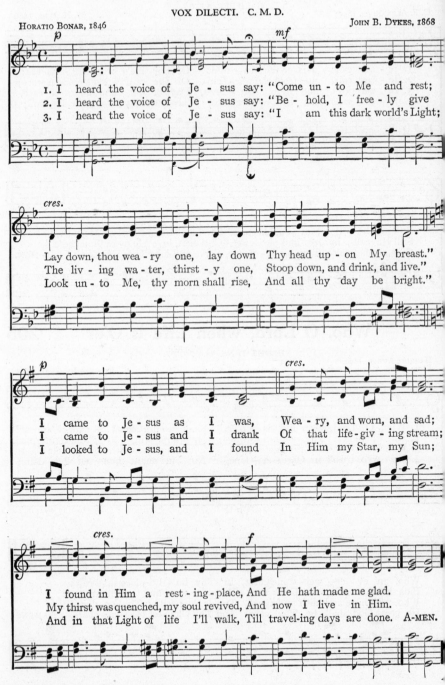

1. I heard the voice of Je - sus say: "Come un - to Me and rest;
2. I heard the voice of Je - sus say: "Be - hold, I freely give
3. I heard the voice of Je - sus say: "I am this dark world's Light;

Lay down, thou wea - ry one, lay down Thy head up - on My breast."
The liv - ing wa - ter, thirst - y one, Stoop down, and drink, and live."
Look un - to Me; thy morn shall rise, And all thy day be bright."

I came to Je - sus as I was, Wea - ry, and worn, and sad;
I came to Je - sus and I drank Of that life - giv - ing stream;
I looked to Je - sus, and I found In Him my Star, my Sun;

I found in Him a rest - ing - place, And He hath made me glad.
My thirst was quenched, my soul revived, And now I live in Him.
And in that Light of life I'll walk, Till travel-ing days are done. A-MEN.

In stanzas 2 and 3, for music of lines 5 and 6, substitute the following:—

I came to Je - sus and I drank Of that life - giv - ing stream;
I looked to Je - sus, and I found In Him my Star, my Sun;

Pass Me Not, O Gentle Saviour   207

PASS ME NOT. 8 5, 8 5. With Refrain.

FANNY J. CROSBY, 1868

WILLIAM H. DOANE, 1870

1. Pass me not, O gen - tle Sav - iour, Hear my hum - ble cry;
2. Let me at the throne of mer - cy Find a sweet re - lief;
3. Trust - ing on - ly in Thy mer - it, Would I seek Thy face;
4. Thou the Spring of all my com - fort More than life to me,

While on oth - ers Thou art call - ing Do not pass me by.
Kneel - ing there in deep con - tri - tion, Help my un - be - lief:
Heal my wound - ed, bro - ken spir - it, Save me by Thy grace.
Whom have I on earth be - side Thee? Whom in Heaven but Thee?

REFRAIN

Sav - iour, Sav - iour, hear my hum - ble cry, While on

oth - ers Thou art call - ing, Do not pass me by. A - MEN.

208   Feeble, Helpless, how Shall I

VIENNA. 77,77.

WM. HENRY FURNESS, 1844

JUSTIN H. KNECHT, 1799

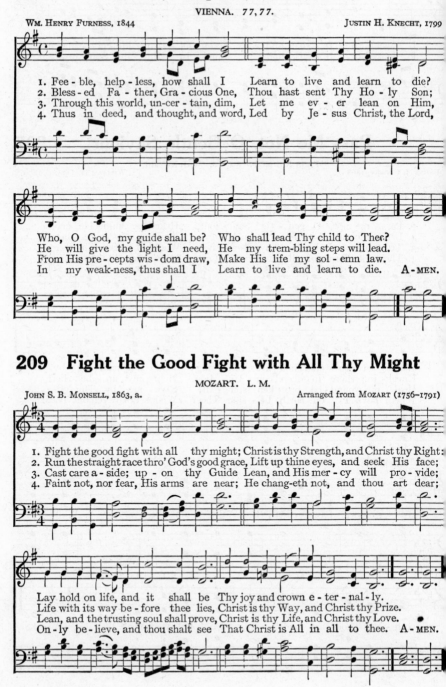

1. Fee - ble, help - less, how shall I   Learn to live and learn to die?
2. Bless - ed Fa - ther, Gra - cious One,   Thou hast sent Thy Ho - ly Son;
3. Through this world, un - cer - tain, dim,   Let me ev - er lean on Him,
4. Thus in deed, and thought, and word,   Led by Je - sus Christ, the Lord,

Who, O God, my guide shall be?   Who shall lead Thy child to Thee?
He will give the light I need,   He my trem-bling steps will lead.
From His pre - cepts wis - dom draw,   Make His life my sol - emn law.
In my weak-ness, thus shall I   Learn to live and learn to die.   A - MEN.

209   **Fight the Good Fight with All Thy Might**

MOZART. L. M.

JOHN S. B. MONSELL, 1863, a.

Arranged from MOZART (1756–1791)

1. Fight the good fight with all thy might; Christ is thy Strength, and Christ thy Right:
2. Run the straight race thro' God's good grace, Lift up thine eyes, and seek His face;
3. Cast care a - side; up - on thy Guide Lean, and His mer - cy will pro - vide;
4. Faint not, nor fear, His arms are near; He chang-eth not, and thou art dear;

Lay hold on life, and it shall be Thy joy and crown e - ter - nal - ly.
Life with its way be - fore thee lies, Christ is thy Way, and Christ thy Prize.
Lean, and the trusting soul shall prove, Christ is thy Life, and Christ thy Love.
On - ly be - lieve, and thou shalt see That Christ is All in all to thee.   A - MEN.

I Lay My Sins on Jesus

MOSCOW. 7 6, 7 6. D.

HORATIUS BONAR, 1837

JOHN B. CALKIN, 1867

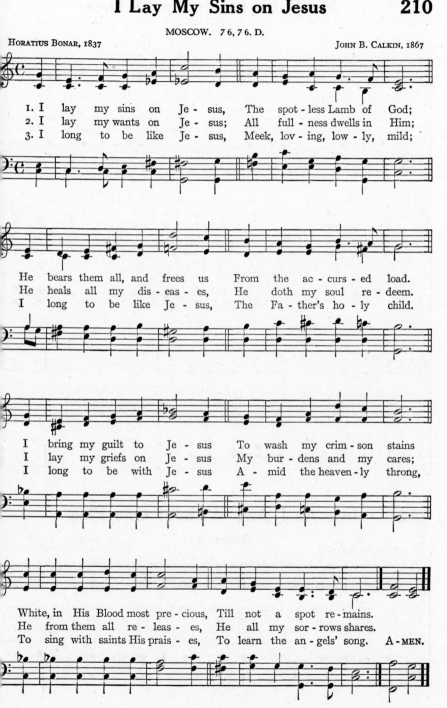

1. I lay my sins on Je - sus, The spot - less Lamb of God;
2. I lay my wants on Je - sus; All full - ness dwells in Him;
3. I long to be like Je - sus, Meek, lov - ing, low - ly, mild;

He bears them all, and frees us From the ac - curs - ed load.
He heals all my dis - eas - es, He doth my soul re - deem.
I long to be like Je - sus, The Fa - ther's ho - ly child.

I bring my guilt to Je - sus To wash my crim - son stains
I lay my griefs on Je - sus My bur - dens and my cares;
I long to be with Je - sus A - mid the heaven - ly throng,

White, in His Blood most pre - cious, Till not a spot re - mains.
He from them all re - leas - es, He all my sor - rows shares.
To sing with saints His prais - es, To learn the an - gels' song. A - MEN.

211 My Faith Looks Up to Thee

OLIVET. 6 6 4, 6 6 6 4.

RAY PALMER, 1830

LOWELL MASON, 1832

1. My faith looks up to Thee, Thou Lamb of Cal - va - ry,
2. May Thy rich grace im - part Strength to my faint - ing heart,
3. While life's dark maze I tread, And griefs a - round me spread,
4. When ends life's tran - sient dream, When death's cold sul - len stream

Sav - iour di - vine! Now hear me while I pray: Take all my
My zeal in - spire; As Thou hast died for me, O may my
Be Thou my Guide; Bid dark - ness turn to day, Wipe sor - row's
Shall o'er me roll; Blest Sav - iour, then, in love Fear and dis -

guilt a - way, O let me from this day Be whol - ly Thine.
love to Thee, Pure, warm, and changeless be, A liv - ing fire.
tears a - way, Nor let me ev - er stray From Thee a - side.
trust re - move; O bear me safe a - bove, A ran - somed soul. A - MEN.

212 Just As I Am, Without One Plea

QUEBEC. L M.

CHARLOTTE ELLIOTT, 1836

HENRY BAKER, 1866
Modified by JAMES PEARCE, 1868

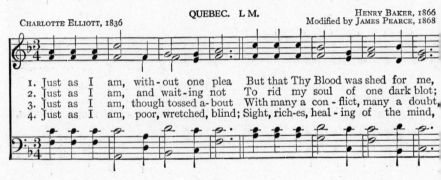

1. Just as I am, with - out one plea But that Thy Blood was shed for me,
2. Just as I am, and wait - ing not To rid my soul of one dark blot;
3. Just as I am, though tossed a - bout With many a con - flict, many a doubt,
4. Just as I am, poor, wretched, blind; Sight, rich - es, heal - ing of the mind,

And that Thou bidst me come to Thee, O Lamb of God, I come, I come!
To Thee, Whose Blood can cleanse each spot, O Lamb of God, I come, I come!
Fight-ings and fears with-in, with-out, O Lamb of God, I come, I come!
Yea, all I need, in Thee to find, O Lamb of God, I come, I come! A - MEN.

5 Just as I am; Thou wilt receive,
Wilt welcome, pardon, cleanse, relieve;
Because Thy promise I believe,
O Lamb of God, I come, I come!

6 Just as I am; Thy love unknown
Has broken every barrier down;
Now to be Thine, yea, Thine alone,
O Lamb of God, I come, I come!

Jesus, Thou Art My Righteousness 213

ST. AGNES. C. M.

CHARLES WESLEY, 1740

JOHN B. DYKES, 1866

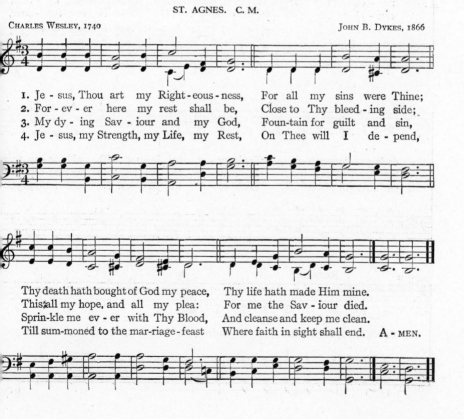

1. Je - sus, Thou art my Right-eous-ness, For all my sins were Thine;
2. For - ev - er here my rest shall be, Close to Thy bleed-ing side;
3. My dy - ing Sav - iour and my God, Foun-tain for guilt and sin,
4. Je - sus, my Strength, my Life, my Rest, On Thee will I de - pend,

Thy death hath bought of God my peace, Thy life hath made Him mine.
This all my hope, and all my plea: For me the Sav - iour died.
Sprin-kle me ev - er with Thy Blood, And cleanse and keep me clean.
Till sum-moned to the mar-riage-feast Where faith in sight shall end. A - MEN.

214 Yield Not to Temptation

PALMER. 11 11, 11 12. With Refrain.

HORATIO R. PALMER, 1868   HORATIO R. PALMER, 1868

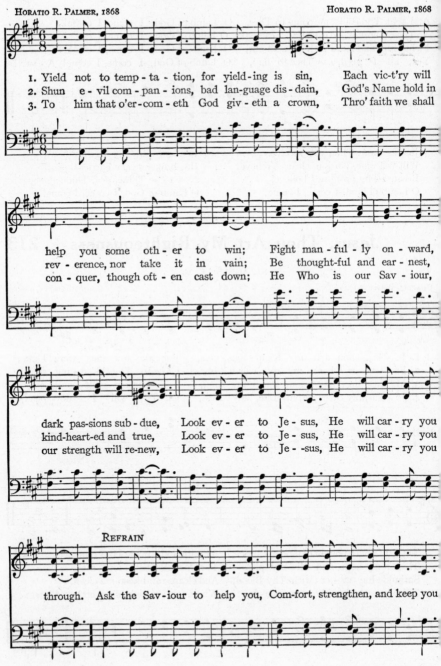

1. Yield not to temp-ta-tion, for yield-ing is sin, Each vic-t'ry will
2. Shun e-vil com-pan-ions, bad lan-guage dis-dain, God's Name hold in
3. To him that o'er-com-eth God giv-eth a crown, Thro' faith we shall

help you some oth-er to win; Fight man-ful-ly on-ward,
rev-erence, nor take it in vain; Be thought-ful and ear-nest,
con-quer, though oft-en cast down; He Who is our Sav-iour,

dark pas-sions sub-due, Look ev-er to Je-sus, He will car-ry you
kind-heart-ed and true, Look ev-er to Je-sus, He will car-ry you
our strength will re-new, Look ev-er to Je--sus, He will car-ry you

REFRAIN

through. Ask the Sav-iour to help you, Com-fort, strengthen, and keep you

He is will-ing to aid you, He will car-ry you through.

Jesus, Still Lead on

215

SEELENBRÄUTIGAM. 5 5, 8 8, 5 5.

Nicolaus L. v. Zinzendorf, 1721
Tr. Jane Borthwick, 1846, a.

Adam Drese (1620–1701)
Geistreiches Gesangbuch, Darmstadt, 1698

1. Je - sus, still lead on, Till our rest be won; And al-though the
2. If the way be drear, If the foe be near, Let not faith - less
3. When we seek re - lief From a long-felt grief, When temp-ta - tions
4. Je - sus, still lead on, Till our rest be won; Heaven-ly Lead - er,

way be cheer - less, We will fol - low, calm and fear - less;
fears o'er-take us, Let not faith and hope for-sake us;
come al - lur - ing, Make us pa - tient and en-dur - ing;
still di - rect us, Still sup-port, con - sole, pro - tect us,

Guide us by Thy hand To our fa - ther - land.
For through many a foe To our home we go.
Show us that bright shore Where we weep no more.
Till we safe - ly stand In our fa - ther - land. A - MEN.

216 How Firm a Foundation

ADESTE FIDELES. 11 11, 11 11.

"K" in RIPPON's *Sel.*, 1787   JOHN F. WADE's *Cantus Diversi*, 1751

1. How firm a foun-da-tion, ye saints of the Lord, Is laid for your
2. "Fear not, I am with thee; O be not dis-mayed! For I am thy
3. "When thro' fi-ery tri-als thy path-way shall lie, My grace, all-suf-

faith in His ex-cel-lent Word! What more can He say than to
God, and will still give thee aid; I'll strength-en thee, help thee, and
fi-cient, shall be thy sup-ply: The flames shall not hurt thee; I

you He hath said, You, who un-to Je-sus for
cause thee to stand, Up-held by My right-eous, om-
on-ly de-sign Thy dross to con-sume, and thy

ref-uge have fled? You, who un-to Je-sus for ref-uge have fled?
nip-o-tent hand, Up-held by My right-eous, om-nip-o-tent hand.
gold to re-fine, Thy dross to con-sume, and thy gold to re-fine.

4 "E'en down to old age all My people shall prove
   My sovereign, eternal, unchangeable love;
   And then, when gray hairs shall their temples adorn,
||:Like lambs they shall still in My bosom be borne. :||

5 "The soul that on Jesus hath leaned for repose
   I will not—I cannot desert to His foes;
   That soul, though all hell should endeavor to shake,
||:I'll never—no, never—no, never forsake!":||

Nearer, My God, to Thee! through Word 217

ST. MARK'S. 6 4, 6 4, 6 6 4.

HENRY E. JACOBS, 1887

GEORGE C. F. HAAS, 1915

1. Near - er, my God, to Thee! Near - er to Thee! Through Word and
2. A - ges on a - ges rolled Ere earth ap - peared, Yet Thine un-
3. Thy Son has come to earth, My sin to bear, My ev - 'ry
4. Lo! all my debt is paid, My guilt is gone. See! He is

Sac - ra - ment Thou com'st to me. Thy grace is ev - er near,
meas - ured love The way pre - pared; Long hast Thou yearned for me,
wound to heal, My pain to share. "God in the flesh" for me,
risen for me, My throne is won. Thanks, O my God, to Thee!

Thy Spir - it ev - er here, Draw - ing to Thee.
That I might near - er be, Near - er to Thee!
Brings me now near - er Thee, Near - er to Thee!
None now can near - er be, Near - er to Thee! A - MEN.

5 Welcome, then, to Thy home,
   Blest One in Three!
As Thou hast promised, come!
   Come, Lord, to me!
Work Thou, O God, through me,
Live Thou, O God, in me,
   Ever in me!

6 Surely, it matters not
   What earth may bring;
Death is of no account;
   Grace will I sing.
Nothing remains for me,
Save to be nearer Thee,
   Nearer to Thee!

218   Rock of Ages, Cleft for Me

REDHEAD No. 76. *77, 77, 77.*

First Tune

AUGUSTUS M. TOPLADY, 1776, a.   RICHARD REDHEAD, 1853

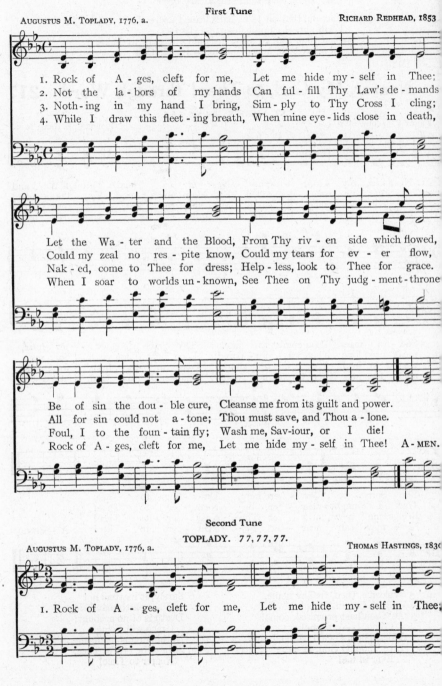

1. Rock of A - ges, cleft for me, Let me hide my - self in Thee;
2. Not the la - bors of my hands Can ful - fill Thy Law's de - mands
3. Noth - ing in my hand I bring, Sim - ply to Thy Cross I cling;
4. While I draw this fleet - ing breath, When mine eye - lids close in death,

Let the Wa - ter and the Blood, From Thy riv - en side which flowed,
Could my zeal no res - pite know, Could my tears for ev - er flow,
Nak - ed, come to Thee for dress; Help - less, look to Thee for grace.
When I soar to worlds un - known, See Thee on Thy judg - ment - throne

Be of sin the dou - ble cure, Cleanse me from its guilt and power.
All for sin could not a - tone; Thou must save, and Thou a - lone.
Foul, I to the foun - tain fly; Wash me, Sav - iour, or I die!
Rock of A - ges, cleft for me, Let me hide my - self in Thee! A - MEN.

Second Tune

TOPLADY. *77, 77, 77.*

AUGUSTUS M. TOPLADY, 1776, a.   THOMAS HASTINGS, 1830

1. Rock of A - ges, cleft for me, Let me hide my - self in Thee;

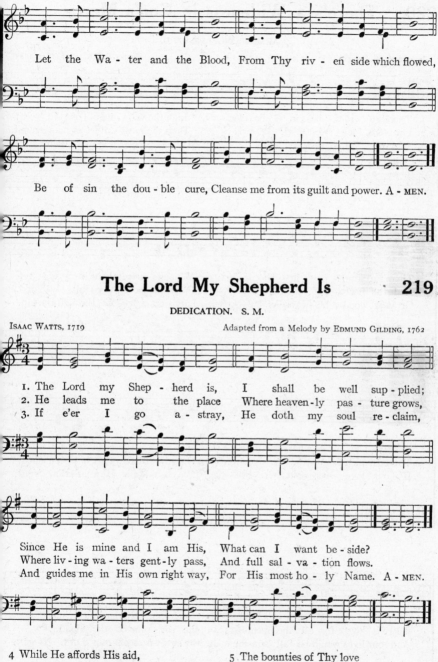

Let the Wa - ter and the Blood, From Thy riv - en side which flowed,

Be of sin the dou - ble cure, Cleanse me from its guilt and power. A - MEN.

The Lord My Shepherd Is · 219

DEDICATION. S. M.

ISAAC WATTS, 1719

Adapted from a Melody by EDMUND GILDING, 1762

1. The Lord my Shep - herd is, I shall be well sup - plied;
2. He leads me to the place Where heaven - ly pas - ture grows,
3. If e'er I go a - stray, He doth my soul re - claim,

Since He is mine and I am His, What can I want be - side?
Where liv - ing wa - ters gent - ly pass, And full sal - va - tion flows.
And guides me in His own right way, For His most ho - ly Name. A - MEN.

4 While He affords His aid,
　I cannot yield to fear;
Though I should walk thro' death's dark
　My Shepherd's with me there. [shade,

5 The bounties of Thy love
　Shall crown my following days;
Nor from Thy house will I remove,
　Nor cease to speak Thy praise.

220 There's a Wideness in God's Mercy

ARMSTRONG. 8 7, 8 7. D.

FREDERICK W. FABER, 1862

HENRY B. RICHARDS (1817–1885)

1. There's a wide - ness in God's mer - cy, Like the wide - ness of the sea;
2. For the love of God is broad - er Than the meas - ures of man's mind
3. 'Tis not all we owe to Je - sus; It is some-thing more than all;

There's a kind - ness in His jus - tice, Which is more than lib - er - ty.
And the heart of the E - ter - nal Is most won - der - ful - ly kind.
Great-er good be - cause of e - vil, Larg - er mer - cy through the fall.

There is no place where earth's sor-rows Are more felt than up in heaven;
There is plen - ti - ful re - demp-tion In the Blood that has been shed;
If our love were but more sim - ple, We should take Him at His word;

There is no place where earth's failings Have such kind-ly judgment giv'n.
There is joy for all the mem-bers In the sor - rows of the Head.
And our lives would be all sun-shine In the sweet-ness of our Lord. A - MEN.

I Am Thine, O Lord   **221**

CROSBY. 10 7, 10 7. With Refrain.

Fanny J. Crosby, 1875   William H. Doane, 1875

1. I am Thine, O Lord, I have heard Thy voice, And it told Thy love to me;
2. Con-se-crate me now to Thy serv-ice, Lord, By the pow'r of grace di - vine;
3. O, the pure de-light of a sin - gle hour That be-fore Thy throne I spend,
4. There are depths of love that I can-not know Till I cross the nar - row sea,

But I long to rise in the arms of faith, And be clos - er drawn to Thee.
Let my soul look up with a stead-fast hope, And my will be lost in Thine.
When I kneel in prayer, and with Thee, my God, I com-mune as friend with friend!
There are heights of joy that I may not reach Till I rest in peace with Thee.

Refrain

Draw me near - er,   nearer, blessed Lord, To the Cross where Thou hast died;
near - er, near-er,

Draw me nearer, nearer, nearer, blessed Lord, To Thy precious bleeding side. A-men.

222 My Hope is Built on Nothing Less

SOLID ROCK. 8 8, 8 8. With Refrain.

EDWARD MOTE, c. 1834

WILLIAM B. BRADBURY

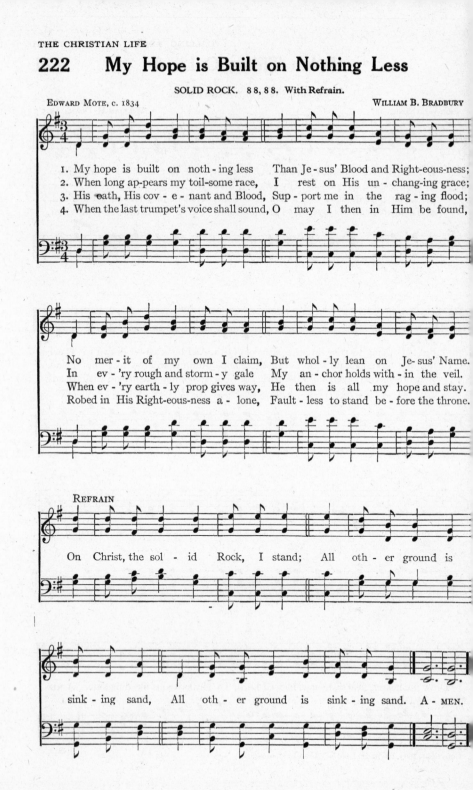

1. My hope is built on noth - ing less   Than Je - sus' Blood and Right-eous-ness;
2. When long ap-pears my toil-some race,   I   rest on His un - chang-ing grace;
3. His oath, His cov - e - nant and Blood,   Sup - port me in the   rag - ing flood;
4. When the last trumpet's voice shall sound, O   may I then in   Him be found,

No mer - it of my own I claim,   But whol - ly lean on   Je - sus' Name.
In   ev - 'ry rough and storm - y gale   My   an - chor holds with - in the veil.
When ev - 'ry earth - ly prop gives way,   He   then is all   my hope and stay.
Robed in His Right-eous-ness a - lone,   Fault - less to stand be - fore the throne.

REFRAIN

On   Christ, the sol - id   Rock, I stand;   All   oth - er ground is

sink - ing sand,   All   oth - er ground is   sink - ing sand. A - MEN.

Dear Lord and Father of Mankind   223

WHITTIER. 8 6, 8 8 6.

JOHN G. WHITTIER, 1872   FREDERICK C. MAKER, 1887

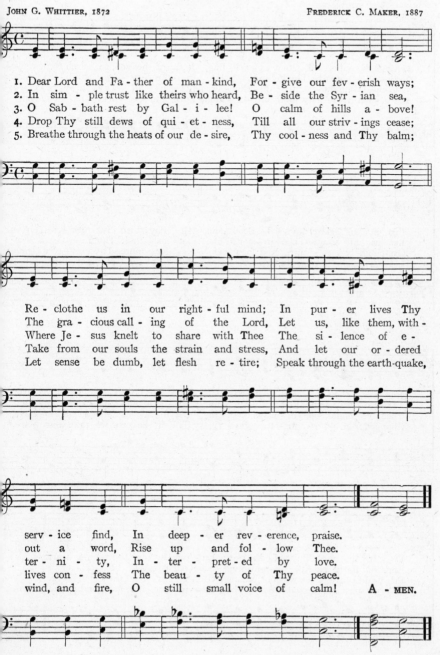

1. Dear Lord and Fa - ther of man - kind,   For - give our fev - erish ways;
2. In sim - ple trust like theirs who heard,   Be - side the Syr - ian   sea,
3. O Sab - bath rest by Gal - i - lee!   O   calm of hills a - bove!
4. Drop Thy still dews of qui - et - ness,   Till all   our striv - ings cease;
5. Breathe through the heats of our de - sire,   Thy cool - ness and Thy balm;

Re - clothe us in our right - ful mind;   In   pur - er lives Thy
The gra - cious call - ing   of   the Lord,   Let   us, like them, with -
Where Je - sus knelt to share with Thee   The   si - lence of e -
Take from our souls the strain and stress,   And   let our or - dered
Let sense be dumb, let flesh re - tire;   Speak through the earth - quake,

serv - ice   find,   In   deep - er rev - erence,   praise.
out   a   word,   Rise   up   and fol - low   Thee.
ter - ni - ty,   In - ter - pret - ed   by   love.
lives con - fess   The beau - ty of   Thy   peace.
wind, and   fire,   O   still   small voice of   calm!   A - MEN.

224 Love Divine, All Love Excelling

THEODORET. 87, 87. D.

First Tune

CHARLES WESLEY, 1747, a.   J. F. OHL, 1887

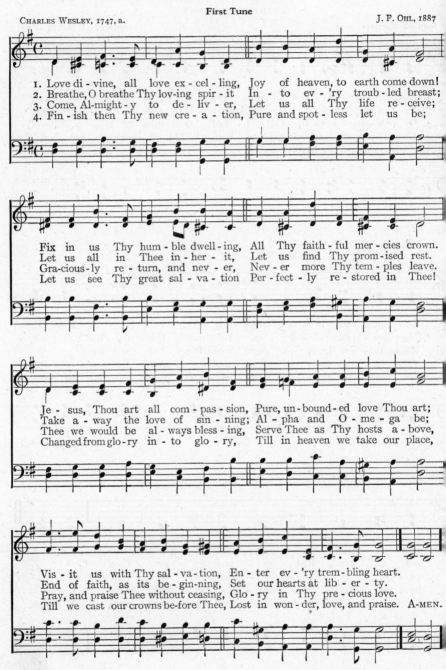

1. Love di - vine, all love ex - cel - ling, Joy of heaven, to earth come down!
2. Breathe, O breathe Thy lov-ing spir - it In - to ev - 'ry troub-led breast;
3. Come, Al-might - y to de - liv - er, Let us all Thy life re - ceive;
4. Fin - ish then Thy new cre - a - tion, Pure and spot - less let us be;

Fix in us Thy hum - ble dwell - ing, All Thy faith - ful mer - cies crown.
Let us all in Thee in - her - it, Let us find Thy prom - ised rest.
Gra - cious - ly re - turn, and nev - er, Nev - er more Thy tem - ples leave.
Let us see Thy great sal - va - tion Per - fect - ly re - stored in Thee!

Je - sus, Thou art all com - pas - sion, Pure, un - bound - ed love Thou art;
Take a - way the love of sin - ning; Al - pha and O - me - ga be;
Thee we would be al - ways bless - ing, Serve Thee as Thy hosts a - bove,
Changed from glo - ry in - to glo - ry, Till in heaven we take our place,

Vis - it us with Thy sal - va - tion, En - ter ev - 'ry trem - bling heart.
End of faith, as its be - gin - ning, Set our hearts at lib - er - ty.
Pray, and praise Thee without ceasing, Glo - ry in Thy pre - cious love.
Till we cast our crowns be-fore Thee, Lost in won - der, love, and praise. A-MEN.

Love Divine, All Love Excelling

BEECHER. 8 7, 8 7. D.

Second Tune

CHARLES WESLEY, 1747, a.

JOHN ZUNDEL, 1870

1. Love di-vine, all love ex-cel-ling, Joy of heaven, to earth come down!
2. Breathe, O breathe Thy lov-ing spir-it In-to ev-'ry troub-led breast;
3. Come, Al-might-y to de-liv-er, Let us all Thy life re-ceive;
4. Fin-ish then Thy new cre-a-tion, Pure and spot-less let us be;

Fix in us Thy hum-ble dwell-ing, All Thy faith-ful mer-cies crown.
Let us all in Thee in-her-it, Let us find Thy prom-ised rest.
Gra-cious-ly re-turn, and nev-er, Nev-er more Thy tem-ples leave.
Let us see Thy great sal-va-tion Per-fect-ly re-stored in Thee!

Je-sus, Thou art all com-pas-sion, Pure, un-bound-ed love Thou art;
Take a-way the love of sin-ning; Al-pha and O-me-ga be;
Thee we would be al-ways bles-sing, Serve Thee as Thy hosts a-bove,
Changed from glo-ry in-to glo-ry, Till in heaven we take our place,

Vis-it us with Thy sal-va-tion, En-ter ev-'ry trem-bling heart.
End of faith, as its be-gin-ning, Set our hearts at lib-er-ty.
Pray, and praise Thee without ceasing, Glo-ry in Thy pre-cious love.
Till we cast our crowns be-fore Thee, Lost in won-der, love, and praise. A-MEN.

225 Shepherd of Tender Youth

KIRBY BEDON. 664, 6664.

CLEMENT OF ALEXANDRIA, about 200 A.D.
Tr. by HENRY M. DEXTER, 1846

EDWARD BUNNETT, 1887

1. Shep - herd of ten - der youth, Guid - ing in love and truth
2. Thou art our ho - ly Lord, The all - sub - du - ing Word,
3. Ev - er be near our side, Our Shep - herd and our Guide,
4. So now, and till we die, Sound we Thy prais - es high,

Through devious ways; Christ, our tri - um - phant King, We come Thy Name to sing;
Heal - er of strife; Thou didst Thy-self a - base, That from sin's deep dis-grace,
Our staff and song; Je - sus, Thou Christ of God, By Thine en-dur-ing Word,
And joy - ful sing; Let all the ho - ly throng Who to Thy Church be-long,

Hith - er Thy chil - dren bring Trib - utes of praise.
Thou might - est save our race, And give us life.
Lead us where Thou hast trod; Make our faith strong.
U - nite to swell the song To Christ our King! A - MEN.

226 As Pants the Hart for Cooling Streams

SPOHR. C. M.

TATE and BRADY, 1696

LOUIS SPOHR, 1835

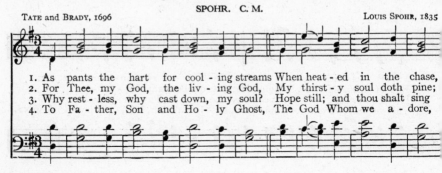

1. As pants the hart for cool - ing streams When heat - ed in the chase,
2. For Thee, my God, the liv - ing God, My thirst - y soul doth pine;
3. Why rest - less, why cast down, my soul? Hope still; and thou shalt sing
4. To Fa - ther, Son and Ho - ly Ghost, The God Whom we a - dore,

So longs my soul, O God, for Thee, And Thy re - fresh-ing grace.
O when shall I be - hold Thy face. Thou Ma - jes - ty Di - vine!
The praise of Him Who is thy God, Thy health's e - ter - nal spring.
Be glo - ry, as it was, is now, And shall be ev - er - more. A - MEN.

Guide Me, O Thou Great Jehovah 227

PILGRIM. 8 7, 8 7, 4 7.

From the Welsh of WILLIAM WILLIAMS, 1746
Tr. St. 1, PETER WILLIAMS, 1771
St. 2 and 3, WILLIAM WILLIAMS, 1772

J. F. OHL, 1889

1. Guide me, O Thou great Je - ho - vah, Pil - grim thro' this bar - ren land;
2. O - pen now the crys - tal foun-tain Whence the heal-ing streams do flow;
3. When I tread the verge of Jor - dan, Bid my anx - ious fears sub - side;

I am weak, but Thou art might - y, Hold me with Thy pow'r - ful hand;
Let the fier - y, cloud - y pil - lar Lead me all my jour - ney through;
Death of death and hell's De-struc-tion, Land me safe on Ca - naan's side;

Bread of heav - en, Feed me till I want no more!
Strong De - liv - er - er, Be Thou still my Strength and Shield!
Songs of prais - es I will ev - er give to Thee. A - MEN.

228 Saviour, Like a Shepherd Lead Us

SHEPHERD. 8 7, 8 7, 4 7.

Anon.
Hymns for the Young, 1832

WILLIAM B. BRADBURY, 1859

1. Sav - iour, like a shep-herd lead us; Much we need Thy ten-d'rest care;
2. We are Thine; do Thou be - friend us, Be the Guard-ian of our way;
3. Thou hast prom-ised to re - ceive us, Poor and sin - ful though we be;
4. Ear - ly let us seek Thy fa - vor, Ear - ly let us do Thy will;

In Thy pleas-ant pas - tures feed us, For our use Thy folds pre-pare.
Keep Thy flock, from sin de - fend us, Seek us when we go a - stray;
Thou hast mer - cy to re - lieve us, Grace to cleanse, and pow-'r to free.
Bless - ed Lord and on - ly Sav - iour, With Thy love our bos-oms fill.

Bless - ed Je - sus, Bless-ed Je - sus, Thou hast bought us: Thine we are,
Bles-sed Je - sus, Bless-ed Je - sus, Hear us chil - dren when we pray,
Bless - ed Je - sus, Bless-ed Je - sus, Ear - ly let us turn to Thee,
Bless - ed Je - sus, Bless-ed Je - sus, Thou hast loved us, love us still,

Bless - ed Je - sus, Bless-ed Je - sus, Thou hast bought us: Thine we are.
Bless - ed Je - sus, Bless-ed Je - sus, Hear us chil-dren when we pray.
Bless - ed Je - sus, Bless-ed Je - sus, Ear - ly let us turn to Thee.
Bless - ed Je - sus, Bless-ed Je - sus, Thou hast loved us, love us still. A - MEN.

Lead, Kindly Light

LUX BENIGNA.   10 4, 10 4, 10 10.

John Henry Newman, 1833
Stanza 4 by Joseph A. Seiss, 1902

John B. Dykes, 1865

1. Lead, kind-ly Light, a-mid the en-cir-cling gloom, Lead Thou me on;
2. I was not ev - er thus, nor prayed that Thou Shouldst lead me on;
3. So long Thy pow'r hath blest me, sure it still Will lead me on
4. Till then, a - long the path Thy-self hast trod, Je - sus lead on:

The night is dark, and I am far from home; Lead Thou me on;
I loved to choose and see my path; but now Lead Thou me on.
O'er moor and fen, o'er crag and tor - rent, till The night is gone;
Be Thou my Strength, my Help, O Son of God, Till heaven is won,—

Keep Thou my feet; I do not ask to see . . . . .
I loved the gar - ish day, and, spite of fears, ...
And with the morn those an - gel fa - ces smile, ...
Till with Thy fold - ed flock my soul shall rest. . . . . .

The dis - tant scene; one step e - nough for me.
Pride ruled my will: Re - mem - ber not past years.
Which I have loved long since, and lost a - while.
In that calm peace where all Thy saints are blest.   A - MEN.

230

Jesus, Saviour, Pilot Me

PILOT. 77,77,77.

EDWARD HOPPER, 1872

JOHN E. GOULD, 1871

1. Je - sus, Sav - iour, pi - lot me, O - ver life's tem - pest - uous sea;
2. As a moth - er stills her child, Thou canst hush the o - cean wild;
3. When at last I near the shore, And the fear - ful break - ers roar

Un-known waves be-fore me roll, Hid - ing rock and treach'rous shoal;
Boist'rous waves o - bey Thy will When Thou say'st to them, "Be still!"
'Twixt me and the peace-ful rest, Then, while lean-ing on Thy breast,

Chart and com-pass come from Thee; Je - sus, Sav - iour, pi - lot me.
Wondrous Sovereign of the sea, Je - sus, Sav - iour, pi - lot me.
May I hear Thee say to me, "Fear not, I will pi - lot thee!" A - MEN.

231

Lord, Teach Us How to Pray

ST. JAMES. C. M.

JAMES MONTGOMERY, 1818

RAPHAEL COURTEVILLE, 1697

1. Lord, teach us how to pray a - right With rev'rence and with fear;
2. Bur-dened with guilt, con-vinced of sin, In weak-ness, want, and woe,
3. God of all grace, we come to Thee With bro - ken, con - trite hearts;
4. Give deep hu - mil - i - ty; the sense Of god - ly sor - row give;

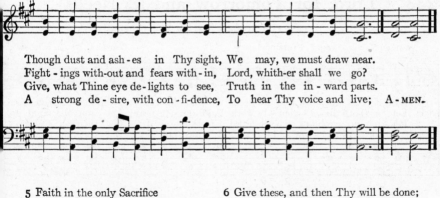

Though dust and ash-es in Thy sight, We may, we must draw near.
Fight-ings with-out and fears with-in, Lord, whith-er shall we go?
Give, what Thine eye de-lights to see, Truth in the in-ward parts.
A strong de-sire, with con-fi-dence, To hear Thy voice and live; A-MEN.

5 Faith in the only Sacrifice
  That can for sin atone;
  To cast our hopes, to fix our eyes,
  On Christ, on Christ alone;

6 Give these, and then Thy will be done;
  Thus strengthened with all might,
  We, through Thy Spirit and Thy Son,
  Shall pray, and pray aright.

O That the Lord Would Guide My Ways   232

EVAN. C. M.

ISAAC WATTS, 1719   WILLIAM H. HAVERGAL, 1847

1. O that the Lord would guide my ways To keep His stat-utes still!
2. Or-der my foot-steps by Thy Word, And make my heart sin-cere;
3. As-sist my soul, too apt to stray, A strict-er watch to keep;
4. Make me to walk in Thy com-mands; 'Tis a de-light-ful road;

O that my God would grant me grace To know and do His will!
Let sin have no do-min-ion, Lord, But keep my con-science clear.
And should I e'er for-get Thy way, Re-store Thy wand'ring sheep.
Nor let my head, or heart, or hands Of-fend a-gainst my God. A-MEN.

233   Lord, for Tomorrow and Its Needs

JUST FOR TO-DAY.   8 4, 8 4.   With Refrain.

Sister MARY XAVIER (SYBIL F. PARTRIDGE), 1876   GEORGE C. STEBBINS (1846-)

1. Lord, for to - mor-row and its needs I do not pray; Keep me, O God, from
2. Let me both dil - i - gent - ly work And du - ly pray; Let me be kind in
3. Let me no wrong or i - dle word Un-think-ing say; Set thou a seal up -
4. So, for to - mor - row and its needs I do not pray; But keep me, guide me,

REFRAIN

stain of sin, Just for to - day, Just for to - day, Just for to - day,
word and deed, Just for to - day, Just for to - day, Just for to - day,
on my lips, Just for to - day, Just for to - day, Just for to - day,
love me, Lord, Just for to - day, Just for to - day, Just for to - day,

Keep me, O God, from stain of sin, Just for to - day.
Let me be kind in word and deed, Just for to - day.
Set thou a seal up - on my lips, Just for to - day.
But keep me, guide me, love me, Lord, Just for to - day. A - MEN.

234   Holy, Holy, Holy Lord

WEBER.   77,77.

BENJAMIN WILLIAMS, 1778, a.   C. M. VON WEBER, 1826

1. Ho - ly, ho - ly, ho - ly Lord! Be Thy glo - rious Name a - dored,
2. Though un-wor-thy, Lord, Thine ear Deign our hum - ble songs to hear.
3. There no tongue shall si - lent be; All shall join in har - mo - ny;
4. Lord, Thy mer - cies nev - er fail: Hail, ce - les - tial Good-ness, hail!

Lord, Thy mer-cies nev-er fail: Hail, ce-les-tial Good-ness, hail!
Pur-er praise we hope to bring, When a-round Thy throne we sing.
That through heaven's capacious round Praise to Thee may ev-er sound.
Ho-ly, ho-ly, ho-ly Lord! Be Thy glo-rious Name a-dored. A-MEN.

Jesus, from Thy Throne on High 235

LITANY. 777, 6.

THOMAS B. POLLOCK (1836–1896)   St. Alban's Tune Book, 1866

1. Je - sus, from Thy throne on high, Far a - bove the bright blue sky,
2. Lit - tle hearts may love Thee well, Lit - tle lips Thy love may tell,
3. Be Thou with us ev - 'ry day, In our work and in our play,

Look on us with lov-ing eye; Hear us, Ho-ly Je-sus.
Lit-tle hymns Thy prais-es swell; Hear us, Ho-ly Je-sus.
When we learn and when we pray; Hear us, Ho-ly Je-sus. A-MEN.

4 May we grow from day to day,
　Glad to learn each holy way,
　Ever ready to obey;
　　Hear us, Holy Jesus.

5 May our thoughts be undefiled;
　May our words be true and mild;
　Make us each a holy child;
　　Hear us, Holy Jesus.

6 Jesus, Son of God Most High,
　Who didst in the manger lie,
　Who upon the Cross didst die;
　　Hear us, Holy Jesus.

7 Jesus, from Thy heavenly throne
　Watching o'er each little one,
　Till our life on earth is done,
　　Hear us, Holy Jesus.

236

I Need Thee Every Hour

6 4, 6 4. With Refrain.

ANNIE S. HAWKS, 1872

ROBERT LOWRY, 1872

1. I need Thee ev - 'ry hour, Most gra - cious Lord;   No ten - der voice like
2. I need Thee ev - 'ry hour; Stay Thou near by;   Temp-ta-tions lose their
3. I need Thee ev - 'ry hour; Teach me Thy will;   And Thy rich prom - is -
4. I need Thee ev - 'ry hour, Most Ho - ly One;   O make me Thine in-

REFRAIN.

Thine   Can peace af - ford.
power   When Thou art nigh.   I need Thee, O I need Thee, Ev - 'ry hour I
es   In me ful - fil.
deed,   Thou bless - ed Son.

need Thee; O bless me now, my Sav-iour, I come to Thee. A - MEN.

237   Give to Our God Immortal Praise

DUKE SRTEET. L. M.

ISAAC WATTS, 1719

JOHN HATTON, 1793

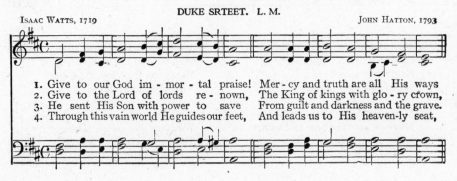

1. Give to our God im - mor - tal praise! Mer - cy and truth are all His ways
2. Give to the Lord of lords re - nown, The King of kings with glo - ry crown,
3. He sent His Son with power to save From guilt and darkness and the grave.
4. Through this vain world He guides our feet, And leads us to His heaven-ly seat,

Won-ders of grace to God be - long; Re-peat His mer-cies in your song.
His mer-cies ev - er shall en - dure, When lords and kings are known no more.
Won-ders of grace to God be - long; Re-peat His mer-cies in your song.
His mer-cies ev - er shall en - dure, When this vain world shall be no more. A-MEN.

Praise, My Soul, the King of Heaven 238

PRAISE. 8 7, 8 7, 8 7.

HENRY FRANCIS LYTE, 1834, a.   JOHN GOSS, 1869

1. Praise, my soul, the King of heav - en;   To His feet thy trib-ute bring;
2. Praise Him for His grace and fa - vor   To our fa - thers in dis - tress;
3. Fa - ther - like He tends and spares us,   Well our fee - ble frame He knows;
4. An - gels in the height a - dore Him,   Who be - hold Him face to face;

Ransomed, healed, re-stored, for - giv - en,   Who like thee His praise should sing?
Praise Him, still the same as ev - er,   Slow to chide, and swift to bless:
In His hands He gent - ly bears us,   Res - cues us from all our foes:
Sun and moon bow down be - fore Him;   Dwell-ers in all time and space:

Al - le - lu - ia! Al - le - lu - ia!   Praise the ev - er - last - ing King!
Al - le - lu - ia! Al - le - lu - ia!   Glo - rious in His faith-ful - ness!
Al - le - lu - ia! Al - le - lu - ia!   Wide - ly as His mer - cy flows!
Al - le - lu - ia! Al - le - lu - ia!   Praise with us the God of grace!   A-MEN.

239 Sweet Hour of Prayer

WALFORD. L. M. D.

WILLIAM W. WALFORD, 1849

WILLIAM B. BRADBURY, 1859

Moderato

1. Sweet hour of prayer! sweet hour of prayer! That calls me from a world of care,
2. Sweet hour of prayer! sweet hour of prayer! Thy wings shall my pe - ti - tion bear

And bids me at my Fa-ther's throne Make all my wants and wish - es known;
To Him Whose truth and faith-ful-ness En - gage the wait - ing soul to bless;

In sea - sons of dis - tress and grief, My soul has oft - en found re - lief;
And since He bids me seek His face, Be - lieve His Word, and trust His grace,

And oft es - caped the temp-ter's snare, By thy re - turn, sweet hour of prayer.
I'll cast on Him my ev - 'ry care, And wait for thee, sweet hour of prayer!

And oft es - caped the temp-ter's snare, By thy re - turn, sweet hour of prayer.
I'll cast on Him my ev - 'ry care And wait for thee, sweet hour of prayer.

What a Friend We Have in Jesus   240

ERIE. 87, 87. D.

Joseph Scriven, 1855

C. C. Converse, 1868

1. What a friend we have in Je - sus,   All   our sins and griefs to bear!
2. Have we tri - als and temp - ta - tions?   Is   there trou-ble an - y - where?
3. Are we weak and heav-y - la - den,   Cum-bered with a load of   care?

What   a priv - i - lege to car - ry   Ev - 'ry-thing to God in   prayer!
We   should nev-er be dis - cour - aged;   Take   it   to the Lord in   prayer.
Pre - cious Sav-iour, still our ref - uge!   Take   it   to the Lord in   prayer.

O   what peace we oft - en for - feit,   O   what need-less pain we bear,
Can we find a friend so faith - ful,   Who will all our sor-rows share?
Do Thy friends de-spise, for-sake thee?   Take   it   to the Lord in prayer;

All   be-cause we do not car - ry   Ev - 'ry thing to God in prayer!
Je - sus knows our ev-'ry weak-ness,   Take it to the Lord in prayer.
In   His arms He'll take and shield thee,   Thou, wilt find a sol - ace there. A - MEN.

241 Lord, with Glowing Heart I'd Praise Thee

SANCTUARY. 87, 87. D.

FRANCIS SCOTT KEY, 1823   JOHN B. DYKES, 1871

1. Lord, with glow-ing heart I'd praise Thee For the bliss Thy love be-stows,
2. Praise, my soul, the God that sought thee, Wretch-ed wan-d'rer, far a-stray;
3. Lord, this bos-om's ar-dent feel-ing Vain-ly would my lips ex-press;

For the par-d'ning grace that saves me, And the peace that from it flows.
Found thee lost, and kind-ly brought thee From the paths of death a-way.
Low be-fore Thy foot-stool kneel-ing, Deign Thy sup-pliant's prayer to bless.

Help, O God, my weak en-deav-or; This dull soul to rap-ture raise;
Praise, with love's de-vout-est feel-ing, Him Who saw thy guilt-born fear,
Let Thy grace, my soul's chief treas-ure, Love's pure flame with-in me raise;

Thou must light the flame, or nev-er   Can my love be warmed to praise.
And, the light of hope re-veal-ing,   Bade the blood-stained Cross appear.
And, since words can nev-er meas-ure,   Let my life show forth Thy praise. A-MEN.

Now Thank We All Our God 242

NUN DANKET ALLE GOTT. 67, 67, 66, 66.

MARTIN RINKART, d. 1648
Tr. CATHERINE WINKWORTH, 1858, a.

JOHANN CRÜGER, 1648

1. Now thank we all our God With heart and hands and voic - es,
2. O may this bount-eous God Through all our life be near us,
3. All praise and thanks to God The Fa - ther now be giv - en,

Who won-drous things hath done, In Whom His world re - joic - es;
With ev - er joy - ful hearts And bless - ed peace to cheer us;
The Son, and Him Who reigns With Them in high - est heav - en:

Who, from our moth - er's arms, Hath blessed us on our way
And keep us in His grace, And guide us when per - plexed,
The One E - ter - nal God Whom earth and heaven a - dore;

With count - less gifts of love, And still is ours to - day.
And free us from all ills In this world and the next.
For thus it was, is now, And shall be ev - er - more. A - MEN.

243 Praise the Lord, Ye Heavens Adore Him

FABEN. 87, 87. D.

London Foundling Hospital Collection, 1796

J. H. WILLCOX, 1849

1. Praise the Lord, ye heavens, a - dore Him, Praise Him, an - gels, in the height;
2. Praise the Lord for He is glo-rious; Nev - er shall His prom-ise fail;

Sun and moon, re - joice be - fore Him, Praise Him, all ye stars and light;
God hath made His saints vic - to - rious, Sin and death shall not pre - vail.

Praise the Lord, for He hath spok - en, Worlds His might - y voice o - beyed;
Praise the God of our sal - va - tion; Hosts on high, His power pro-claim;

Laws, which nev - er shall be bro - ken, For their guid-ance He hath made.
Heaven and earth, and all cre - a - tion, Laud and mag - ni - fy His Name. A - MEN.

Let All the World in Every Corner Sing 244

UNDIQUE GLORIA. 10 4, 6 6, 6 6, 10 4.

GEORGE HERBERT, 1633
Doxology, Anon. 1872

GEORGE J. ELVEY, 1872

1. Let all the world in ev - 'ry cor - ner sing "My God and King!"
2. Let all the world in ev - 'ry cor - ner sing "My God and King!"
3. Let all the world in ev - 'ry cor - ner sing "My God and King!"

The heavens are not too high, His praise may thith - er fly;
The Church with psalms must shout, No door can keep them out;
The Fa - ther, and the Son, And Spir - it, Three in One,

The earth is not too low, His prais - es there may grow.
But, a - bove all, the heart Must bear the long - est part.
One ev - er - last - ing Lord, Be ev - er - more a - dored!

Let all the world in ev - 'ry cor - ner sing "My God and King!"

245   # O Worship the King

LYONS. 10 10, 11 11.

ROBERT GRANT, 1833, a.
Based on W. KETHES' Paraphrase, 1561

MICHAEL HAYDN (1737-1806)

1. O wor-ship the King, all - glo - rious a - bove, And grate-ful - ly sing His
2. O tell of His might and sing of His grace, Whose robe is the light, Whose
3. Thy boun-ti-ful care what tongue can re - cite? It breathes in the air, it
4. Frail chil-dren of dust, and fee - ble as frail, In Thee do we trust, nor

won - der - ful love; Our Shield and De - fend - er, the An - cient of Days,
can - o - py space; His char - iots of wrath the deep thun-der-clouds form,
shines in the light, It streams from the hills, it de - scends to the plain,
find Thee to fail; Thy mer - cies how ten - der! how firm to the end,

Pa - vil - ioned in splen - dor and gird - ed with praise.
And dark is His path on the wings of the storm.
And sweet - ly dis - tills in the dew and the rain.
Our Mak - er, De - fend - er, Re - deem - er, and Friend. A - MEN.

246 **We Thank Thee, Lord, for This Fair Earth**

ERNAN. L. M.

GEORGE E. L. COTTON, 1856

LOWELL MASON, 1850

1. We thank thee, Lord, for this fair earth, The glit-t'ring sky, the sil - ver sea;
2. Thine are the flow'rs that clothe the ground, The trees that wave their arms a - bove,
3. Yet teach us still how far more fair, More glo-rious, Fa-ther, in Thy sight,
4. So while we gaze with thought-ful eye On all the gifts Thy love has given,

For all their beau-ty, all their worth, Their light and glo-ry, come from Thee.
The hills that gird our dwell-ings 'round, As Thou dost gird Thine own with love.
Is one pure deed, one ho - ly prayer, One heart that owns Thy Spir-it's might.
Help us in Thee to live and die, By Thee to rise from earth to heaven. A-MEN.

Glory Be to God the Father 247

ST. RAPHAEL. 87, 87, 47.

HORATIUS BONAR, 1866

EDWARD J. HOPKINS, 1862

1. Glo - ry be to God the Fa-ther! Glo - ry be to God the Son!
2. Glo - ry be to Him Who loved us, Washed us from each spot and stain!
3. Glo - ry to the King of an-gels! Glo - ry to the Church's King!
4. Glo - ry, bless-ing, praise, e - ter - nal! Thus the choir of an - gels sings,

Glo - ry be to God the Spir - it! Great Je - ho - vah, Three in One!
Glo - ry be to Him Who bought us, Made us kings with Him to reign!
Glo - ry to the King of na-tions! Heaven and earth, your prais - es bring:—
Hon - or, rich - es, power, do - min-ion! Thus its praise cre - a - tion brings;

Glo - ry, glo - ry, While e - ter - nal a - ges run!
Glo - ry, glo - ry, To the Lamb that once was slain!
Glo - ry, glo - ry, To the King of Glo - ry bring!
Glo - ry, glo - ry, Glo - ry to the King of kings! A-MEN.

248 Praise to the Lord

LOBE DEN HERREN. 14 14, 4 7 8.

JOACHIM NEANDER, 1680
Tr. CATHERINE WINKWORTH, 1863

Stralsund Gesangbuch, 1665
Present form since 1708

1. Praise to the Lord, the Al-might-y, the King of cre - a - tion!
2. Praise to the Lord! Who o'er all things so won-drous-ly reign - eth,
3. Praise to the Lord! Who doth pros-per thy work and de - fend thee;
4. Praise to the Lord! O let all that is in me a - dore Him!

O my soul, praise Him, for He is thy health and sal - va - tion!
Shel-ters thee un - der His wings, yea, so gen - tly sus - tain - eth;
Sure - ly His good - ness and mer - cy here dail - y at - tend thee.
All that hath life and breath, come now with prais - es be - fore Him!

All ye who hear, Now to His tem - ple draw near;
Hast thou not seen How thy de - sires e'er have been
Pon - der a - new What the Al - might - y can do,
Let the A - men Sound from His peo - ple a - gain;

Praise Him in glad ad - o - ra - tion.
Grant - ed in what He or - dain - eth?
If with His love He be - friend thee!
Glad - ly for aye we a - dore Him. A - MEN.

Mighty God, while Angels Bless Thee 249

PRAISE. 8 7, 8 7. With Alleluia.

ROBERT ROBINSON, 1774

ALBERT LOWE, 1876

1. Might - y God, while an - gels bless Thee, May a mor - tal sing Thy Name?
2. Lord of ev - 'ry land and na - tion, An - cient of e - ter - nal days,
3. For the gran - deur of Thy na - ture, Grand be - yond a ser - aph's thought;
4. For Thy prov - i - dence, that gov - erns Through Thine em-pire's wide do-main,

ORGAN

Lord of men, as well as an - gels, Thou art ev - 'ry crea-ture's theme.
Sound-ed through the wide cre - a - tion Be Thy just and end - less praise.
For the won - ders of cre - a - tion, Works with skill and kind-ness wrought:
Wings an an - gel, guides a spar - row: Bless - ed be Thy gen - tle reign.

Al - le - lu - ia, Al - le - lu - ia, Al - le - lu - ia. A - MEN.

5 But Thy rich, Thy free Redemption,
Bright, though veiled in darkness long,
Thought is poor, and poor expression,—
Who can sing that wondrous song?

6 From the highest throne in glory
To the cross of deepest woe!
All to ransom guilty captives!
Flow, my praise, for ever flow.

250   Alleluia! Song of Gladness

ALLELUIA, DULCE CARMEN. 8 7, 8 7, 8 7.

From the Latin
Tr. COOKE and DENTON's *Hymnal*, 1853

Ascribed to MICHAEL HAYDN (1737-1806)

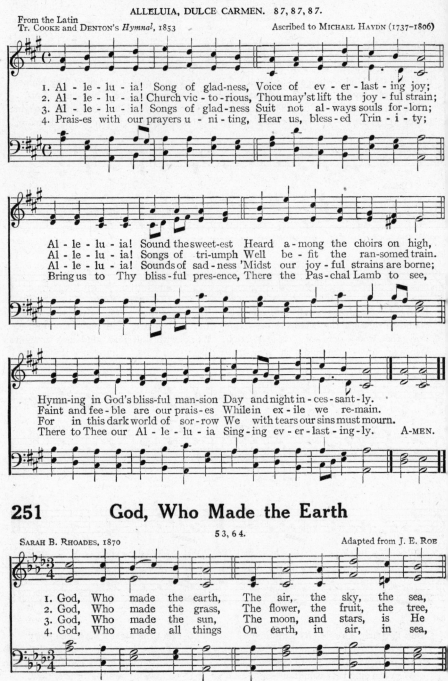

1. Al - le - lu - ia! Song of glad-ness, Voice of ev - er - last - ing joy;
2. Al - le - lu - ia! Church vic - to - rious, Thou may'st lift the joy - ful strain;
3. Al - le - lu - ia! Songs of glad-ness Suit not al - ways souls for-lorn;
4. Prais-es with our prayers u - ni - ting, Hear us, bless - ed Trin - i - ty;

Al - le - lu - ia! Sound the sweet-est Heard a - mong the choirs on high,
Al - le - lu - ia! Songs of tri-umph Well be - fit the ran-somed train.
Al - le - lu - ia! Sounds of sad - ness 'Midst our joy - ful strains are borne;
Bring us to Thy bliss-ful pres-ence, There the Pas-chal Lamb to see,

Hymn-ing in God's bliss-ful man-sion Day and night in - ces - sant-ly.
Faint and fee - ble are our prais-es While in ex - ile we re-main.
For in this dark world of sor-row We with tears our sins must mourn.
There to Thee our Al - le - lu - ia Sing-ing ev - er - last - ing - ly. A-MEN.

251   God, Who Made the Earth

5 3, 6 4.

SARAH B. RHOADES, 1870

Adapted from J. E. ROE

1. God, Who made the earth, The air, the sky, the sea,
2. God, Who made the grass, The flower, the fruit, the tree,
3. God, Who made the sun, The moon, and stars, is He
4. God, Who made all things On earth, in air, in sea,

Who gave the light its birth, Car - eth for me.
The day and night to pass, Car - eth for me.
Who, when life's clouds come on, Car - eth for me.
Who chang - ing sea - sons brings, Car - eth for me. A - MEN.

5 God, Who sent His Son
    To die on Calvary,
  He, if I lean on Him,
    Will care for me.

6 When in heaven's bright land
    I all His loved ones see,
  I'll sing with that blest band,
    God cared for me.

Praise the Lord of Heaven   252

DAVID. 6 5, 6 5. D.

THOMAS B. BROWNE, 1844   THOMAS MORLEY, 1867

1. Praise the Lord of heav - en, Praise Him in the height, Praise Him, all ye
2. Praise the Lord, ye foun - tains Of the deeps and seas, Rocks and hills, and
3. Praise Him, fowls and cat - tle, Prin - ces and all kings; Praise Him, men and

an - gels, Praise Him, stars and light; Praise Him, clouds and wa-ters, Which a-bove the
moun-tains, Ce - dars, and all trees; Praise Him, clouds and va-pors, Snow, and hail, and
maid - ens, All cre - at - ed things; For the Name of God is Ex - cel-lent a-

skies, When His word com-mand-ed, Did es - tab - lished rise.
fire, Storm - y wind, ful - fill - ing On - ly His de - sire.
lone, Ov - er earth His foot-stool, Ov - er heaven His throne. A - MEN.

253 The God of Abraham Praise

LEONI. 6 6, 8 4. D.

THOMAS OLIVERS, 1770, a.
Based on the Hebrew Yigdal

Adapted from a Hebrew Melody

1. The God of Abra - ham praise Who reigns en - throned a - bove,
2. The God who reigns on high The great arch - an - gels sing,
3. Be - fore the Sav - iour's face The ran - somed na - tions bow,
4. The whole tri - um - phant host Give thanks to God on high;

An - cient of ev - er - last - ing days, And God of love;
And "Ho - ly, Ho - ly, Ho - ly," cry, "Al - might - y King!
O'er - whelmed at His al - might - y grace, For - ev - er new;
"Hail! Fa - ther, Son and Ho - ly Ghost," They ev - er cry;

To Him up - lift your voice, At Whose su - preme com - mand
Who was, and is, the same, And ev - er - more shall be;
He shows His prints of love,— They kin - dle to a flame,
Hail! Abra - ham's God, and mine! (I join the heaven - ly lays),

From earth we rise, and seek the joys At His right hand.
E - ter - nal Fa - ther, great I AM, We wor - ship Thee."
And sound thro' all the worlds a - bove, "Wor - thy the Lamb."
All might and maj - es - ty are Thine, And end - less praise. A - MEN.

Blessing and Honor, and Glory and Power 254

AMERICAN HYMN. 10 10, 10 10.

HORATIUS BONAR, 1866

MATTHIAS KELLER (1813–1890)

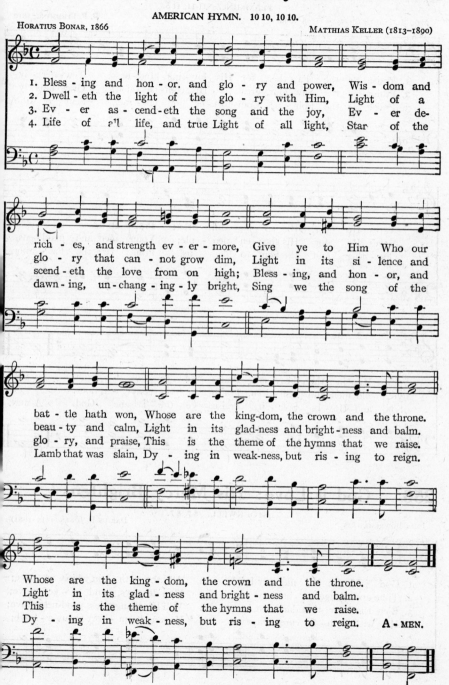

1. Bless - ing and hon - or. and glo - ry and power, Wis - dom and
2. Dwell - eth the light of the glo - ry with Him, Light of a
3. Ev - er as - cend-eth the song and the joy, Ev - er de-
4. Life of all life, and true Light of all light, Star of the

rich - es, and strength ev - er - more, Give ye to Him Who our
glo - ry that can - not grow dim, Light in its si - lence and
scend - eth the love from on high; Bless - ing, and hon - or, and
dawn - ing, un - chang - ing - ly bright, Sing we the song of the

bat - tle hath won, Whose are the king-dom, the crown and the throne.
beau - ty and calm, Light in its glad-ness and bright - ness and balm.
glo - ry, and praise, This is the theme of the hymns that we raise.
Lamb that was slain, Dy - ing in weak-ness, but ris - ing to reign.

Whose are the king - dom, the crown and the throne.
Light in its glad - ness and bright - ness and balm.
This is the theme of the hymns that we raise.
Dy - ing in weak - ness, but ris - ing to reign. A - MEN.

255 Praise Ye the Father

FLEMMING. 11 11, 11 5.

Mrs. Elizabeth Charles (1828-1896)

F. F. Flemming, 1810

1. Praise ye the Fa - ther, for His lov - ing - kind - ness: Ten - der - ly
2. Praise ye the Sav - iour, great is His com - pas - sion; Gra - cious - ly
3. Praise ye the Spir - it, Com - fort - er of Is - rael, Sent of the

cares He for His err - ing chil - dren; Praise Him, ye an - gels,
cares He for His chos - en peo - ple; Young men and maid - ens,
Fa - ther and the Son to bless us, Praise ye the Fa - ther,

praise Him in the heav - ens, Praise ye Je - ho - vah.
ye old men and chil - dren, Praise ye the Sav - iour.
Son, and Ho - ly Spir - it, Praise ye the Tri - une God. A-MEN.

256 God is Love: His Mercy Brightens

STOCKWELL. 87, 87.

John Bowring, 1825

Darius E. Jones (1815-1881)

1. God is Love: His mer - cy bright - ens All the path in which we rove;
2. Time and change are bu - sy ev - er; Man de - cays, and a - ges move;
3. E'en the hour that dark - est seem - eth Will His change - less good-ness prove;
4. He with earth - ly cares en - twin - eth Hope and com - fort from a - bove;

Bliss He wakes, and woe He light-ens; God is Wis-dom, God is Love.
But His mer-cy wan-eth nev-er; God is Wis-dom, God is Love.
From the gloom His brightness streameth; God is Wis-dom, God is Love.
Ev - 'ry-where His glo-ry shin-eth; God is Wis-dom, God is Love. A-MEN.

Singing for Jesus, Our Saviour and King 257

BROMHAM. 10 10, 10 10.

FRANCES R. HAVERGAL, 1872

TIMOTHY R. MATTHEWS, 1886

1. Sing - ing for Je - sus, our Sav - iour and King, Sing - ing for
2. Sing - ing for Je - sus, and try - ing to win Man - y to
3. Sing - ing for Je - sus, our Shep - herd and Guide, Sing - ing for
4. Sing - ing for Je - sus, yes, sing - ing for joy; Thus will we

Je - sus, the Lord Whom we love; All ad - o - ra - tion we
love Him, and join in the song; Call - ing the wear - y and
glad - ness of heart that He gives; Sing - ing for won - der and
praise Him and tell out His love; Till He shall call us to

joy - ous - ly bring, Long - ing to praise as they praise Him a - bove.
wan - der - ing in, Roll - ing the cho - rus of glad - ness a - long.
praise that He died, Sing - ing for bless - ing and joy that He lives.
bright - er em - ploy, Sing - ing for Je - sus, for ev - er a - bove. A-MEN.

258 The Heavens Declare Thy Glory

CHENIES. 7 6, 7 6. D.

THOMAS R. BIRKS, 1874

TIMOTHY R. MATTHEWS, 1855

1. The heavens de-clare Thy glo-ry, The fir-ma-ment Thy power;
2. The sun with roy-al splen-dor Goes forth to chant Thy praise;
3. How per-fect, just and ho-ly The pre-cepts Thou hast given!
4. All heaven on high re-joic-es To do its Mak-er's will;

Day un-to day the sto-ry Re-peats from hour to hour;
And moon-beams soft and ten-der Their gen-tler an-them raise;
Still mak-ing wise the low-ly, They lift the thoughts to heaven;
The stars with sol-emn voic-es Re-sound Thy prais-es still;

Night un-to night re-ply-ing, Pro-claims in ev-'ry land,
O'er ev-'ry tribe and na-tion That mu-sic strange is poured,
Thy word hath rich-er treas-ure Than dwells with-in the mine,
So let my whole be-hav-ior, Tho'ts, words and ac-tions be,

O Lord, with voice un-dy-ing, The won-ders of Thy hand.
The song of all cre-a-tion, To Thee, cre-a-tion's Lord.
And sweet-ness be-yond meas-ure, At-tends Thy voice di-vine.
O Lord, my strength, my Sav-iour, One cease-less song to Thee. A-MEN.

Jesus, Thy Love Unbounded

EVERTS. 7 6, 7 6. D.

BOSWORTH'S *Hymns*, 1865

German

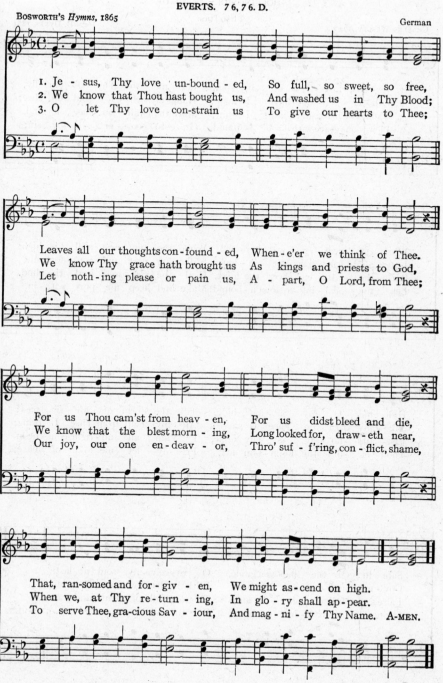

1. Je - sus, Thy love un-bound - ed, So full, so sweet, so free,
2. We know that Thou hast bought us, And washed us in Thy Blood;
3. O let Thy love con-strain us To give our hearts to Thee;

Leaves all our thoughts con-found - ed, When-e'er we think of Thee.
We know Thy grace hath brought us As kings and priests to God,
Let noth-ing please or pain us, A - part, O Lord, from Thee;

For us Thou cam'st from heav - en, For us didst bleed and die,
We know that the blest morn - ing, Long looked for, draw-eth near,
Our joy, our one en-deav - or, Thro' suf - f'ring, con - flict, shame,

That, ran-somed and for - giv - en, We might as-cend on high.
When we, at Thy re-turn - ing, In glo - ry shall ap-pear.
To serve Thee, gra-cious Sav - iour, And mag - ni - fy Thy Name. A-MEN.

260 ## Jesus, Lover of My Soul

HOLLINGSIDE. 77,77. D.

First Tune

CHARLES WESLEY, 1740

JOHN B. DYKES, 1861

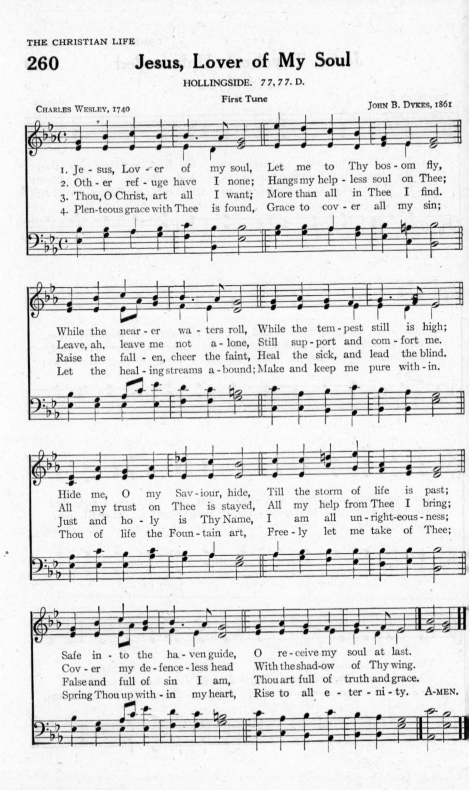

1. Je - sus, Lov - er of my soul, Let me to Thy bos - om fly,
2. Oth - er ref - uge have I none; Hangs my help - less soul on Thee;
3. Thou, O Christ, art all I want; More than all in Thee I find.
4. Plen-teous grace with Thee is found, Grace to cov - er all my sin;

While the near - er wa - ters roll, While the tem - pest still is high;
Leave, ah, leave me not a - lone, Still sup - port and com - fort me.
Raise the fall - en, cheer the faint, Heal the sick, and lead the blind.
Let the heal - ing streams a - bound; Make and keep me pure with - in.

Hide me, O my Sav - iour, hide, Till the storm of life is past;
All my trust on Thee is stayed, All my help from Thee I bring;
Just and ho - ly is Thy Name, I am all un - right-eous - ness;
Thou of life the Foun - tain art, Free - ly let me take of Thee;

Safe in - to the ha - ven guide, O re - ceive my soul at last.
Cov - er my de - fence - less head With the shad-ow of Thy wing.
False and full of sin I am, Thou art full of truth and grace.
Spring Thou up with - in my heart, Rise to all e - ter - ni - ty. A-MEN.

Second Tune

MARTYN. 77,77. D.

CHARLES WESLEY, 1740

SIMEON B. MARSH, 1834

FINE

1. { Je - sus, Lov - er of my soul, Let me to Thy bos - om fly,
While the near-er wa-ters roll, While the tem-pest still is high; }

D.C.—Safe in - to the ha - ven guide, O re - ceive my soul at last.

Hide me, O my Sav-iour, hide, Till the storm of life is past; A-MEN.

D.C.

Lamb of God, I Look to Thee   261

EDYFIELD. 77,77.

CHARLES WESLEY, 1742

CHRISTIAN I. LA TROBE (1758–1836)

1. Lamb of God, I look to Thee; Thou shalt my ex - am - ple be;
2. Fain I would be as Thou art, Give me Thy o - be-dient heart.
3. Lov - ing Je - sus, gen - tle Lamb, In Thy gra-cious hands I am.
4. I shall then show forth Thy praise, Serve Thee all my hap - py days;

Thou art gen - tle, meek, and mild, Thou wast once a lit - tle child. A-MEN.
Thou art pit - i - ful and kind: Let me have Thy lov-ing mind.
Make me, Sav - iour, what Thou art, Live Thy-self with-in my heart.
Then the world shall al - ways see Christ, the ho - ly Child, in me.

262   Jesus, My Lord, My God, My All

ST. CHRYSOSTOM. 8 8, 8 8, 8 8.

HENRY COLLINS, 1854

JOSEPH BARNBY, 1872

1. Je-sus, my Lord, my God, my All, Hear me, blest Sav-iour, when I call!
2. Je-sus, too late I Thee have sought; How can I love Thee as I ought?
3. Je-sus, what didst Thou find in me, That Thou hast dealt so lov-ing-ly?
4. Je-sus, of Thee shall be my song, To Thee my heart and soul be-long;

Hear me, and from Thy dwell-ing-place Pour down the rich-es of Thy grace.
And how ex-tol Thy match-less fame, The glo-rious beau-ty of Thy Name?
How great the joy that Thou hast brought, So far ex-ceed-ing hope or thought!
All that I have or am is Thine, And Thou, blest Saviour, Thou art mine.

Je-sus, my Lord, I Thee a-dore, O make me love Thee more and more. A-MEN.

263   O Jesus, King Most Wonderful

WINCHESTER. C. M.

BERNARD OF CLAIRVAUX. d. 1153
Tr. EDWARD CASWELL, 1849

THOMAS EST's *Psalter*, 1592

1. O Je-sus, King most won-der-ful, Thou Con-quer-or re-nowned,
2. When once Thou vis-it-est the heart, Then truth be-gins to shine,
3. O Je-sus, Light of all be-low, Thou fount of life and fire,

Thou sweet-ness most in - ef - fa - ble, In Whom all joys are found!
Then earth - ly van - i - ties de-part, Then kin-dles love di - vine.
Sur - pass ing all the joys we know, All that we can de - sire, A-MEN.

4 May every heart confess Thy Name
  And ever Thee adore,
And seeking Thee, itself inflame
  To seek Thee more and more.

5 Thee may our tongues forever bless;
  Thee may we love alone;
And ever in our lives express
  The image of Thine own.

Jesus, Thou Joy of Loving Hearts 264

MT. AIRY. L. M.

BERNARD OF CLAIRVAUX, d. 1153
Tr. RAY PALMER, 1858

In HOYTE's *Book of Litanies*

1. Je - sus, Thou Joy of lov - ing hearts! Thou Fount of life! Thou Light of men!
2. Thy truth un-changed hath ev-er stood; Thou sav-est those that on Thee call;
3. We taste Thee, O Thou liv - ing Bread, And long to feast up - on Thee still;

From the best bliss that earth im - parts We turn un-filled to Thee a-gain.
To them that seek Thee, Thou art good, To them that find Thee, all in all.
We drink of Thee, the Foun-tain-head, And thirst our souls from Thee to fill. A-MEN.

4 Our restless spirits yearn for Thee,
  Where'er our changeful lot is cast;
Glad, when Thy gracious smile we see,
  Blest, when our faith can hold Thee fast.

5 O Jesus, ever with us stay;
  Make all our moments calm and bright;
Chase the dark night of sin away,
  Shed o'er the world Thy holy light.

265 Jesus! the Very Thought of Thee

ST. AGNES. C. M.

BERNARD OF CLAIRVAUX, d. 1153
Tr. EDWARD CASWALL, 1849

JOHN B. DYKES, 1866

1. Je - sus! the ver - y thought of Thee With sweet-ness fills the breast;
2. Nor voice can sing, nor heart can frame, Nor can the mem - 'ry find
3. O Hope of ev - 'ry con - trite heart, O Joy of all the meek,

But sweet-er far Thy face to see, And in Thy pres-ence rest.
A sweet-er sound than Thy blest Name, O Sav-iour of man-kind!
To those who fall, how kind Thou art, How good to those who seek! A - MEN.

4 But what to those who find? Ah, this
   Nor tongue nor pen can show;
   The love of Jesus, what it is,
   None but His loved ones know.

5 Jesus, our only Joy be Thou,
   As Thou our Prize wilt be;
   Jesus, be Thou our Glory now
   And through eternity!

266 My Hope, My All, My Saviour Thou!

THANKSGIVING. L. M.

Unknown, 1774

JOHN B. DYKES, c. 1889

1. My Hope, my All, my Sav-iour Thou! To Thee, O Lord, my soul I bow.
2. Be Thou my Strength, be Thou my Way, Pro-tect me thro' my life's short day;
3. Cor - rect, re - prove, and com-fort me; As I have need, my Sav-iour be;
4. In fierce temp - ta-tion's dark-est hour, Save me from sin and Sa-tan's power

I seek the bliss Thy wounds im-part, I long to find Thee in my heart.
In all my acts let wis-dom guide, And keep me, Saviour, near Thy side.
And if I would from Thee de-part, Then clasp me, Saviour, to Thy heart.
Tear ev-'ry i-dol from Thy throne, And reign, my Sav-iour, reign a-lone. A-MEN.

Jesus, Thy Name I Love 267

FIAT LUX. 664, 6664.

JAMES G. DECK, 1842

HENRY HILES (1826–1904)

1. Je - sus, Thy Name I love, All oth - er names a - bove,
2. Thou, bless-ed Son of God, Hast bought me with Thy blood,
3. When un - to Thee I flee, Thou wilt my ref - uge be,
4. Soon Thou wilt come a - gain! I shall be hap - py then,

Je - sus, my Lord! Oh, Thou art all to me! Noth - ing to
Je - sus, my Lord! Oh, how great is Thy love, All oth - er
Je - sus, my Lord! What need I now to fear? What earth - ly
Je - sus, my Lord! Then Thine own face I'll see, Then I shall

please I see, Noth - ing a - part from Thee, Je - sus, my Lord!
loves a - bove, Love that I dai - ly prove, Je - sus, my Lord!
grief or care, Since Thou art ev - er near, Je - sus, my Lord!
like Thee be, Then ev - er-more with Thee, Je - sus, my Lord! A-MEN.

268 I Need Thee, Precious Jesus

ST. CHRISTOPHER. 7 6, 7 6. D.

FREDERICK WHITFIELD, 1855

FREDERICK C. MAKER, 1881

1. I need Thee, pre-cious Je - sus, For I am full of sin;
My soul is dark and guilt - y, My heart is dead with - in;
I need the cleans-ing foun - tain Where I can al - ways flee,
The Blood of Christ most pre-cious, The sin - ner's per - fect plea.

2. I need Thee, pre-cious Je - sus, For I am ver - y poor;
A stran - ger and a pil - grim, I have no earth - ly store.
I need the love of Je - sus To cheer me on my way,
To guide my doubt-ing foot-steps, To be my strength and stay.

3. I need Thee, pre-cious Je - sus; I need a Friend like Thee,
A Friend to soothe and pit - y, A Friend to care for me.
I need the heart of Je - sus To feel each anx - ious care,
To tell my ev - 'ry trou - ble And all my sor-rows share. A-MEN.

O Saviour, Precious Saviour

269

ANGEL'S STORY. 7 6, 7 6, D.

Frances R. Havergal, 1870

Arthur H. Mann, 1818

1. O Sav-iour, pre-cious Sav-iour, Whom, yet un-seen, we love;
2. O Bring-er of sal - va-tion, Who won-drous-ly hast wrought,
3. In Thee all full-ness dwell-eth, All grace and power di - vine;
4. O grant the con-sum-ma-tion Of this our song a-bove,

O Name of might and fa - vor, All oth-er names a-bove;
Thy-self the rev-e-la-tion Of Love be-yond our thought;
The glo-ry that ex-cell-eth, O Son of God, is Thine.
In end-less ad-o-ra-tion And ev-er-last-ing love;

We wor-ship Thee, we bless Thee, To Thee a-lone we sing;
We wor-ship Thee, we bless Thee, To Thee a-lone we sing;
We wor-ship Thee, we bless Thee, To Thee a-lone we sing;
Then shall we praise and bless Thee Where per-fect prais-es ring,

We praise Thee and con-fess Thee, Our Ho-ly Lord and King.
We praise Thee and con-fess Thee, Our Gra-cious Lord and King.
We praise Thee and con-fess Thee, Our Glo-rious Lord and King.
And ev-er-more con-fess Thee, Our Sav-iour and our King. A-men.

270 Thou Art the Way; to Thee Alone

ST. JAMES. C. M.

GEORGE W. DOANE, 1824

RAPHAEL COURTEVILLE, 1697

1. Thou art the Way; to Thee a - lone From sin and death we flee;
2. Thou art the Truth; Thy Word a - lone True wis - dom can im - part;
3. Thou art the Life; the rend - ing tomb Pro - claims Thy con - quering arm;
4. Thou art the Way, the Truth, the Life; Grant us that Way to know,

And he who would the Fa - ther seek Must seek Him, Lord, by Thee.
Thou on - ly canst in - form the mind, And pur - i - fy the heart.
And those who put their trust in Thee Nor death nor hell shall harm.
That Truth to keep, that Life to win, Whose joys e - ter - nal flow. A-MEN.

271 The King of Love My Shepherd Is

DOMINUS REGIT ME. 8 7, 8 7. Iambic.

HENRY W. BAKER, 1868

JOHN B. DYKES, 1868

1. The King of love my Shep-herd is, Whose good - ness fail - eth nev - er;
2. Where streams of liv-ing wa - ter flow My ran - somed soul He lead - eth.
3. Per-verse and fool - ish, oft I strayed, But yet in love He sought me,
4. In death's dark vale I fear no ill With Thee, dear Lord, be - side me,

I noth - ing lack if I am His And He is mine for ev - er.
And, where the verdant pastures grow With food ce - les - tial feed - eth.
And on His shoul-der gent - ly laid, And home, re-joic-ing, brought me.
Thy rod and staff my com-fort still, Thy Cross be-fore to guide me. A-MEN.

5 Thou spread'st a table in my sight;
Thy unction grace bestoweth;
And O, what transport and delight
From Thy pure chalice floweth!

6 And so through all the length of days
Thy goodness faileth never;
Good Shepherd! may I sing Thy praise
Within Thy house for ever.

I Lift My Heart to Thee   272

BUDLEIGH.   6 4, 6 4, 10 10.

CHARLES E. MUDIE, 1872

THOMAS M. MUDIE (1809–1876)

1. I lift my heart to Thee, Sav-iour Di-vine; For Thou art all to me, And I am Thine. Is there on earth a clos-er bond than this: That "my Be-lov-ed's mine, and I am His"?

2. Thine am I by all ties; But chief-ly Thine, That thro' Thy sac-ri-fice Thou, Lord, art mine. By Thine own cords of love, so sweet-ly wound A-round me, I to Thee am close-ly bound.

3. To Thee, Thou bleeding Lamb, I all things owe; All that I have and am, And all I know. All that I have is now no long-er mine, And I am not mine own,—Lord, I am Thine. A-MEN.

4 How can I, Lord, withhold
Life's brightest hour
From Thee: or gathered gold,
Or any power?
Why should I keep one precious thing from Thee,
When Thou hast given Thine own dear self for me?

5 I pray Thee, Saviour, keep
Me in Thy love,
Until death's holy sleep
Shall me remove
To that fair realm, where sin and sorrow o'er,
Thou and Thine own are one for evermore.

273 Break Thou the Bread of Life

BREAD OF LIFE. 6 4, 6 4. D.

MARY A. LATHBURY, 1880

WILLIAM F. SHERWIN, 1877

1. Break Thou the bread of life, Dear Lord, to me, As Thou didst
2. Bless Thou the truth, dear Lord, To me—to me— As Thou didst
3. Thou art the Bread of Life, O Lord, to me, Thy ho - ly
4. O send Thy Spir - it, Lord, Now un - to me, That He may

break the loaves Be - side the sea; Be - yond the sa - cred page
bless the bread By Gal - i - lee; Then shall all bond - age cease,
Word the truth That sav - eth me; Give me to eat and live
touch my eyes, And make me see: Show me the truth con-cealed

I seek Thee, Lord; My spir - it pants for Thee, O liv - ing Word.
All fet-ters fall; And I shall find my peace, My All in all.
With Thee a - bove; Teach me to love Thy truth, For Thou art love.
With-in Thy Word, And in Thy book re-vealed I see the Lord. A-MEN.

274 Blest Are the Pure in Heart

GORTON. S. M.

St. 1, 3, JOHN KEBLE, 1819
St. 2, 4, Mitre Hymn Book, 1835

Arranged from BEETHOVEN, 1807

1. Blest are the pure in heart, For they shall see their God;
2. The Lord Who left the sky Our life and peace to bring,
3. He to the low - ly soul Doth still Him - self im - part,
4. Lord, we Thy pres-ence seek, Ours may this bless - ing be;

The se - cret of the Lord is theirs, Their soul is Christ's a - bode.
And dwell in low - li - ness with men, Their Pat-tern and their King;
And for His dwell-ing and His throne Choos-eth the pure in heart.
Give us the pure and low - ly heart, A tem-ple meet for Thee! A-MEN.

O Love That Wilt Not Let Me Go 275

ST. MARGARET. 8 8, 8 8 6.

GEORGE MATHESON, 1882   ALBERT L. PEACE, 1885

1. O Love that wilt not let me go,   I rest my wea-ry soul in
2. O Light that follow-est all my way,   I yield my flick-'ring torch to
3. O Joy that seek-est me thro' pain,   I can-not close my heart to
4. O Cross that lift-est up my head,   I dare not ask to fly from

Thee;   I give Thee back the life I owe,
Thee;   My heart re-stores its bor-rowed ray,
Thee;   I trace the rain-bow thro' the rain,
Thee;   I lay in dust life's glo-ry dead,

That in Thine o-cean depths its flow May rich - er, full - er be.
That in Thy sun-shine's blaze its day May bright-er, fair - er be.
And feel the prom-ise is not vain That morn shall tear - less be.
And from the ground there blossoms red Life that shall end - less be. A-MEN.

276   Saviour! Thy Dying Love

SOMETHING FOR THEE.   6 5, 6 4, 6 6 6, 4.

S. D. PHELPS, 1862   ROBERT LOWRY, 1872

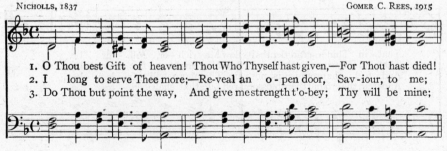

1. Sav-iour! Thy dy - ing love Thou gav - est me,   Nor should I aught with-hold,
2. Give me a faith-ful heart, Like-ness to Thee,   That each de-part-ing day
3. All that I am and have, Thy gifts so free,   Ev - er in joy or grief,

Dear Lord, from Thee; In love my soul would bow, My heart ful -
Hence-forth may see   Some work of love be - gun, Some deed of
My Lord, for Thee;   And when Thy face I see,   My ran-somed

fil   its vow, Some off-'ring bring Thee now, Some-thing for Thee.
kind-ness done, Some wan-d'rer sought and won, Some-thing for Thee.
soul shall be, Through all e - ter - ni - ty,   Some-thing for Thee. A-MEN.

Copyright, 1890, by Robert Lowry. Renewal. Used by permission

277   O Thou Best Gift of Heaven

RESOLVEN. 6 6 4, 6 6 4.

NICHOLLS, 1837   GOMER C. REES, 1915

1. O Thou best Gift of heaven! Thou Who Thyself hast given,—For Thou hast died!
2. I   long to serve Thee more;—Re-veal an o - pen door, Sav-iour, to me;
3. Do Thou but point the way, And give me strength t'o-bey; Thy will be mine;

This hast Thou done for me; What have I done for Thee, Thou Cru-ci-fied?
Then, count-ing all but loss, I'll glo-ry in Thy Cross, And fol-low Thee.
Then can I think it joy To suf-fer or to die, Since I am Thine. A-MEN.

Take My Life, and Let it Be 278

HENDON. 77, 77.

FRANCES R. HAVERGAL, 1874

H. A. C. MALAN, 1827

1. Take my life, and let it be   Con - se - crat - ed, Lord, to Thee;
2. Take my hands, and let them move   At the im - pulse of Thy love;
3. Take my voice, and let me sing   Al - ways, on - ly, for my King;
4. Take my sil - ver and my gold,   Not a mite would I with - hold;

Take my mo - ments and my days,   Let them flow in
Take my feet, and let them be   Swift and beau - ti -
Take my lips, and let them be   Filled with mes - sa -
Take my in - tel - lect, and use   Ev - 'ry power as

cease - less praise,   Let them flow in   cease - less praise.
ful for Thee,   Swift and beau - ti -   ful for Thee.
ges from Thee,   Filled with mes - sa -   ges from Thee.
Thou shalt choose,   Ev - 'ry power as   Thou shalt choose. A-MEN.

5 Take my will and make it Thine;
  It shall be no longer mine;
  Take my heart, it is Thine own;
  It shall be Thy royal throne.

6 Take my love; my Lord, I pour
  At Thy feet its treasured store;
  Take myself, and I will be,
  Ever, only, all, for Thee.

279 Lord, Speak to Me, That I May Speak

CANONBURY. L. M.

FRANCES R. HAVERGAL, 1872   Arranged from ROBERT SCHUMANN, 1839

1. Lord, speak to me, that I may speak In liv-ing ech-oes of Thy tone;
2. O lead me, Lord, that I may lead The wan-d'ring and the wav-'ring feet;
3. O strength-en me, that, while I stand Firm on the Rock, and strong in Thee,

As Thou hast sought, so let me seek Thy err-ing chil-dren lost and lone.
O feed me, Lord, that I may feed Thy hun-g'ring ones with man-na sweet.
I may stretch out a lov-ing hand To wrest-lers with the trou-bled sea. A-MEN.

4 O teach me, Lord, that I may teach
   The precious things Thou dost impart;
And wing my words, that they may reach
   The hidden depths of many a heart.

5 O give Thine own sweet rest to me,
   That I may speak with soothing power
A word in season, as from Thee,
   To weary ones in needful hour.

6 O fill me with Thy fulness, Lord,
   Until my very heart o'erflow
In kindling thought and glowing word,
   Thy love to tell, Thy praise to show.

7 O use me, Lord, use even me,
   Just as Thou wilt, and when, and where;
Until Thy blessèd face I see,
   Thy rest, Thy joy, Thy glory share.

280 We Give Thee But Thine Own

ST. GEORGE. S. M.

WM. W. HOW, c. 1858   HENRY J. GAUNTLETT, 1852

1. We give Thee but Thine own, What-e'er the gift may be;
2. May we Thy boun-ties thus As stew-ards true re-ceive,
3. O hearts are bruised and dead, And homes are bare and cold,
4. To com-fort and to bless, To find a balm for woe,

All that we have is Thine a-lone, A trust, O Lord, from Thee.
And glad-ly, as Thou bless-est us, To Thee our first-fruits give.
And lambs for whom the Shep-herd bled Are stray-ing from the fold.
To tend the lone and fa-ther-less, Is an-gels' work be-low. A-MEN.

5 The captive to release,
   The lost to God to bring,
To teach the way of life and peace,—
   It is a Christ-like thing.

6 And we believe Thy word,
   Though dim our faith may be;
Whate'er for Thine we do, O Lord,
   We do it unto Thee.

May We Thy Precepts, Lord, Fulfil   281

MERIBAH. 8 8 6. D.

EDWARD OSLER, 1836, a.   LOWELL MASON, 1839

1. May we Thy pre-cepts, Lord, ful-fil, And do on earth our Fa-ther's will,
2. So may we join Thy Name to bless, Thy grace a-dore, Thy power con-fess,
3. Spir-it of life, of love and peace, U - nite our hearts, our joy in-crease,

As an-gels do a-bove; Still walk in Christ, the liv-ing Way,
From sin and strife to flee; One is our call-ing, one our name,
Thy gra-cious help sup-ply; To each of us the bless-ing give,

With all Thy chil-dren, and o-bey The law of Chris-tian love.
The end of all our hopes the same: A crown of life with Thee.
In Chris-tian fel-low-ship to live, In joy-ful hope to die. A-MEN.

282 Come, Let Us Join with Faithful Souls

MEDFIELD. C. M.

WM. G. TARRANT, 1892

WILLIAM MATHER (1756–1808)

1. Come, let us join with faith-ful souls Our song of faith to sing,
2. Faith-ful are all who love the truth And dare the truth to tell,
3. And faith-ful are the gen-tle hearts, To whom the power is given
4. O Lord of hosts, our faith re-new, And grant us, in Thy love,

One broth-er-hood in heart are we, And one our Lord and King.
Who stead-fast stand at God's right hand, And strive to serve Him well.
Of ev-'ry hearth to make a home, Of ev-'ry home a heaven.
To sing the songs of vic-to-ry With faith-ful souls a-bove. A-MEN.

283 O Lord of Heaven and Earth and Sea

ALMSGIVING. 8 8 8, 4.

CHRISTOPHER WORDSWORTH, 1863

JOHN B. DYKES, 1865

1. O Lord of heaven and earth and sea, To Thee all praise and glo-ry be;
2. The gold-en sun-shine, ver-nal air, Sweet flowers and fruit Thy love de-clare,
3. For peace-ful homes, and health-ful days, For all the bless-ings earth dis-plays,
4. Thou didst not spare Thine on-ly Son, But gav'st Him for a world un-done,

How shall we show our love to Thee, Who giv-est all?
When har-vests rip-en, Thou art there, Who giv-est all.
We owe Thee thank-ful-ness and praise, Who giv-est all.
And free-ly with that bless-ed One, Thou giv-est all. A-MEN.

5 Thou giv'st the Holy Spirit's dower,
Spirit of life and love and power,
And dost His sevenfold graces shower
Upon us all.

6 For souls redeemed, for sins forgiven,
For means of grace and hopes of heaven,
Father, what can to Thee be given,
Who givest all?

7 We lose what on ourselves we spend;
We have as treasure without end
Whatever, Lord, to Thee we lend,
Who givest all.

8 To Thee, from Whom we all derive
Our life, our gifts, our power to give,
O may we ever with Thee live,
Who givest all.

Jesus, Master, Whose I Am 284

ST. CHRYSOSTOM. 77,77,77.

FRANCES R. HAVERGAL, 1865

J. F. OHL, 1910

1. Je-sus, Mas-ter, Whose I am, Pur-chased, Thine a-lone to be,
2. Oth-er lords have long held sway; Now, Thy Name a-lone to bear,
3. Je-sus, Mas-ter, I am Thine: Keep me faith-ful, keep me near;
4. Je-sus, Mas-ter, Whom I serve, Though so fee-bly and so ill,

By Thy Blood, O spot-less Lamb, Shed so will-ing-ly for me,
Thy dear voice a-lone o-bey, Is my dai-ly, hour-ly prayer:
Let Thy pres-ence in me shine, All my home-ward way to cheer.
Strength-en hand and heart and nerve All Thy bid-ding to ful-fill;

Let my heart be all Thine own, Let me live for Thee a-lone.
Whom have I in heaven but Thee? Noth-ing else my joy can be.
Je-sus, at Thy feet I fall, O be Thou my All in all.
O-pen Thou mine eyes to see All the work Thou hast for me. A-MEN.

5 Lord, Thou needest not, I know,
Service such as I can bring;
Yet I long to prove and show
Full allegiance to my King.
Thou an honor art to me;
Let me be a praise to Thee.

6 Jesus, Master, wilt Thou use
One who owes Thee more than all?
As Thou wilt! I would not choose;
Only let me hear Thy call.
Jesus, let me always be
In Thy service glad and free.

285 I Love to Tell the Story

HANKEY. 7 6, 7 6. D. With Refrain.

KATHERINE HANKEY, 1865   WILLIAM G. FISCHER, 1869

1. I love to tell the sto - ry Of un - seen things a - bove,
2. I love to tell the sto - ry; More won - der - ful it seems
3. I love to tell the sto - ry; 'Tis pleas - ant to re - peat
4. I love to tell the sto - ry; For those who know it best

Of Je - sus and his glo - ry, Of Je - sus and His love.
Than all the gold - en fan - cies Of all our gold - en dreams.
What seems, each time I tell it, More won - der - ful - ly sweet.
Seem hun - ger - ing and thirst - ing To hear it, like the rest.

I love to tell the sto - ry, Be - cause I know 'tis true;
I love to tell the sto - ry, It did so much for me;
I love to tell the sto - ry, For some have nev - er heard
And when, in scenes of glo - ry, I sing the new, new song,

It sat - is - fies my long - ings As noth - ing else could do.
And that is just the rea - son I tell it now to thee.
The mes - sage of sal - va - tion From God's own ho - ly word.
'Twill be the old, old sto - ry That I have loved so long.

REFRAIN

I love to tell the sto - ry, 'Twill be my theme in glo - ry,

To tell the old, old sto - ry Of Je - sus and His love. A-MEN.

Awake, My Soul, Stretch Every Nerve 286

CHRISTMAS. C. M.

PHILIP DODDRIDGE, d. 1751   Arranged from GEORG F. HANDEL, 1728

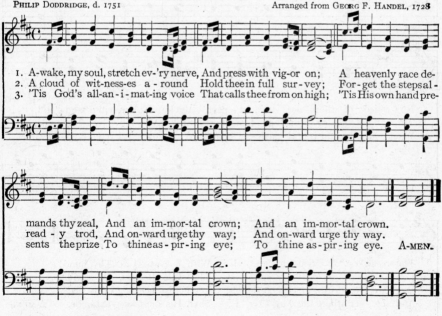

1. A-wake, my soul, stretch ev-'ry nerve, And press with vig-or on; A heavenly race de-
2. A cloud of wit-ness-es a - round Hold thee in full sur-vey; For-get the steps al -
3. 'Tis God's all-an-i-mat-ing voice That calls thee from on high; 'Tis His own hand pre-

mands thy zeal, And an im-mor-tal crown; And an im-mor-tal crown.
read - y trod, And on-ward urge thy way; And on-ward urge thy way.
sents the prize To thine as-pir-ing eye; To thine as-pir-ing eye. A-MEN.

4 That prize with peerless glories bright,
    Which shall new lustre boast
When victors' wreaths and monarchs' gems
    Shall blend in common dust.

5 Blest Saviour, introduced by Thee,
    Have I my race begun;
And crowned with victory, at Thy feet
    I'll lay my honors down.

287 How Blessed, from the Bonds of Sin

ST. LEONARD. C. M. D.

Karl Johann P. Spitta, 1833
Tr. Jane Borthwick, 1853

Henry Hiles, 1867

1. How bless-ed, from the bonds of sin   And earth-ly fet-ters free,
2. With will-ing heart and long-ing eyes   To watch be-fore Thy gate,
3. Thus may we serve Thee, gra-cious Lord! Thus ev-er Thine a-lone,
4. How hap-pi-ly the work-ing days   In this dear serv-ice fly!

In sin-gle-ness of heart and aim   Thy serv-ant, Lord, to be!
Read-y to run the wea-ry race,   To bear the heav-y weight;
Our souls and bod-ies given to Thee,   The pur-chase Thou hast won;
How rap-id-ly the clos-ing hour,   The time of rest, draws nigh!

The hard-est toil to un-der-take   With joy at Thy com-mand,
No voice of thun-der to ex-pect,   But fol-low, calm and still,
Through e-vil or through good re-port   Still keep-ing by Thy side,
When all the faith-ful gath-er home,   A joy-ful com-pa-ny,

The mean-est of-fice to re-ceive   With meek-ness at Thy hand!
For love can eas-i-ly di-vine   The One Be-lov-ed's will.
By life or death, in this poor flesh   Let Christ be mag-ni-fied!
And ev-er where the Mas-ter is,   Shall His blest serv-ants be.   A-men.

O Master, Let Me Walk With Thee   288

SAXBY. L. M.

WASHINGTON GLADDEN, 1879

TIMOTHY R. MATTHEWS, 1883

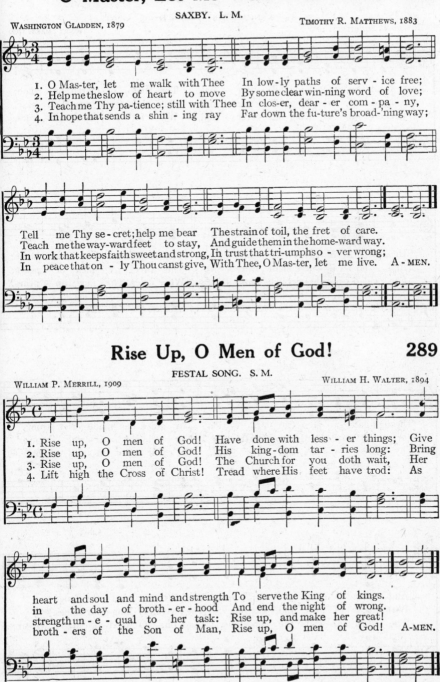

1. O Mas-ter, let me walk with Thee   In low-ly paths of serv-ice free;
2. Help me the slow of heart to move   By some clear win-ning word of love;
3. Teach me Thy pa-tience; still with Thee   In clos-er, dear-er com-pa-ny,
4. In hope that sends a shin-ing ray   Far down the fu-ture's broad-'ning way;

Tell me Thy se-cret; help me bear   The strain of toil, the fret of care.
Teach me the way-ward feet to stay,   And guide them in the home-ward way.
In work that keeps faith sweet and strong, In trust that tri-umphs o-ver wrong;
In peace that on-ly Thou canst give, With Thee, O Mas-ter, let me live.   A-MEN.

Rise Up, O Men of God!   289

FESTAL SONG. S. M.

WILLIAM P. MERRILL, 1909

WILLIAM H. WALTER, 1894

1. Rise up, O men of God!   Have done with less-er things;   Give
2. Rise up, O men of God!   His king-dom tar-ries long: Bring
3. Rise up, O men of God!   The Church for you doth wait,   Her
4. Lift high the Cross of Christ!   Tread where His feet have trod: As

heart and soul and mind and strength To serve the King of kings.
in the day of broth-er-hood And end the night of wrong.
strength un-e-qual to her task: Rise up, and make her great!
broth-ers of the Son of Man, Rise up, O men of God!   A-MEN.

290 Lead on, O King Eternal

LANCASHIRE. 7 6, 7 6. D.

ERNEST W. SHURTLEFF, 1888

HENRY SMART, 1836

1. Lead on, O King E - ter - nal, The day of march has come;
2. Lead on, O King E - ter - nal, Till sin's fierce war shall cease,
3. Lead on, O King E - ter - nal, We fol - low, not with fears,

Hence-forth in fields of con - quest Thy tents shall be our home:
And ho - li - ness shall whis - per The sweet A - men of peace;
For glad - ness breaks like morn - ing Wher - e'er Thy face ap - pears:

Through days of prep - a - ra - tion Thy grace has made us strong,
For not with swords loud clash - ing, Nor roll of stir - ring drums,
Thy Cross is lift - ed o'er us; We jour - ney in its light;

And now, O King E - ter - nal, We lift our bat - tle song.
With deeds of love and mer - cy, The heaven-ly king-dom comes.
The crown a - waits the con - quest; Lead on, O God of Might. A-MEN.

The Son of God Goes Forth to War 291

ALL SAINTS NEW. C. M. D.

REGINALD HEBER, 1812   HENRY S. CUTLER, 1872

1. The Son of God goes forth to war, A king - ly crown to gain;
2. The mar - tyr first, whose ea - gle eye Could pierce be-yond the grave,
3. A glo - rious band, the cho - sen few, On whom the Spir - it came,
4. A no - ble ar - my— men and boys, The ma - tron and the maid,

His blood - red ban - ner streams a - far;— Who fol - lows in His train?
Who saw his Mas - ter in the sky, And called on Him to save;
Twelve val-iant saints, their hope they knew, And mocked the cross and flame.
A - round the Sav-iour's throne re - joice In robes of light ar - rayed.

Who best can drink His cup of woe, Tri - umph - ant o - ver pain,
Like Him, with par - don on his tongue, In midst of mor - tal pain,
They met the ty - rant's brandished steel, The li - on's go - ry mane;
They climbed the steep as - cent of heaven Through per-il, toil, and pain!

Who pa-tient bears his cross be-low, He fol - lows in His train.
He prayed for them that did the wrong;— Who fol - lows in His train?
They bowed their necks the death to feel;— Who fol - lows in their train?
O God! to us may grace be given To fol - low in their train! A-MEN.

292   Forward! Be Our Watchword

ST. BOTOLPH.   6 5, 6 5.   12 lines.

HENRY ALFORD, 1871   HENRY SMART, 1872

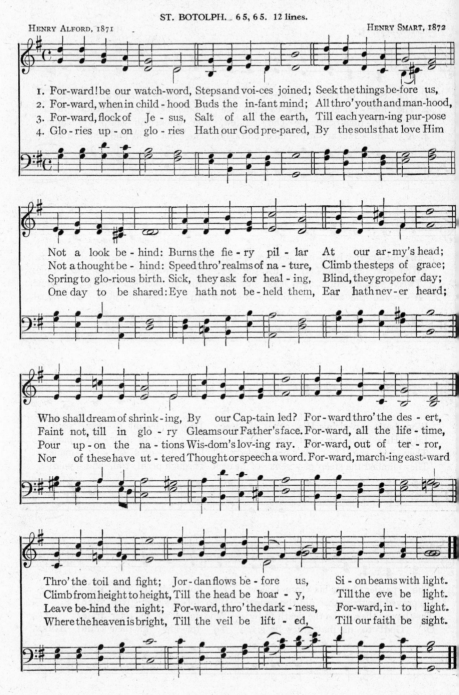

1. For-ward! be our watch-word, Steps and voi-ces joined; Seek the things be-fore us,
2. For-ward, when in child-hood Buds the in-fant mind; All thro' youth and man-hood,
3. For-ward, flock of Je-sus, Salt of all the earth, Till each yearn-ing pur-pose
4. Glo-ries up-on glo-ries Hath our God pre-pared, By the souls that love Him

Not a look be-hind: Burns the fie-ry pil-lar At our ar-my's head;
Not a thought be-hind: Speed thro' realms of na-ture, Climb the steps of grace;
Spring to glo-rious birth. Sick, they ask for heal-ing, Blind, they grope for day;
One day to be shared: Eye hath not be-held them, Ear hath nev-er heard;

Who shall dream of shrink-ing, By our Cap-tain led? For-ward thro' the des-ert,
Faint not, till in glo-ry Gleams our Father's face. For-ward, all the life-time,
Pour up-on the na-tions Wis-dom's lov-ing ray. For-ward, out of ter-ror,
Nor of these have ut-tered Thought or speech a word. For-ward, march-ing east-ward

Thro' the toil and fight; Jor-dan flows be-fore us, Si-on beams with light.
Climb from height to height, Till the head be hoar-y, Till the eve be light.
Leave be-hind the night; For-ward, thro' the dark-ness, For-ward, in-to light.
Where the heaven is bright, Till the veil be lift-ed, Till our faith be sight.

Onward, Christian Soldiers

ST. GERTRUDE. 6 5, 6 5. D. With Refrain.

S. BARING-GOULD, 1865

ARTHUR S. SULLIVAN, 1871

1. On-ward, Chris-tian sol - diers, March-ing as to war, With the Cross of
2. Like a might-y ar - my, Moves the Church of God: Broth-ers, we are
3. Crowns and thrones may per-ish, King-doms rise and wane, But the Church of
4. On-ward, then, ye faith - ful, Join our hap - py throng, Blend with ours your

Je - sus Go - ing on be - fore. Christ, the roy - al Mas - ter,
tread - ing Where the saints have trod. We are not di - vid - ed,
Je - sus Con-stant will re - main. Gates of hell can nev - er
voi - ces, In the tri-umph-song; Glo - ry, laud, and hon - or,

Leads a-gainst the foe; For-ward in - to bat - tle, See, His ban-ners go!
All one bod-y we, One in hope and doc - trine, One in char - i - ty.
'Gainst that Church pre-vail; We have Christ's own prom-ise, And that can-not fail.
Un - to Christ the King; This, thro' count-less a - ges, Men and an-gels sing.

REFRAIN

On - ward, Chris - tian sol - diers, March - ing as to war,

With the Cross of Je - sus Go - ing on be - fore. A-MEN.

294   O Christians! Leagued Together

LUTHER LEAGUE HYMN. P. M.

LILLIAN WEAVER CASSADAY, 1893
Refrain by MARGARET R. SEEBACH, 1915   GEORGE C. F. HAAS, 1893

1. O Chris-tians! leagued to-geth-er, To bat-tle for the right,
2. Then on-ward be the war-cry And on-ward still, so long
3. We proud-ly bear as ban-ner A cross with-in the heart,

A-rise and don your ar-mor, Put the foe to flight.
As we have self to con-quer, Souls to cheer with song.
To show that we have cho-sen Christ, the bet-ter part.

We've giv-en our al-le-giance, To serve with-out sur-cease
Let sound the mar-tial mu-sic, Ring out the bu-gle call
Then joy and peace and com-fort Shall blos-som as a rose,

The might-y Lord of Ar-mies And gen-tle Prince of Peace.
To ral-ly for the con-flict Our peo-ple one and all.
Un-til our earth-ly bless-ings The worth of heaven dis-close.

REFRAIN

All hail, our glo-rious Sav-iour! We march where Thou hast trod,

To seek Thy House of Tri-umph, The Cit-y of our God. A-MEN.

Soldiers of Christ, to Arms   295

NATIONAL HYMN.   10 10, 10 10.

C. ARMAND MILLER (1864–1917)   GEORGE W. WARREN, 1892

1. Sol - diers of Christ, to arms, and take your stand! Forth to the fight! Our
2. Christ is our strength; 'tis He Who makes us strong. We live in Him, to
3. Broth-ers are we, and broth-ers to our Lord; One in His life and

Cap - tain gives com-mand, Strong Son of God! He leads His
Him our lives be - long. His Church we love, His Cross is
nour - ished by His Word; One in His love Who crowns our

Church to war. We fal - ter not, while He goes on be - fore.
all our boast! Him we would praise, with all His ran-somed host!
lives with good; "Quit ye like men," be strong in broth - er - hood. A-MEN.

296   Christian, Dost Thou See Them

ST. ANDREW OF CRETE. 6 5, 6 5. D.

St. ANDREW OF CRETE, d. 732
Tr. JOHN MASON NEALE, 1862

JOHN B. DYKES, 1868

1. Chris - tian, dost thou see them   On the ho - ly ground,
2. Chris - tian, dost thou feel them,   How they work with - in,
3. Chris - tian, dost thou hear them,   How they speak thee fair:
4. Hear the words of Je - sus: "O My serv - ant true,

How the hosts of dark - ness Com - pass thee a - round?
Striv - ing, tempt - ing, lur - ing, Goad - ing in - to sin?
"Al - ways fast and vig - il? Al - ways watch and prayer?"
Thou art ver - y wea - ry,— I was wea - ry too;

Chris - tian, up and smite them, Count - ing gain but loss;
Chris - tian, nev - er trem - ble; Nev - er be down - cast;
Chris - tian, an - swer bold - ly, "While I breathe, I pray."
But that toil shall make thee Some day all Mine own,

Smite them by the mer - it Of the ho - ly Cross.
Gird thee for the bat - tle, Watch and pray and fast.
Peace shall fol - low bat - tle, Night shall end in day.
And the end of sor - row Shall be near My throne." A-MEN.

The Lord My Pasture Shall Prepare

ST. CATHERINE. 8 8, 8 8, 8 8.

JOSEPH ADDISON, 1712

HENRI F. HEMY, 1865
Altered by JAMES G. WALTON, 1871

1. The Lord my pas - ture shall pre - pare, And feed me with a
2. When in the sul - try glebe I faint, Or in the thirst - y
3. Though in a bare and rug - ged way, Through de-vious, lone - ly

shep - herd's care; His pres - ence shall my wants sup - ply,
moun - tains pant, To fer - tile vales and dew - y meads,
wilds I stray, His boun - ty shall my pains be - guile;

And guard me with a watch - ful eye: My noon - day walks He
My wea - ry, wan - d'ring steps He leads, Where peace-ful riv - ers
The bar - ren wil - der - ness shall smile, With live - ly green and

shall at - tend, And all my mid - night hours de - fend.
soft and slow, A - mid the ver - dant land - scape flow.
herb - age crowned And streams shall mur - mur all a - round. A - MEN.

298 One There is Above All Others

AMEN, JESUS HAN SKAL RAADE. 87,87,77.

JOHN NEWTON, 1779

A. P. BERGGREEN, 1849

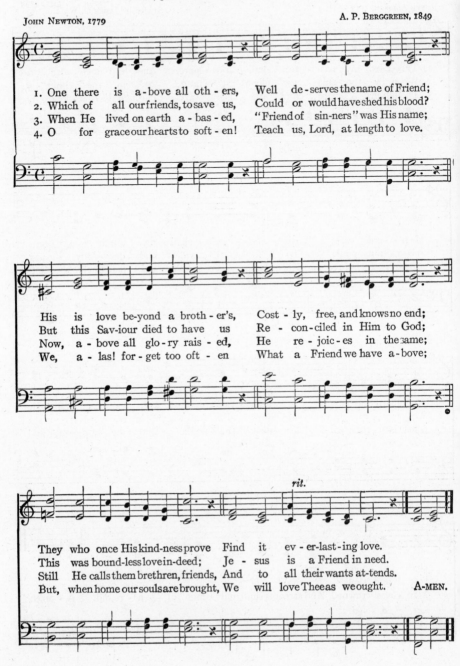

1. One there is a-bove all oth-ers, Well de-serves the name of Friend;
2. Which of all our friends, to save us, Could or would have shed his blood?
3. When He lived on earth a-bas-ed, "Friend of sin-ners" was His name;
4. O for grace our hearts to soft-en! Teach us, Lord, at length to love.

His is love be-yond a broth-er's, Cost-ly, free, and knows no end;
But this Sav-iour died to have us Re-con-ciled in Him to God;
Now, a-bove all glo-ry rais-ed, He re-joic-es in the same;
We, a-las! for-get too oft-en What a Friend we have a-bove;

rit.

They who once His kind-ness prove Find it ev-er-last-ing love.
This was bound-less love in-deed; Je-sus is a Friend in need.
Still He calls them brethren, friends, And to all their wants at-tends.
But, when home our souls are brought, We will love Thee as we ought. A-MEN.

Nearer, My God, to Thee

BETHANY. 6 4, 6 4, 6 6 4.

SARAH FOWLER ADAMS, 1841

LOWELL MASON, 1856

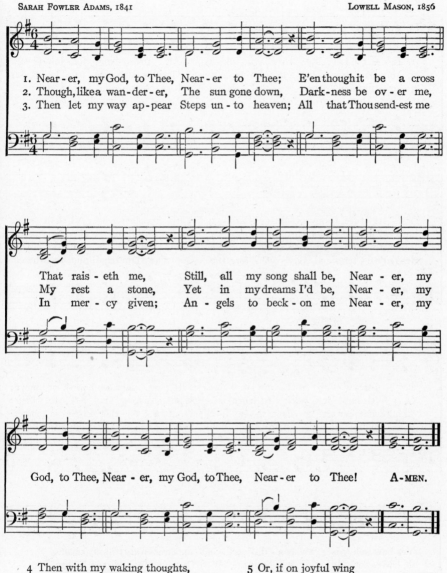

1. Near - er, my God, to Thee, Near - er to Thee; E'en though it be a cross
2. Though, like a wan - der - er, The sun gone down, Dark - ness be ov - er me,
3. Then let my way ap - pear Steps un - to heaven; All that Thou send-est me

That rais - eth me, Still, all my song shall be, Near - er, my
My rest a stone, Yet in my dreams I'd be, Near - er, my
In mer - cy given; An - gels to beck - on me Near - er, my

God, to Thee, Near - er, my God, to Thee, Near - er to Thee! A-MEN.

4 Then with my waking thoughts,
    Bright with Thy praise,
Out of my stony griefs
    Bethel I'll raise;
So by my woes to be
Nearer, my God, to Thee
    Nearer to Thee!

5 Or, if on joyful wing
    Cleaving the sky,
Sun, moon, and stars forgot,
    Upward I fly;
Still, all my song shall be,
Nearer, my God, to Thee,
    Nearer to Thee!

300   Jesus, I My Cross Have Taken

FALFIELD. 8 7, 8 7. D.

HENRY F. LYTE, 1824   ARTHUR S. SULLIVAN, 1867

1. Je - sus, I   my   cross have tak - en,   All   to leave and fol - low Thee;
2. Man may trou - ble and dis - tress me,   'Twill but drive me to Thy breast;
3. Take, my soul, thy full sal - va - tion;   Rise o'er sin, and fear, and care;
4. Haste, then, on from grace to   glo - ry,   Armed by faith and winged by prayer;

Des - ti - tute, de - spised, for - sak - en,   Thou from hence my All shalt be.
Life with tri - als hard may press me,   Heaven will bring me sweet-er rest.
Joy   to find   in ev - 'ry sta - tion,   Some-thing still to do or bear.
Heaven's e - ter - nal day's be - fore thee,   God's own hand shall guide thee there.

Per - ish ev - 'ry fond am - bi - tion,   All I've sought, or hoped, or known;
O,   'tis not   in grief   to harm me,   While Thy love is   left   to   me;
Think what Spir - it dwells with - in thee,   What a Fa - ther's smile is thine,
Soon   shall close thine earth - ly mis - sion,   Swift shall pass thy pil - grim days;

Yet how rich   is   my con - di - tion: God and heaven are still my own.
O, 'twere not   in   joy to charm me, Were that joy un - mixed with Thee.
What a Sav - iour died to win thee; Child of heaven, shouldst thou re - pine?
Hope soon change to glad fru - i - tion, Faith to sight, and prayer to praise. A-MEN.

In the Hour of Trial

PENITENCE. 6 5, 6 5. D.

JAMES MONTGOMERY, 1834
Revised by FRANCES A. HUTTON, c. 1875

SPENCER LANE, 1879

1. In the hour of tri - al, Je - sus, plead for me,
2. With for - bid - den pleas - ures Should this vain world charm
3. Should Thy mer - cy send me Sor - row, toil, and woe;
4. When my last hour com - eth, Fraught with strife and pain,

Lest by base de - ni - al, I de - part from Thee;
Or its tempt - ing treas - ures Spread, to work me harm,
Or should pain at - tend me On my path be - low;
When my dust re - turn - eth To the dust a - gain;

When Thou seest me wa - ver, With a look re - call,
Bring to my re - mem-brance Sad Geth - sem - a - ne,
Grant that I may nev - er Fail Thy hand to see;
On Thy truth re - ly - ing Thro' that mor - tal strife,

Nor for fear or fa - vor Suf - fer me to fall.
Or, in dark - er sem - blance, Cross-crowned Cal-va - ry.
Grant that I may ev - er Cast my care on Thee.
Je - sus, take me, dy - ing, To e - ter - nal life. A-MEN.

302 My Jesus, As Thou Wilt

RESIGNATION. 6 6, 6 6. D.

Benjamin Schmolk, 1704
Tr. Jane Borthwick, 1854

First Tune

J. F. Ohl, 1926

1. My Je - sus, as Thou wilt! O may Thy will be mine!
2. My Je - sus, as Thou wilt! If need - y here and poor,
3. My Je - sus, as Thou wilt! Though seen thro' many a tear,

In - to Thy hand of love I would my all re - sign.
Give me Thy peo - ple's bread, Their por - tion rich and sure.
Let not my star of hope Grow dim or dis - ap - pear;

Thro' sor - row or thro' joy Con - duct me as Thine own,
The man - na of Thy Word Let my soul feed up - on;
Since Thou on earth hast wept And sor - rowed oft a - lone,

And help me still to say: My Lord, Thy will be done!
And if all else should fail, My Lord, Thy will be done!
If I must weep with Thee, My Lord, Thy will be done! A-men.

If God Himself Be for Me

HOLY CHURCH. 7 6, 7 6. D.

PAUL GERHARDT, 1656
Tr. RICHARD MASSIE, 1857

ARTHUR H. BROWN, 1862

1. If God Him - self be for me, I may a host de - fy;
2. I build on this foun - da - tion, That Je - sus and His Blood
3. His Ho - ly Spir - it dwell - eth With - in my will - ing heart,
4. To mine His Spir - it speak - eth Sweet words of sooth - ing power,

For when I pray, be - fore me My foes con - found - ed fly.
A - lone are my sal - va - tion, The true e - ter - nal good:
Tames it when it re - bel - leth, And soothes the keen - est smart.
How God to him that seek - eth For rest, hath rest in store—

If Christ, the Head, be - friend me, If God be my sup - port,
With - out Him, all that pleas - es Is val - ue - less on earth:
He crowns His work with bless - ing, And help - eth me to cry
How God Him - self pre - par - eth My her - it - age and lot,

The mis - chief they in - tend me Shall quick - ly come to naught.
The gifts I owe to Je - sus A - lone my love are worth.
"My Fa - ther!" with - out ceas - ing To Him Who reigns on high.
And though my bod - y wear - eth, My heaven shall fail me not. A-MEN.

304 He Leadeth Me: O, Blessed Thought

HE LEADETH ME. L. M. With Refrain.

J. H. GILMORE, 1859

W. B. BRADBURY, 1864

1. He lead-eth me: O, bless-ed thought! O, words with heaven-ly com-fort fraught!
2. Some-times 'mid scenes of deep-est gloom, Some-times where E-den's bow-ers bloom,
3. Lord, I would clasp Thy hand in mine, Nor ev-er mur-mur nor re-pine;
4. And when my task on earth is done, When by Thy grace the vic-t'ry's won,

What-e'er I do, wher-e'er I be, Still 'tis God's hand that lead-eth me.
By wa-ter's calm, o'er troub-led sea,— Still 'tis His hand that lead-eth me.
Con-tent, what-ev-er lot I see, Since 'tis God's hand that lead-eth me.
E'en death's cold wave I will not flee, Since God thro' Jor-dan lead-eth me.

REFRAIN

mf   *mp*

He lead-eth me, He lead-eth me! By His own hand He lead-eth me;

His faith-ful fol-lower I would be, For by His hand He lead-eth me. A-MEN.

When Peace, Like a River, Attendeth My Way 305

11 8, 11 9. With Refrain.

H. G. SPAFFORD, 1876   PHILIP P. BLISS, 1876

1. When peace, like a riv - er, at - tend - eth my way, When sor - rows, like
2. Though Sa - tan should buf - fet, though tri - als should come, Let this blest as -
3. My sin— O, the bliss of this glo - ri - ous thought—My sin— not in
4. And, Lord, haste the day when the faith shall be sight, The clouds be rolled

sea bil - lows, roll; What - ev - er my lot, Thou hast taught me to
sur - ance con - trol, That Christ hath re - gard - ed my help - less es -
part, but the whole, Is nailed to His Cross and I bear it no
back as a scroll, The trump shall re - sound, and the Lord shall de -

REFRAIN

say, It is well, it is well with my soul.
tate, And hath shed His own blood for my soul. It is well........
more,— Praise the Lord, praise the Lord, O my soul.
scend, "E - ven so"— it is well with my soul. It is

.... with my soul,........

well   with my soul, It is well, it is well ⌈with my soul. A-MEN.

306   O Happy Home

WINDSOR. 11 10, 11 10.

CARL J. P. SPITTA, 1833
Tr. by SARAH BORTHWICK FINDLATER, 1853

JOSEPH BARNBY (1838-1896)

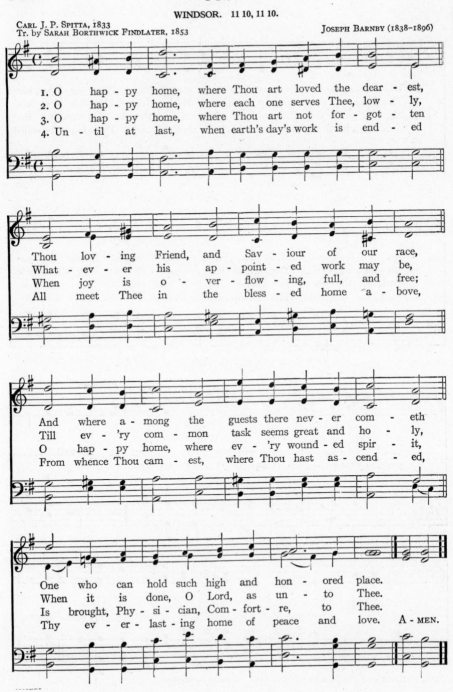

1. O hap - py home, where Thou art loved the dear - est,
Thou lov - ing Friend, and Sav - iour of our race,
And where a - mong the guests there nev - er com - eth
One who can hold such high and hon - ored place.

2. O hap - py home, where each one serves Thee, low - ly,
What - ev - er his ap - point - ed work may be,
Till ev - 'ry com - mon task seems great and ho - ly,
When it is done, O Lord, as un - to Thee.

3. O hap - py home, where Thou art not for - got - ten
When joy is o - ver - flow - ing, full, and free;
O hap - py home, where ev - 'ry wound - ed spir - it,
Is brought, Phy - si - cian, Com - fort - re, to Thee.

4. Un - til at last, when earth's day's work is end - ed
All meet Thee in the bless - ed home a - bove,
From whence Thou cam - est, where Thou hast as - cend - ed,
Thy ev - er - last - ing home of peace and love. A - MEN.

Sleep, Baby, Sleep!

SCHLAF, KINDLEIN, SCHLAF. 4, 6, 8 8, 4.

FERDINAND F. BUERMEYER, 1876

LOUISE REICHARDT (1780–1826)

1. Sleep, ba - by, sleep! Thy moth - er watch doth keep, With love that knows no wea - ri - ness, Un - tir - ing in its ten - der - ness. Sleep, ba - by, sleep!

2. Sleep, ba - by, sleep! The an - gels watch will keep, And whis - per as they hov - er nigh Of heaven-ly love be - yond the sky. Sleep, ba - by, sleep!

3. Sleep, ba - by, sleep! God grant thee slum - bers deep; And peace - ful - ly as dews of heaven Lie cra - dled in the flowers at even. Sleep, ba - by, sleep!

4. Sleep, ba - by, sleep! No wear - y watch we'll keep; When Je - sus calls us to His breast There sweet - ly we'll to - geth - er rest. Sleep, ba - by, sleep!

TIMES AND SEASONS

OPENING HYMNS

308   Open Now Thy Gates of Beauty

NEANDER. 87, 87, 77.

Benjamin Schmolck, 1732
Tr. Catherine Winkworth, 1863

Joachim Neander, 1680

1. O - pen now thy gates of beau - ty, Zi - on, let me en - ter there,
2. Gra - cious God, I come be - fore Thee, Come Thou al - so down to me;
3. Here Thy praise is glad - ly chant - ed, Here Thy seed is du - ly sown;

Where my soul, in joy - ful du - ty, Waits for Him Who an - swers prayer.
Where we find Thee and a - dore Thee, There a heaven on earth must be.
Let my soul, where it is plant - ed, Bring forth pre - cious sheaves a - lone.

O how bless - ed is this place, Filled with so - lace, light and grace!
To my heart O en - ter Thou, Let it be Thy tem - ple now.
So that all I hear may be Fruit - ful un - to life in me. A-MEN.

4 Thou my faith increase and quicken,
    Let me keep Thy gift divine;
Howsoe'er temptations thicken,
    May Thy Word still o'er me shine,
As my pole-star through my life,
As my comfort in my strife.

5 Speak, O God, and I will hear Thee,
    Let Thy will be done indeed;
May I undisturbed draw near Thee
    While Thou dost Thy people feed.
Here of life the fountain flows,
Here is balm for all our woes.

God Himself is Present

ARNSBERG. 6 6 8, D., 3 3, 6 6

GERHARD TERSTEEGEN, 1729
Tr. F. W. FOSTER and J. MILLER, 1789, a.

JOACHIM NEANDER'S *Bundes-Lieder*, 1680

1. God Him-self is pres - ent: Let us now a - dore Him. And with awe ap-
2. God Him-self is pres - ent: Hear the harps re-sound - ing! See the crowds the
3. O Thou Fount of bless - ing, Pur - i - fy my spir - it; Trust-ing on - ly

pear be - fore Him. God is in His tem - ple— All with - in keep si - lence,
throne sur-round-ing. "Ho - ly, ho - ly, ho - ly," Hear the hymn as-cend - ing,
in Thy mer - it. Like the ho - ly an - gels Who be - hold Thy glo - ry,

Pros - trate lie with deep-est rev - erence Him a - lone God we own,
An - gels, saints, their voi-ces blend - ing! Bow Thine ear To us here:
May I cease - less - ly a - dore Thee. Let Thy will Ev - er still

Him, our God and Sav - iour; Praise His Name for - ev - er.
Hear, O Christ, the prais - es That Thy Church now rais - es.
Rule Thy Church ter - res - trial, As the hosts ce - les - tial. A - MEN.

310 Father, Again in Jesus' Name We Meet

LANGRAN. 10 10, 10 10.

LUCY E. G. WHITMORE, 1824

JAMES LANGRAN, 1861

1. Fa - ther, a - gain in Je - sus' Name we meet, And bow in pen - i -
2. O we would bless Thee for Thy cease-less care, And all Thy work from
3. We are un - wor - thy of Thy bound-less love, Too oft with care - less
4. O by that Name in which all ful-ness dwells, O by that Love which

tence be-neath Thy feet: A - gain to Thee our fee - ble voi - ces raise,
day to day de - clare! Is not our life with hour - ly mer-cies crowned?
feet from Thee we rove; But now, en - cour - aged by Thy voice, we come,
ev - 'ry love ex - cels, O by that Blood so free - ly shed for sin,

To sue for mer - cy, and to sing Thy praise.
Does not Thine arm en - cir - cle us a - round?
Re - turn - ing sin - ners, to a Fa - ther's home.
O - pen blest Mer - cy's gate, and take us in. A - MEN.

311 To Thy Temple I Repair

PLEYEL'S HYMN. 77, 77.

JAMES MONTGOMERY, 1812

Arranged from IGNAZ J. PLEYEL, 1790

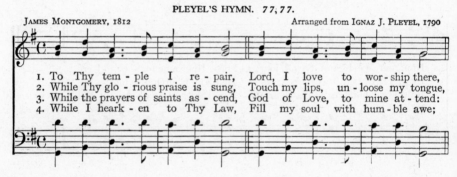

1. To Thy tem - ple I re - pair, Lord, I love to wor - ship there,
2. While Thy glo - rious praise is sung, Touch my lips, un - loose my tongue,
3. While the prayers of saints as - cend, God of Love, to mine at - tend:
4. While I heark - en to Thy Law, Fill my soul with hum - ble awe;

When, with-in the veil, I meet Christ be-fore the mer-cy-seat.
That my joy-ful soul may bless Thee, the Lord my Right-eous-ness.
Hear me for Thy Spir-it pleads; Hear, for Je-sus in-ter-cedes.
Till Thy Gos-pel bring to me Life and im-mor-tal-i-ty. A-MEN

5 While Thy ministers proclaim
Peace and pardon in Thy name,
Through their voice, by faith may I
Hear Thee speaking from the sky.

6 From Thy house when I return,
May my heart within me burn;
And at evening let me say,
I have walked with God to-day.

God of Mercy, God of Grace   312

HEATHLANDS. 77,77,77.

HENRY FRANCIS LYTE, 1834

HENRY SMART, 1867

1. God of Mer-cy, God of Grace, Show the bright-ness of Thy face;
2. Let the peo-ple praise Thee, Lord; Be by all that live a-dored;
3. Let the peo-ple praise Thee, Lord; Earth shall then her fruits af-ford:

Shine up-on us, Sav-iour, shine, Fill Thy Church with light di-vine;
Let the na-tions shout and sing Glo-ry to their Sav-iour King;
God to man His bless-ing give, Man to God de-vo-ted live;

And Thy sav-ing health ex-tend To the earth's re-mot-est end.
At Thy feet their trib-ute pay, And Thy ho-ly will o-bey.
All be-low, and all a-bove, One in joy, and light, and love. A-MEN

313   Behold Us, Lord, a Little Space

BEATITUDO. C. M.

JOHN ELLERTON, 1870

JOHN B. DYKES, 1874

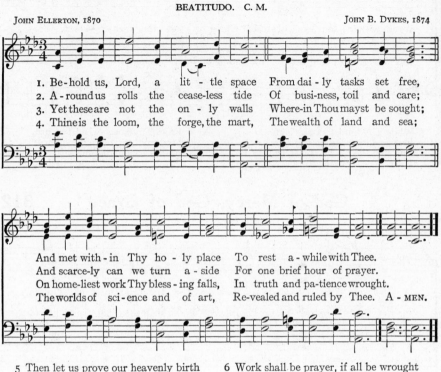

1. Be-hold us, Lord, a lit - tle space   From dai - ly tasks set free,
2. A - round us rolls the cease-less tide   Of busi-ness, toil and care;
3. Yet these are not the on - ly walls   Where-in Thou mayst be sought;
4. Thine is the loom, the forge, the mart,   The wealth of land and sea;

And met with - in Thy ho - ly place   To rest a - while with Thee.
And scarce-ly can we turn a - side   For one brief hour of prayer.
On home-liest work Thy bless - ing falls,   In truth and pa-tience wrought.
The worlds of sci - ence and of art,   Re-vealed and ruled by Thee. A - MEN.

5 Then let us prove our heavenly birth
    In all we do and know:
And claim the kingdom of the earth
    For Thee, and not Thy foe.

6 Work shall be prayer, if all be wrought
    As Thou wouldst have it done;
And prayer, by Thee inspired and taught,
    Itself with work be one.

314   Lord Jesus Christ, Be Present Now

HERR JESU CHRIST, DICH ZU UNS WEND. L. M.

WILHELM II, DUKE OF SAXE-WEIMER, 1648, 1651
Tr. CATHERINE WINKWORTH, 1863

Cantionale Sacrum, Gotha, 1651

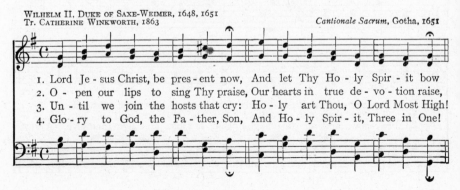

1. Lord Je - sus Christ, be pres - ent now, And let Thy Ho - ly Spir - it bow
2. O - pen our lips to sing Thy praise, Our hearts in true de - vo - tion raise,
3. Un - til we join the hosts that cry: Ho - ly art Thou, O Lord Most High!
4. Glo - ry to God, the Fa - ther, Son, And Ho - ly Spir - it, Three in One!

All hearts in love and fear to - day, To hear the truth and keep Thy way.
Strengthen our faith, increase our light, That we may know Thy Name a-right;
And 'mid the light of that blest place Shall gaze up - on Thee face to face.
To Thee, O bless-ed Trin - i - ty, Be praise through-out e - ter-ni - ty! A-MEN.

Blessed Jesus, at Thy Word   315

LIEBSTER JESU, WIR SIND HIER.   7 8, 7 8, 8 8.

TOBIAS CLAUSSNITZER, 1663
Tr. CATHERINE WINKWORTH, 1858

JOHANN R. AHLE, 1664

1. Bless - ed Je - sus, at Thy word We are gath-ered all to hear Thee;
2. All our knowl-edge, sense, and sight Lie in deep - est dark-ness shroud - ed,
3. Glo-rious Lord, Thy-self im - part! Light of Light, from God pro - ceed - ing,

Let our hearts and souls be stirred Now to seek and love and fear Thee;
Till Thy Spir - it breaks our night With the beams of truth un - cloud - ed.
O - pen Thou our ears and heart, Help us by Thy Spir - it's plead - ing,

By Thy teach-ings sweet and holy Drawn from earth to love Thee sole - ly.
Thou a - lone to God canst win us, Thou must work all good with-in us.
Hear the cry Thy peo-ple rais - es, Hear, and bless our prayers and prais-es. A-MEN.

316 Rejoice, Ye Pure in Heart

MARION. S. M. With Refrain.

EDWARD A. PLUMTRE, 1865

ARTHUR H. MESSITER, 1883

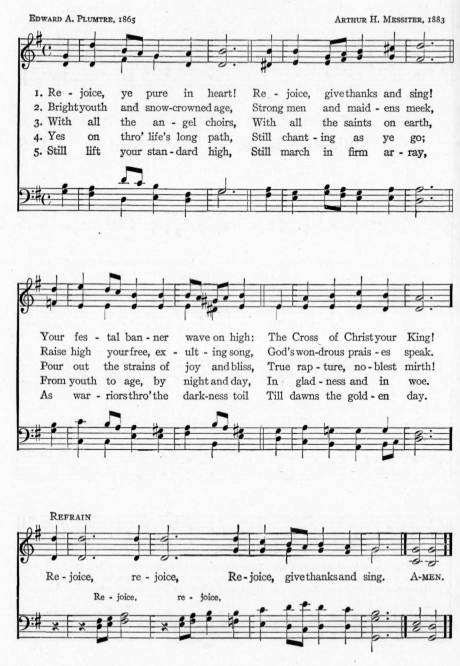

1. Re - joice, ye pure in heart! Re - joice, give thanks and sing!
2. Bright youth and snow-crowned age, Strong men and maid - ens meek,
3. With all the an - gel choirs, With all the saints on earth,
4. Yes on thro' life's long path, Still chant - ing as ye go;
5. Still lift your stan - dard high, Still march in firm ar - ray,

Your fes - tal ban - ner wave on high: The Cross of Christ your King!
Raise high your free, ex - ult - ing song, God's won-drous prais - es speak.
Pour out the strains of joy and bliss, True rap - ture, no - blest mirth!
From youth to age, by night and day, In glad - ness and in woe.
As war - riors thro' the dark-ness toil Till dawns the gold - en day.

REFRAIN

Re - joice, re - joice, Re-joice, give thanks and sing. A-MEN.

Re - joice, re - joice,

Lord, Dismiss Us With Thy Blessing 317

SICILIAN MARINERS' HYMN. 8 7, 8 7, 4 7.

Sicilian Folksong

JOHN FAWCETT ? 1773

J. MERRICK and W. D. TATTERSALL'S *Psalms,* 1794

1. Lord, dis - miss us   with Thy bless - ing, Fill our hearts with joy and peace!
2. Thanks we give and   ad - o - ra - tion For Thy Gos - pel's joy - ful sound.
3. So, when-e'er the   sig - nal's giv - en   Us from earth to   call a - way,

Let us each, Thy   love pos - sess - ing, Tri-umph in   re - deem-ing grace.
May the fruits of   Thy   sal - va - tion   In our hearts and lives a - bound;
Borne on an - gels' wings to   heav - en,   Glad the sum - mons to   o - bey,

O re - fresh us, O   re - fresh us,   Trav-'ling thro' this wil - der-ness.
Ev - er faith-ful, Ev - er faith-ful, To Thy truth may we   be found.
May we, rea - dy,   May we rea-dy,   Rise and reign in   end-less day.   A-MEN.

318   Abide With Us, Our Saviour

CHRISTUS, DER IST MEIN LEBEN. 76,76.

JOSHUA STEGMANN, 1628
Tr. UNKNOWN, 1848

MELCHIOR VULPIUS, 1609

1. A - bide with us, our Sav - iour, Nor let Thy mer - cy cease;
2. A - bide with us, our Sav - iour, Sus - tain us by Thy Word;
3. A - bide with us, our Sav - iour, Thou Light of end - less Light,

From Sa - tan's might de - fend us, And grant our souls re - lease.
That we with all Thy peo - ple To life may be re - stored.
In - crease to us Thy bless - ings, And save us by Thy might. A - MEN.

319   May the Grace of Christ Our Saviour

STUTTGART. 87,87.

Adapted from a Melody in

JOHN NEWTON, 1779

LUDWIG and WITT'S *Psalmodia Sacra*, GOTHA, 1715

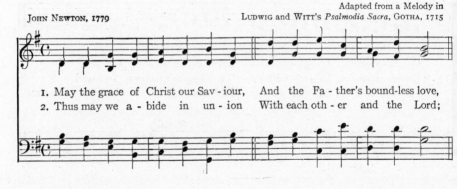

1. May the grace of Christ our Sav - iour, And the Fa - ther's bound-less love,
2. Thus may we a - bide in un - ion With each oth - er and the Lord;

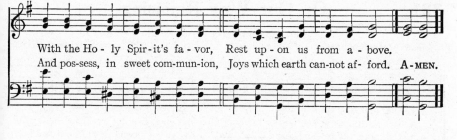

With the Ho - ly Spir-it's fa - vor, Rest up - on us from a - bove.
And pos-sess, in sweet com-mun-ion, Joys which earth can-not af- ford. A-MEN.

Saviour, Again to Thy Dear Name   320

ELLERS.   10 10, 10 10.

JOHN ELLERTON, 1866, a.   EDWARD J. HOPKINS, 1869

1. Sav - iour, a - gain   to   Thy dear Name we raise With one ac - cord our
2. Grant us Thy peace up - on our home-ward way; With Thee be - gan, with
3. Grant us Thy peace, Lord, thro' the com-ing night, Turn Thou for us   its
4. Grant us Thy peace through-out our earth-ly life, Our balm in sor - row,

part - ing hymn of praise; Once more we bless Thee   ere our wor-ship
Thee shall end the day;   Guard Thou the lips   from   sin, the hearts from
dark-ness in - to light: From harm and dan - ger keep Thy chil - dren
and our stay in strife; Then, when Thy voice shall bid our con - flict

cease, Then, low - ly bend - ing, wait Thy word of peace.
shame, That in   this house have called up - on Thy Name.
free,   For dark and light are both a - like to Thee.
cease, Call us O Lord, to Thine e - ter - nal peace. A - MEN.

321 On Our Way Rejoicing

HERMAS. 65, 65, D. With Refrain.

John S. B. Monsell, 1863

Frances R. Havergal, 1871

1. On our way re-joic-ing, As we homeward move, Hearken to our prais-es,
2. If with hon-est-heart-ed Love for God and man, Day by day Thou find us
3. On our way re-joic-ing Glad-ly let us go; Conquered hath our Lead-er,
4. Un-to God the Fa-ther Joy-ful songs we sing; Un-to God the Sav-iour

mp

O Thou God of love! Is there grief or sad-ness? Thine it can-not be!
Do-ing what we can, Thou Who giv'st the seed-time Wilt give large in-crease,
Vanquished is our foe! Christ with-out, our safe-ty, Christ with-in, our joy:
Thank-ful hearts we bring; Un-to God the Spir-it Bow we and a-dore,

cres.

REFRAIN

Is our sky be-cloud-ed? Clouds are not from Thee!
Crown the head with blessings, Fill the heart with peace. On our way re-joic-ing,
Who, if we be faith-ful, Can our hope de-stroy?
On our way re-joic-ing Now and ev-er-more!

as we homeward move, Hearken to our prais-es, O Thou God of love! A-MEN.

God Be With You Till We Meet Again 322

DEUS VOBISCUM. 9 8, 9 8. With Refrain.

JEREMIAH E. RANKIN, 1882   WILLIAM G. TOMER, 1882

1. God   be with you till we   meet a - gain,   By   His counsels guide, up-
2. God   be with you till we   meet a - gain,   'Neath His wings se-cure - ly
3. God   be with you till we   meet a - gain,   When life's per - ils thick con-
4. God   be with you till we   meet a - gain,   Keep love's ban-ner float-ing

hold   you,   With   His   sheep se - cure - ly   fold   you,
hide   you,   Dai - ly   man - na   still   di - vide   you,
found you,   Put   His   arms un - fail - ing 'round   you,
o'er   you,   Smite death's threat-ening wave be - fore   you,

REFRAIN

God   be with you till we   meet a - gain.   Till we meet,...... till we
                                            Till we meet, till we

meet,   Till we meet at Je - sus' feet,   Till we
meet a - gain,   Till we meet,

meet,...... till we meet,   God be with you till we meet a - gain.   A-MEN.
Till we meet, till we meet a - gain,

323   Safely Through Another Week

SABBATH. 77,77,77.

JOHN NEWTON, 1774 a.   LOWELL MASON, 1824

1. Safe-ly through an-oth-er week, God has brought us on our way;
2. Mer-cies mul-ti-plied each hour Through the week, our praise de-mand;
3. While we pray for pard-oning grace, Through the dear Re-deem-er's Name,

Let us now a bless-ing seek, Wait-ing in His courts to-day;
Guard-ed by Thy might-y power, Fed and guid-ed by Thy hand;
Show Thy re-con-cil-ed face, Take a-way our sin and shame;

Day of all the week the best, Em-blem of e-ter-nal rest;
Though un-grate-ful we have been, On-ly made re-turns of sin;
From our world-ly care set free, May we rest this day in Thee;

Day of all the week the best, Em-blem of e-ter-nal rest.
Though un-grate-ful we have been, On-ly made re-turns of sin.
From our world-ly cares set free, May we rest this day in Thee. A-MEN.

4 Here we come, Thy Name to praise;
   Let us feel Thy presence near;
   May Thy glory meet our eyes,
   While we in Thy house appear:
   Here afford us, Lord, a taste
   Of our everlasting feast.

5 May the Gospel's joyful sound
   Conquer sinners, comfort saints;
   Make the fruits of grace abound,
   Bring relief for all complaints.
   Thus may all our Sabbaths prove,
   Till we join the Church above.

This Day the Light of Heavenly Birth 324

LUFFENHAM. L. M.

William W. How, 1854, a.

George A. Macfarren, 1872

1. This day the light of heaven-ly birth First streamed up - on the new - born earth; O Lord, this day up - on us shine, And fill our souls with light di - vine.
2. This day the Sav - iour left the grave, And rose, om - nip - o - tent to save; O Je - sus, may we rais - ed be From death of sin to life in Thee.
3. This day the Ho - ly Spir - it came With fier - y tongues of clov - en flame; O Spir - it, fill our hearts this day With grace to hear, and grace to pray.
4. O day of light and life, and grace! From earth - ly toils sweet rest - ing - place! Thy hal - lowed hours, best gift of love, We give a - gain to God a - bove! A - MEN.

325 O Day of Rest and Gladness

DAY OF REST. 7 6, 7 6. D.

CHRISTOPHER WORDSWORTH, 1862   JAMES W. ELLIOTT, 1874

1. O day of rest and glad - ness, O day of joy and light,
2. On thee, at the cre - a - tion, The light first had its birth;
3. To - day on wea - ry na - tions The heaven - ly man - na falls;
4. New gra - ces ev - er gain - ing From this our day of rest,

O balm of care and sad - ness, Most beau - ti - ful, most bright;
On thee, for our sal - va - tion, Christ rose from depths of earth;
To ho - ly con - vo - ca - tions The sil - ver trum - pet calls,
We reach the rest re - main - ing To spir - its of the blest.

On thee the high and low - ly, Be - fore th' e - ter - nal throne,
On thee our Lord, vic - to - rious, The Spir - it sent from heaven;
Where Gos - pel light is glow - ing With pure and ra - diant beams,
To Ho - ly Ghost be prais - es, To Fa - ther, and to Son;

Voices in Unison   *In Harmony*

Sing: Ho - ly, Ho - ly, Ho - ly, To the great Three in One.
And thus on thee, most glo - rious, A tri - ple light was given.
And liv - ing wa - ter flow - ing With soul - re - fresh - ing streams.
The Church her voice up - rais - es To Thee, blest Three in One. A-MEN.

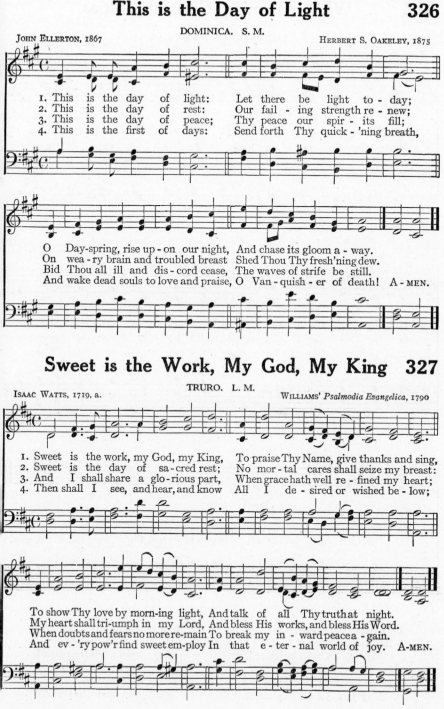

328   When Morning Gilds the Skies

LAUDES DOMINI. 6 6, 6 6, 6 6.

Anon., 1828, Tr. ROBERT BRIDGES, 1899
St. 1, vr. 1–3, EDWARD CASWALL, 1854

JOSEPH BARNBY, 1868

1. When morn - ing gilds the skies, My heart, a - wak - ing, cries:
2. When mirth for mu - sic longs, This is my song of songs:
3. No love - lier an - ti - phon In all high heaven is known

May Je - sus Christ be praised. When eve - ning shad - ows fall,
May Je - sus Christ be praised. God's ho - ly house of prayer
Than: Je - sus Christ be praised. There to th'e - ter - nal Word

This rings my cur - few call: May Je - sus Christ be praised.
Hath none that can com - pare With: Je - sus Christ be praised.
Th'e - ter - nal psalm is heard: May Je - sus Christ be praised. A-MEN.

4 Ye nations of mankind,
  In this your concord find:
    May Jesus Christ be praised.
  Let all the earth around
  Ring joyous with the sound:
    May Jesus Christ be praised.

5 Sing, suns and stars of space,
  Sing, ye that see His face,
    Sing: Jesus Christ be praised.
  God's whole creation o'er,
  For aye and evermore
    Shall Jesus Christ be praised.

Come, My Soul, Thou Must Be Waking 329

HAYDN. 8 4 7. D.

FRIEDRICH R. VON CANITZ, 1700
Tr. HENRY J. BUCKOLL, 1841, a.

Arranged from JOSEPH HAYDN, 1791

1. Come, my soul, thou must be wak-ing; Now is break-ing O'er the earth an-oth-er day, Come to Him Who made the splen-dor; See thou ren-der All thy fee-ble strength can pay.

2. Glad-ly hail the sun re-turn-ing; Read-y burn-ing Be the in-cense of thy powers; For the night is safe-ly end-ed; God hath tend-ed With His care thy help-less hours.

3. Pray that He may pros-per ev-er Each en-deav-or, When thy aim is good and true; But that He may ev-er thwart thee, And con-vert thee, When thou e-vil wouldst pur-sue. A-MEN.

4 Only God's free gift abuse not,
  Light refuse not,
  But His Spirit's voice obey;
Thou with Him shalt dwell, beholding
  Light enfolding
  All things in unclouded day.

5 Glory, honor, exaltation,
  Adoration
  Be to the Eternal One;
To the Father, Son, and Spirit,
  Laud and merit,
  While unending ages run.

330 Christ, Whose Glory Fills the Skies

GOUNOD. 77,77,77.

CHARLES WESLEY, 1740

CHARLES F. GOUNOD, 1872

1. Christ, Whose glo - ry fills the skies, Christ, the true, the on - ly Light,
2. Dark and cheer - less is the morn, Un - ac - com - pa - nied by Thee;
3. Vis - it then this soul of mine: Pierce the gloom of sin and grief;

Sun of Right - eous - ness, a - rise, Tri - umph o'er the shades of night;
Joy - less is the day's re - turn Till Thy mer - cy's beams I see:
Fill me, ra - dian - cy di - vine, Scat - ter all my un - be - lief;

Day-spring from on high, be near; Day-star, in my heart ap - pear.
Till they in - ward light im - part, Glad my eyes, and warm my heart.
More and more Thy-self dis - play, Shin - ing to the per - fect day. A-MEN.

331 O Father, Hear My Morning Prayer

EVERSLEY. C. M.

FRANCES A. PERCY, 1896

ARTHUR COTTMAN, 1875

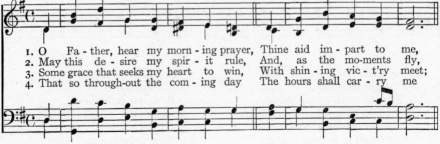

1. O Fa - ther, hear my morn - ing prayer, Thine aid im - part to me,
2. May this de - sire my spir - it rule, And, as the mo-ments fly,
3. Some grace that seeks my heart to win, With shin - ing vic - t'ry meet;
4. That so through-out the com - ing day The hours shall car - ry me

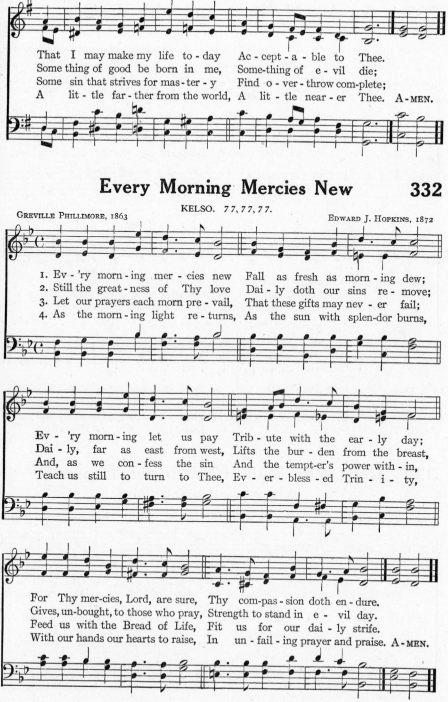

That I may make my life to-day   Ac-cept-a-ble to   Thee.
Some thing of good be born in me,   Some-thing of e-vil   die;
Some sin that strives for mas-ter-y   Find o-ver-throw com-plete;
A lit-tle far-ther from the world,   A lit-tle near-er   Thee. A-MEN.

Every Morning Mercies New   332

KELSO. 7 7, 7 7, 7 7.

GREVILLE PHILLIMORE, 1863

EDWARD J. HOPKINS, 1872

1. Ev-'ry morn-ing mer-cies new   Fall as fresh as morn-ing dew;
2. Still the great-ness of Thy love   Dai-ly doth our sins re-move;
3. Let our prayers each morn pre-vail,   That these gifts may nev-er   fail;
4. As the morn-ing light re-turns,   As the sun with splen-dor burns,

Ev-'ry morn-ing let us pay   Trib-ute with the ear-ly day;
Dai-ly, far as east from west,   Lifts the bur-den from the breast,
And, as we con-fess the sin   And the tempt-er's power with-in,
Teach us still to turn to Thee,   Ev-er-bless-ed Trin-i-ty,

For Thy mer-cies, Lord, are sure,   Thy com-pas-sion doth en-dure.
Gives, un-bought, to those who pray,   Strength to stand in e-vil day.
Feed us with the Bread of Life,   Fit us for our dai-ly strife.
With our hands our hearts to raise,   In un-fail-ing prayer and praise. A-MEN.

333 Awake, My Soul, and with the Sun

MORNING HYMN. L. M.

Thomas Ken, 1695, 1709

Françis H. Barthélémon (1741-1808)

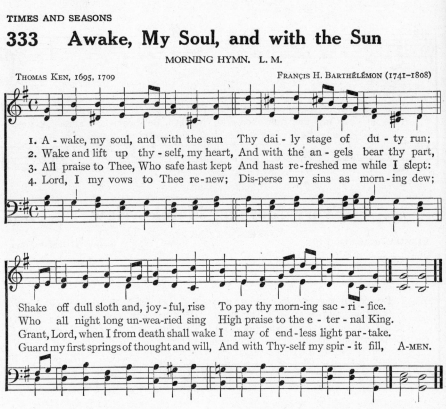

1. A - wake, my soul, and with the sun Thy dai - ly stage of du - ty run;
2. Wake and lift up thy - self, my heart, And with the an - gels bear thy part,
3. All praise to Thee, Who safe hast kept And hast re - freshed me while I slept:
4. Lord, I my vows to Thee re-new; Dis-perse my sins as morn - ing dew;

Shake off dull sloth and, joy - ful, rise To pay thy morn-ing sac - ri - fice.
Who all night long un-wea-ried sing High praise to the e - ter - nal King.
Grant, Lord, when I from death shall wake I may of end - less light par - take.
Guard my first springs of thought and will, And with Thy-self my spir - it fill, A-MEN.

5 Direct, control, suggest, this day,
All I design, or do, or say,
That all my powers, with all their might,
In Thy sole glory may unite.

6 Praise God, from whom all blessings flow;
Praise Him, all creatures here below;
Praise Him above, ye heavenly host;
Praise Father, Son, and Holy Ghost.

334 God, Who Madest Earth and Heaven

GOTT DES HIMMELS. 8 7, 8 7, 7 7.

Heinrich Albert, 1643; Tr. John Christian Jacobi, 1720
Arthur Tozer Russell, 1848. Catherine Winkworth, 1855

Heinrich Albert, 1642

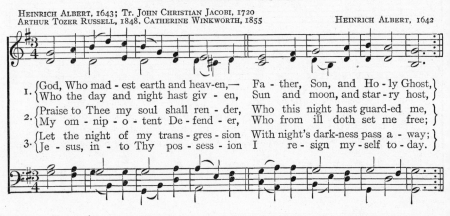

1. {God, Who mad - est earth and heav-en,— Fa - ther, Son, and Ho - ly Ghost,}
   {Who the day and night hast giv - en, Sun and moon, and star - ry host,}
2. {Praise to Thee my soul shall ren - der, Who this night hast guard-ed me,}
   {My om - nip - o - tent De - fend - er, Who from ill doth set me free;}
3. {Let the night of my trans - gres - sion With night's dark-ness pass a - way;}
   {Je - sus, in - to Thy pos - sess - ion I re - sign my-self to - day.}

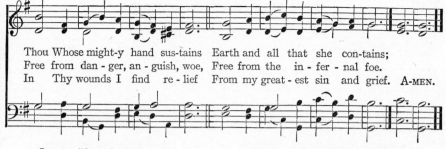

Thou Whose might-y hand sus-tains Earth and all that she con-tains;
Free from dan - ger, an - guish, woe, Free from the in - fer - nal foe.
In Thy wounds I find re - lief From my great - est sin and grief. A-MEN.

4 Let my life and conversation
   Be directed by Thy Word;
Lord, Thy constant preservation
   To Thy erring child afford.
Nowhere but alone in Thee
From all harm can I be free.

5 Wholly to Thy blest protection
   I commit my heart and mind;
Mighty God! to Thy direction
   Wholly may I be resigned.
Lord, my Shield, my Light divine,
O accept, and own me Thine!

Forth in Thy Name, O Lord, I Go   335

CANONBURY. L. M.

CHARLES WESLEY, 1749

Arranged from ROBERT SCHUMANN, 1839

1. Forth in Thy Name, O Lord, I go, My dai-ly la-bor to pur-sue,
2. The task Thy wis-dom hath as-signed, O, let me cheer-ful-ly ful-fill;
3. Thee may I set at my right hand, Whose eyes my in-most sub-stance see,

Thee, on-ly Thee, re-solved to know In all I think, or speak, or do.
In all my works Thy pres-ence find, And prove Thy good and per-fect will.
And la-bor on at Thy com-mand, And of-fer all my works to Thee. A-MEN.

4 Give me to bear Thy easy yoke,
   And every moment watch and pray,
And still to things eternal look,
   And hasten to Thy glorious day;

5 For Thee delightfully employ
   Whate'er Thy bounteous grace hath given,
And run my course with even joy,
   And closely walk with Thee to heaven.

336   Evening and Morning

DIE GÜLDNE SONNE. 5 5, 5 5, 10, 5 6, 5 6, 10.

Paul Gerhardt, 1666
Tr. Richard Massie, 1857

Johann G. Ebeling, 1666

1. Eve-ning and morn - ing,   Sun - set and dawn - ing,   Wealth, peace, and glad-ness,
2. Fa - ther, O hear me: Par-don and spare me;   Calm all my ter - rors,
3. Griefs of God's send - ing   Soon have an end - ing;   Clouds may be pour - ing,

Com - fort in sad - ness, These are Thy works; all the glo - ry be Thine!
Blot out my er - rors, That by Thine eyes they may no more be scanned.
Wind and wave roar - ing; Sun-shine will come when the tem - pest has past.

Times with-out num-ber, A - wake or in slum - ber, Thine eye ob-serves us,
Or - der my go-ings; Di - rect all my do-ings; As it may please Thee,
Joys still in - creas - ing, And peace nev - er ceas - ing, Foun-tains that dry not,

From dan-ger pre-serves us, Caus - ing Thy mer - cy up - on us to shine.
Re - tain or re - lease me; All I com - mit to Thy Fa-ther-ly hand.
And ros - es that die not, Bloom-ing in E - den, a - wait me at last. A-MEN.

Now the Light Has Gone Away

MÜDE BIN ICH, GEH ZUR RUH. 7 7, 7 7.

FRANCES R. HAVERGAL, 1869   FLIEDNER's *Liederbuch für Kleinkinder-Schulen*, 1842

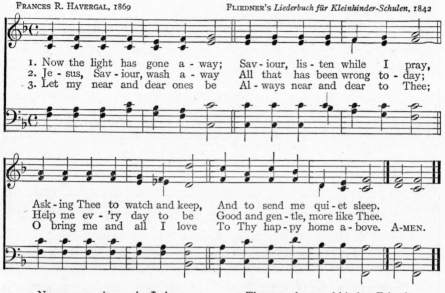

1. Now the light has gone a - way; Sav - iour, lis - ten while I pray,
2. Je - sus, Sav - iour, wash a - way All that has been wrong to - day;
3. Let my near and dear ones be Al - ways near and dear to Thee;

Ask - ing Thee to watch and keep, And to send me qui - et sleep.
Help me ev - 'ry day to be Good and gen - tle, more like Thee.
O bring me and all I love To Thy hap - py home a - bove. A-MEN.

4 Now my evening praise I give;
Thou didst die that I might live:
All my blessings come from Thee;
O how good Thou art to me!

5 Thou, my best and kindest Friend,
Thou wilt love me to the end;
Let me love Thee more and more,
Always better than before.

The Daylight Fades

338

EVENING. 4 4 6. D.

THOMAS O. SUMMERS, 1849   J. F. OHL, 1884

1. The day - light fades, The eve - ning shades Are gath - 'ring round my head;
2. While Thou art near, I need not fear The gloom of mid - night hour;
3. Par - don my sin, And en - ter in To sanc - ti - fy my heart;

Fa - ther a - bove, I praise that love Which night - ly guards my bed;
Blest Je - sus, still From ev - 'ry ill De - fend me with Thy power!
Spir - it Di - vine, O make me Thine, And ne'er from me de - part! A-MEN.

339 All Praise to Thee, My God, This Night

TALLIS' CANON. L. M.

Thomas Ken, 1695, 1709, a.

Thomas Tallis, 1560

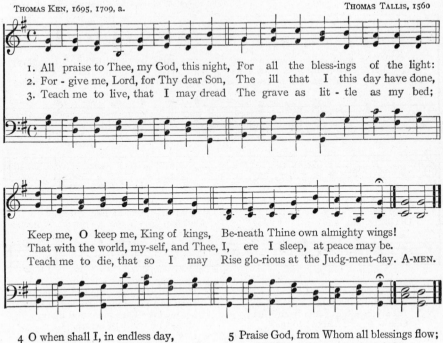

1. All praise to Thee, my God, this night, For all the bless-ings of the light:
2. For-give me, Lord, for Thy dear Son, The ill that I this day have done,
3. Teach me to live, that I may dread The grave as lit-tle as my bed;

Keep me, O keep me, King of kings, Be-neath Thine own almighty wings!
That with the world, my-self, and Thee, I, ere I sleep, at peace may be.
Teach me to die, that so I may Rise glo-rious at the Judg-ment-day. A-MEN.

4 O when shall I, in endless day,
For ever chase dark sleep away,
And hymns divine with angels sing
In endless praise to Thee, my King?

5 Praise God, from Whom all blessings flow;
Praise Him, all creatures here below;
Praise Him above, ye heavenly host;
Praise Father, Son and Holy Ghost.

340 Now the Day is Over

MERRIAL. 6 5, 6 5.

S. Baring-Gould, 1865

Joseph Barnby, 1868

1. Now the day is o - ver,
2. Now the dark-ness gath - ers,
3. Je - sus, give the wea - ry
4. Through the long night-watch-es

Night is draw-ing nigh,
Stars their watch-es keep,
Calm and sweet re - pose.
May Thine an - gels spread

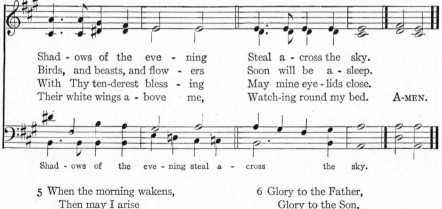

Shad - ows of the eve - ning / Steal a - cross the sky.
Birds, and beasts, and flow - ers / Soon will be a - sleep.
With Thy ten-derest bless - ing / May mine eye - lids close.
Their white wings a - bove me, / Watch-ing round my bed. A-MEN.

Shad - ows of the eve - ning steal a - cross the sky.

5 When the morning wakens,
   Then may I arise
   Pure and fresh and sinless
   In Thy holy eyes.

6 Glory to the Father,
   Glory to the Son,
   And to Thee, blest Spirit,
   Whilst all ages run.

Saviour, Breathe An Evening Blessing 341

EVENING PRAYER. 87, 87.

JAMES EDMESTON, 1820
St. 4, GODFREY THRING, 1882

GEORGE C. STEBBINS, 1878

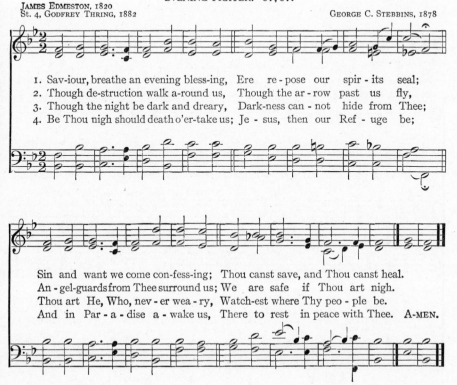

1. Sav-iour, breathe an evening bless-ing, Ere re - pose our spir - its seal;
2. Though de-struction walk a-round us, Though the ar - row past us fly,
3. Though the night be dark and dreary, Dark-ness can - not hide from Thee;
4. Be Thou nigh should death o'er-take us; Je - sus, then our Ref - uge be;

Sin and want we come con-fess-ing; Thou canst save, and Thou canst heal.
An - gel-guards from Thee surround us; We are safe if Thou art nigh.
Thou art He, Who, nev - er wea - ry, Watch-est where Thy peo - ple be.
And in Par - a - dise a - wake us, There to rest in peace with Thee. A-MEN.

342 O Light, O Trinity Most Blest!

GRACE CHURCH. L. M.

Latin Hymn, VII Century
Tr. Composite, 1890

Arranged from IGNAZ J. PLEYEL, 1815

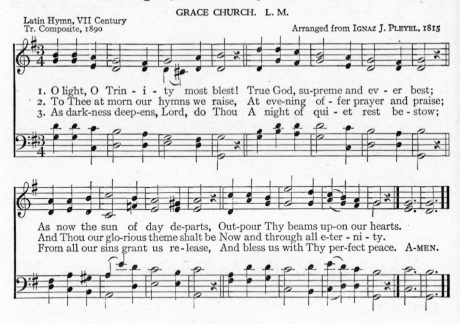

1. O light, O Trin - i - ty most blest! True God, su-preme and ev - er best;
2. To Thee at morn our hymns we raise, At eve-ning of - fer prayer and praise;
3. As dark-ness deep-ens, Lord, do Thou A night of qui - et rest be - stow;

As now the sun of day de-parts, Out-pour Thy beams up-on our hearts.
And Thou our glo-rious theme shalt be Now and through all e-ter - ni - ty.
From all our sins grant us re - lease, And bless us with Thy per-fect peace. A-MEN.

343 Sun of My Soul, Thou Saviour Dear

HURSLEY. L. M.

JOHN KEBLE, 1820

Adapted from melody in *Katholisches Gesangbuch*, Vienna, c. 1774

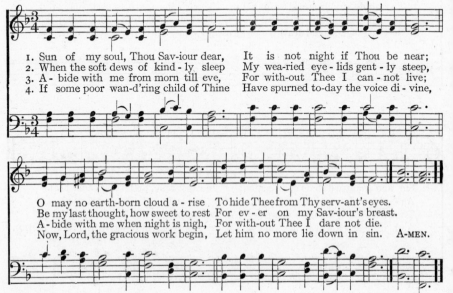

1. Sun of my soul, Thou Sav-iour dear, It is not night if Thou be near;
2. When the soft dews of kind - ly sleep My wea-ried eye - lids gent - ly steep,
3. A - bide with me from morn till eve, For with-out Thee I can - not live;
4. If some poor wan-d'ring child of Thine Have spurned to-day the voice di - vine,

O may no earth-born cloud a - rise To hide Thee from Thy serv-ant's eyes.
Be my last thought, how sweet to rest For ev - er on my Sav-iour's breast.
A - bide with me when night is nigh, For with-out Thee I dare not die.
Now, Lord, the gracious work begin, Let him no more lie down in sin. A-MEN.

5 Watch by the sick; enrich the poor
  With blessings from Thy boundless store;
  Be every mourner's sleep to-night
  Like infant's slumbers, pure and light.

6 Come near and bless us when we wake,
  Ere through the world our way we take;
  Till in the ocean of Thy love
  We lose ourselves in heaven above.

The Day is Past and Over   344

ST. ANATOLIUS. 7 6, 7 6, 8 8.

ANATOLIUS, c. VIII Century
Tr. JOHN MASON NEALE, 1862

JOHN B. DYKES, 1862

1. The day is past and o-ver; All thanks, O Lord, to Thee!
2. The joys of day are o-ver; I lift my heart to Thee,
3. The toils of day are o-ver; I lift my heart to Thee,
4. Be Thou my soul's Pre-serv-er, O God, for Thou dost know

I pray Thee that of-fence-less The hours of dark may be.
And call on Thee that sin-less The hours of gloom may be.
And ask that free from per-il The hours of gloom may be.
How ma-ny are the per-ils Thro' which I have to go.

O Je-sus, keep me in Thy sight, And guard me thro' the com-ing night!
O Je-sus, make their dark-ness light, And save me thro' the com-ing night.
O Je-sus, make their dark-ness light, And guard me thro' the com-ing night!
Lov-er of men, O hear my call, And guard and save me from them all! A-MEN.

345 God, That Madest Earth and Heaven

CHORAL EVENING HYMN. 8 4, 8 4, 8 8 8, 4.

REGINALD HEBER, d.1827
St. 2, RICHARD WHATELY, 1838

JAMES TILLEARD (1827–1876)

1. God, that mad-est earth and heav-en, Dark-ness and light;
2. And when morn a-gain shall call us To run life's way.
3. Guard us wak-ing, guard us sleep-ing, And, when we die,

Who the day for toil hast giv-en, For rest the night;
May we till, what-e'er be-fall us, Thy will o-bey.
May we in Thy might-y keep-ing All peace-ful lie.

May Thine an-gel-guards de-fends us, Slum-ber sweet Thy mer-cy send us,
From the power of e-vil hide us, In the nar-row path-way guide us,
When the last dread call shall wake us, Do not Thou, our Lord, for-sake us,

Ho-ly dreams and hopes at-tend us, This live-long night.
Nor Thy smile be e'er de-nied us, The live-long day.
But to reign in glo-ry take us, With Thee on high. A-MEN.

Abide With Me; Fast Falls the Eventide 346

EVENTIDE. 10 10, 10 10.

HENRY F. LYTE, 1847

WILLIAM H. MONK, 1861

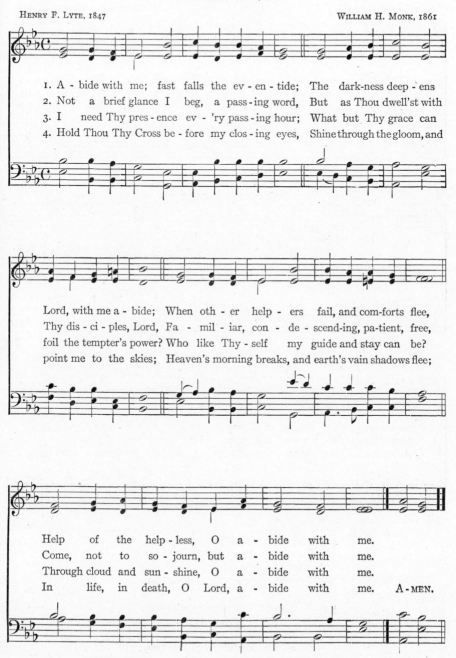

1. A - bide with me; fast falls the ev - en - tide; The dark-ness deep - ens Lord, with me a - bide; When oth - er help - ers fail, and com-forts flee, Help of the help - less, O a - bide with me.

2. Not a brief glance I beg, a pass-ing word, But as Thou dwell'st with Thy dis - ci - ples, Lord, Fa - mil - iar, con - de - scend-ing, pa-tient, free, Come, not to so - journ, but a - bide with me.

3. I need Thy pres - ence ev - 'ry pass-ing hour; What but Thy grace can foil the tempter's power? Who like Thy - self my guide and stay can be? Through cloud and sun - shine, O a - bide with me.

4. Hold Thou Thy Cross be - fore my clos - ing eyes, Shine through the gloom, and point me to the skies; Heaven's morning breaks, and earth's vain shadows flee; In life, in death, O Lord, a - bide with me. A - MEN.

347 The Day Thou Gavest, Lord, is Ended

ST. CLEMENT. 98, 98.

JOHN ELLERTON, 1870 · CLEMENT C. SCHOLEFIELD, 1874

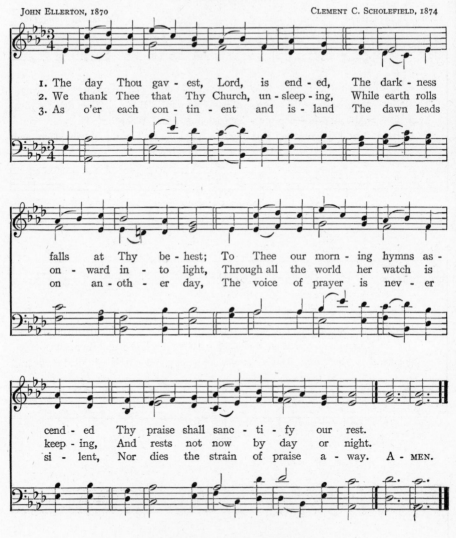

1. The day Thou gav - est, Lord, is end - ed, The dark - ness falls at Thy be - hest; To Thee our morn - ing hymns as - cend - ed Thy praise shall sanc - ti - fy our rest.

2. We thank Thee that Thy Church, un - sleep - ing, While earth rolls on - ward in - to light, Through all the world her watch is keep - ing, And rests not now by day or night.

3. As o'er each con - tin - ent and is - land The dawn leads on an - oth - er day, The voice of prayer is nev - er si - lent, Nor dies the strain of praise a - way. A - MEN.

4 The sun that bids us rest is waking
Our brethren 'neath the western sky,
And hour by hour fresh lips are making
Thy wondrous doings heard on high.

5 So be it, Lord; Thy throne shall never,
Like earth's proud empires, pass away;
Thy kingdom stands, and grows for ever,
Till all Thy creatures own Thy sway.

Day is Dying in the West

CHATAUQUA. 7 7, 7 7, 4. With Refrain.

MARY A. LATHBURY, 1877

WM. F. SHERWIN, 1877

1. Day is dy-ing in the west; Heaven is touch-ing earth with rest;
2. Lord of life, be-neath the dome Of the U - ni-verse, Thy home,

Wait and wor-ship while the night Sets her eve-ning lamps a-light
Gath-er us who seek Thy face To the fold of Thy em-brace,

REFRAIN

Through all the sky. Ho-ly, ho-ly, ho-ly, Lord God of
For Thou art nigh.

Hosts! Heaven and earth are full of Thee! Heaven and earth are

prais-ing Thee, O Lord most high! A - MEN.

349 Great God! We Sing Thy Mighty Hand

DUKE STREET. L. M.

PHILIP DODDRIDGE, d. 1751

JOHN HATTON, 1793

1. Great God! we sing Thy might - y   Hand   By which, sup-port-ed still, we stand;
2. By   day, by night, at home, a - broad,   Still we are guard - ed by our God;
3. With grate-ful hearts the past we   own;   The fu - ture, all to us   un - known,

The opening year Thy mer - cy   shows; Let mercy crown it till   it   close.
By His in - ces - sant boun - ty   fed,   By His un-err - ing coun-sel   led.
We to Thy guard-ian care com - mit,   And, peaceful, leave before Thy feet. A - MEN.

350   For Thy Mercy and Thy Grace

CULBACH. 77, 77.

HENRY DOWNTON, 1841

SCHEFFLER'S *Helige Seelenlust*, 1657

1. For Thy mer - cy and Thy   grace,   Con-stant through an - oth - er   year,
2. In   our weak - ness and dis - stress,   Rock of strength, be Thou our   stay;
3. Who of   us death's aw - ful   road   In   the com - ing year shall tread,—
4. Keep us faith - ful; keep us   pure;   Keep us   ev - er - more Thine own;

Hear our song of thank-ful - ness,   Je - sus, our Re - deem-er, hear.
In   the path - less wil - der - ness,   Be our true and liv - ing way.
With Thy rod and staff, O God,   Com-fort Thou his dy - ing head.
Help, O help us to   en - dure;   Fit us for the prom-ised crown. A - MEN.

Another Year is Dawning

AURELIA. 7 6, 7 6. D.

FRANCES R. HAVERGAL, 1874

SAMUEL S. WESLEY, 1864

1. An - oth - er year is dawn - ing, Dear Fa - ther, let it be
2. An - oth - er year of mer - cies, Of faith - ful - ness and grace,
3. An - oth - er year of serv - ice, Of wit - ness for Thy love,

In work - ing or in wait - ing An - oth - er year with Thee;
An - oth - er year of glad - ness In the shin - ing of Thy face;
An - oth - er year of train - ing For ho - lier work a - bove;

An - oth - er year of lean - ing Up - on Thy lov - ing breast,
An - oth - er year of prog - ress, An - oth - er year of praise,
An - oth - er year is dawn - ing, Dear Fa - ther, let it be

An - oth - er year of trust - ing, Of qui - et, hap - py rest;
An - oth - er year of prov - ing Thy pres - ence all the days;
On earth, or else in heav - en, An - oth - er year for Thee. A-MEN.

352   Our God, Our Help in Ages Past

ST. ANNE. C. M.

ISAAC WATTS, 1719   WILLIAM CROFT, 1708

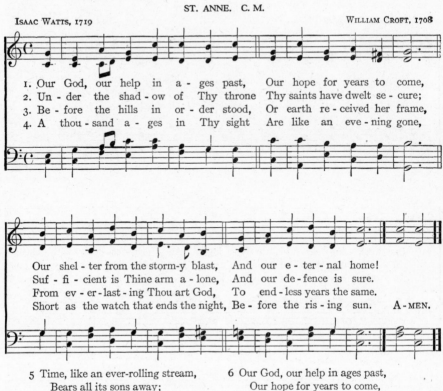

1. Our God, our help in a - ges past,   Our hope for years to come,
2. Un - der the shad - ow of Thy throne   Thy saints have dwelt se - cure;
3. Be - fore the hills in or - der stood,   Or earth re - ceived her frame,
4. A thou - sand a - ges in Thy sight   Are like an eve - ning gone,

Our shel - ter from the storm-y blast,   And our e - ter - nal home!
Suf - fi - cient is Thine arm a - lone,   And our de - fence is sure.
From ev - er - last - ing Thou art God,   To end - less years the same.
Short as the watch that ends the night,   Be - fore the ris - ing sun.   A - MEN.

5 Time, like an ever-rolling stream,
    Bears all its sons away;
    They fly, forgotten as a dream
    Dies at the opening day.

6 Our God, our help in ages past,
    Our hope for years to come,
    Be Thou our guard while troubles last,
    And our eternal home!

HARVEST

353   We Plough the Fields, and Scatter

WIR PFLÜGEN UND WIR STREUEN.   7 6, 7 6. D.   With Refrain.

MATTHIAS CLAUDIUS, 1782
Tr. JANE MONTGOMERY CAMPBELL, 1861   JOHANN A. P. SCHULZ, 1800

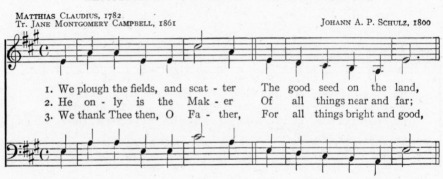

1. We plough the fields, and scat - ter   The good seed on the land,
2. He on - ly is the Mak - er   Of all things near and far;
3. We thank Thee then, O Fa - ther,   For all things bright and good,

But it is fed and wa - tered By God's al - might - y hand;
He paints the way - side flow - er; He lights the eve - ning star;
The seed - time and the har - vest, Our life, our health, our food;

He sends the snow in win - ter, The warmth to swell the grain,
The winds and waves o - bey Him; By Him the birds are fed;
No gifts have we to of - fer For all Thy love im - parts,

The breez - es and the sun - shine, And soft re - fresh - ing rain.
Much more to us, His chil - dren, He gives our dai - ly bread.
But that which Thou de - sir - est, Our hum - ble, thank - ful hearts.

REFRAIN

All good gifts a - round us Are sent from heaven a - bove,

A little slower

Then thank the Lord, O thank the Lord, For all His love. A - MEN.

354 Come, Ye Thankful People, Come

ST. GEORGE'S WINDSOR. 77,77. D.

HENRY ALFORD, 1844, 1865

GEORGE J. ELVEY, 1858

1. Come, ye thank-ful peo-ple, come; Raise the song of har-vest-home.
2. All the world is God's own field, Fruit un-to His praise to yield;
3. For the Lord our God shall come And shall take His har-vest home;
4. Ev-en so, Lord, quick-ly come, To Thy fi-nal har-vest-home;

All is safe-ly gath-ered in Ere the win-ter storms be-gin.
Wheat and tares to-geth-er sown, Un-to joy or sor-row grown;
From His field shall in that day All of-fenc-es purge a-way;
Gath-er Thou Thy peo-ple in, Free from sor-row, free from sin,

God our Mak-er doth pro-vide For our wants to be sup-plied;
First the blade and then the ear, Then the full corn shall ap-pear;
Give His an-gels charge at last In the fire the tares to cast;
There for ev-er pur-i-fied, In Thy pres-ence to a-bide;

Come, to God's own tem-ple come, Raise the song of har-vest-home.
Lord of har-vest, grant that we Whole-some grain and pure may be.
But the fruit-ful ears to store In His gar-ner ev-er-more.
Come with all Thine an-gels, come, Raise the glo-rious har-vest-home! A-MEN.

Praise to God and Thanks We Bring 355

CULFORD. 7 7, 7 7. D.

WM. C. GANNETT, 1872

EDWARD J. HOPKINS, 1867

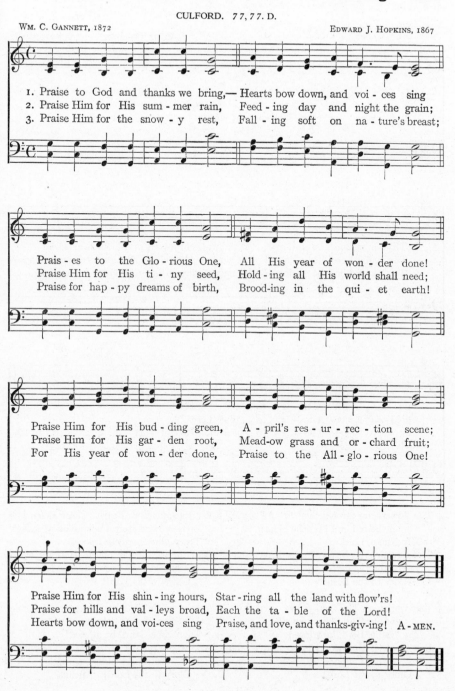

1. Praise to God and thanks we bring,— Hearts bow down, and voi - ces sing
2. Praise Him for His sum - mer rain, Feed - ing day and night the grain;
3. Praise Him for the snow - y rest, Fall - ing soft on na - ture's breast;

Prais - es to the Glo - rious One, All His year of won - der done!
Praise Him for His ti - ny seed, Hold - ing all His world shall need;
Praise for hap - py dreams of birth, Brood-ing in the qui - et earth!

Praise Him for His bud - ding green, A - pril's res - ur - rec - tion scene;
Praise Him for His gar - den root, Mead-ow grass and or - chard fruit;
For His year of won - der done, Praise to the All - glo - rious One!

Praise Him for His shin - ing hours, Star - ring all the land with flow'rs!
Praise for hills and val - leys broad, Each the ta - ble of the Lord!
Hearts bow down, and voi-ces sing Praise, and love, and thanks-giv-ing! A - MEN.

356 For All Thy Love and Goodness

SPRINGTIME. P. M.

FRANCES JANE DOUGLASS, 1848, and
WILLIAM WALSHAM HOW, 1871

Arr. by ARTHUR S. SULLIVAN (1842–1900)

1. For all Thy love and goodness, so bounti - - ful and free,
2. The spring-time breaks all round about, wak-ing from win - ter's night:
3. A voice of joy is in all the earth, a voice is in all the air:

Thy Name, Lord, be a-dored! On the wings of joyous praise our hearts soar
Thy Name, Lord, be a-dored! The sunshine, like God's love, pours down in floods of
Thy Name, Lord, be a-dored! All nature singeth aloud to God; there is glad-ness

Last verse. Slower.

up to Thee: Glo - ry to the Lord!
gold - en light: Glo - ry to the Lord!
ev - 'ry - where: Glo - ry to the Lord! Al - le - lu - ia! A - MEN.

4 The flowers are strewn in field and copse,
 on the hill and | on the plain:
 Thy Name, Lord, be adored!
 The soft air stirs in the tender leaves that
  clothe the | trees again:
 Glory to the Lord!

5 The works of Thy hands are very fair;
 and for Thy | bounteous love,
 Thy Name, Lord, be adored!
 But what, if this world is so fair, is the
  better | land above?
 Glory to the Lord!

6 O to awake from death's short sleep, like
 flowers from their | wintry grave!
 Thy Name, Lord, be adored!
 And to rise all glorious in the day when
  Christ shall | come to save!
 Glory to the Lord!

7 O to dwell in that happy land, where the
 heart cannot | choose but sing!
 Thy Name, Lord, be adored!
 And where the life of the blessed ones is a
  beautiful | endless spring!
 Glory to the Lord! Alleluia!

Summer Suns Are Glowing

RUTH. 6 5, 6 5. D.

WILLIAM W. HOW, 1871

SAMUEL SMITH (1804–1873)

1. Sum - mer suns are glow - ing O - ver land and sea,
2. God's free mer - cy stream - eth O - ver all the world,
3. Lord, up - on our blind - ness Thy pure ra - diance pour;
4. We will nev - er doubt Thee, Though Thou veil Thy light:

Hap - py light is flow - ing Boun - ti - ful and free.
And His ban - ner gleam - eth Ev - 'ry - where un - furled,
For thy lov - ing - kind - ness Make us love Thee more;
Life is dark with - out Thee; Death with Thee is bright.

Ev - 'ry - thing re - joic - es In the mel - low rays,
Broad and deep and glo - rious As the heaven a - bove,
And when clouds are drift - ing Dark a - cross our sky,
Light of Light! shine o'er us On our pil - grim way;

All earth's thousand voi - ces Swell the psalm of praise.
Shines in might vic - to - rious His e - ter - nal Love.
Then, the veil up - lift - ing, Fa - ther, be Thou nigh.
Go Thou still be - fore us To the end - less day. A - MEN.

358   The Year is Swiftly Waning

ST. ALPHEGE. 7 5, 7 6.

WILLIAM W. HOW, 1871

HENRY J. GAUNTLETT, 1852

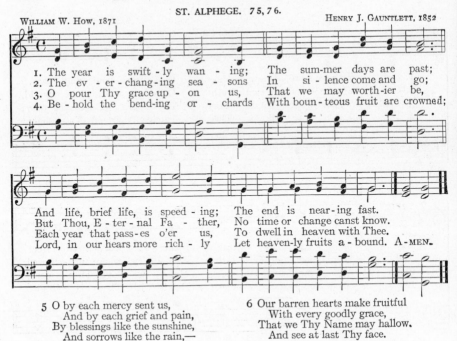

1. The year is swift - ly wan - ing; The sum-mer days are past;
2. The ev - er - chang-ing sea - sons In si - lence come and go;
3. O pour Thy grace up - on us, That we may worth-ier be,
4. Be - hold the bend-ing or - chards With boun - teous fruit are crowned;

And life, brief life, is speed - ing; The end is near-ing fast.
But Thou, E - ter - nal Fa - ther, No time or change canst know.
Each year that pass-es o'er us, To dwell in heaven with Thee.
Lord, in our hears more rich - ly Let heaven-ly fruits a - bound. A -MEN.

5 O by each mercy sent us,
  And by each grief and pain,
By blessings like the sunshine,
  And sorrows like the rain,—

6 Our barren hearts make fruitful
  With every goodly grace,
That we Thy Name may hallow.
  And see at last Thy face.

359   See the Leaves Around Us Falling

STUTTGART. 8 7, 8 7.

GEORGE HORNE, 1795

Adapted from a Melody in
LUDWIG and WITT's *Psalmodia Sacra*, Gotha, 1715

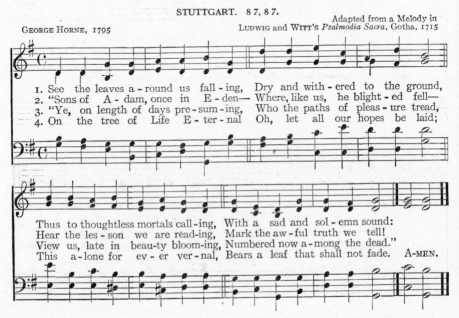

1. See the leaves a - round us fall - ing, Dry and with - ered to the ground,
2. "Sons of A - dam, once in E - den— Where, like us, he blight - ed fell—
3. "Ye, on length of days pre - sum-ing, Who the paths of pleas - ure tread,
4. On the tree of Life E - ter - nal Oh, let all our hopes be laid;

Thus to thoughtless mortals call-ing, With a sad and sol - emn sound;
Hear the les - son we are read-ing, Mark the aw - ful truth we tell!
View us, late in beau-ty bloom-ing, Numbered now a-mong the dead."
This a - lone for ev - er ver-nal, Bears a leaf that shall not fade. A-MEN.

Winter Reigneth O'er the Land 360

CLARENCE. 7 7, 7 7.

WILLIAM W. HOW, 1871   ARR. by ARTHUR S. SULLIVAN (1842–1900)

1. Win - ter reign-eth o'er the land,   Freez - ing with its i - cy breath;
2. Sun - ny days are past and gone;   So   the years go, speed-ing fast,
3. Life is wan - ing, life is brief;   Death, like win - ter, stand - eth nigh;

Dead and bare the tall   trees stand;   All is chill and drear as death.
On - ward ev - er, each   new one   Swift-er speed - ing than the   last.
Each one, like the fall - ing   leaf,   Soon shall fade, and fall, and   die.

4th and 5th stanzas. A little faster

4. But the sleep - ing earth shall wake,   And the flow'rs shall burst in bloom;
5. So the saints, from slum - ber blest   Ris - ing, shall a - wake and sing;

And all na - ture ris - ing, break   Glo - rious from its win - try tomb.
And our flesh in hope shall rest   Till there breaks the end - less spring.

361   My Country, 'Tis of Thee

AMERICA. 6 6 4, 6 6 6 4.

SAMUEL F. SMITH, 1832   *Harmonia Anglicana*, c. 1742

1. My coun - try, 'tis of thee, Sweet land of lib - er - ty,
2. My na - tive coun - try, thee, Land of the no - ble free,

Of thee I sing: Land where my fa-thers died, Land of the pil-grim's pride,
Thy name I love; I love thy rocks and rills, Thy woods and tem-pled hills;

From ev - 'ry moun - tain side Let free - dom ring.
My heart with rap - ture thrills Like that a - bove. A - MEN.

3 Let music swell the breeze,
  And ring from all the trees
    Sweet freedom's song;
  Let mortal tongues awake;
  Let all that breathe partake;
  Let rocks their silence break,
    The sound prolong.

4 Our fathers' God, to Thee,
  Author of liberty,
    To Thee we sing;
  Long may our land be bright
  With freedom's holy light;
  Protect us by Thy might,
    Great God, our King.

362   God Bless Our Native Land

AMERICA. 6 6 4, 6 6 6 4.

Based on a German Hymn by SIGFRIED AUGUST MAHLMANN, 1815
CHARLES TIMOTHY BROOKS, c. 1833; Revised by JOHN S. DWIGHT, 1844

1 God bless our native land!
  Firm may she ever stand
    Through storm and night;
  When the wild tempests rave,
  Ruler of wind and wave,
  Do Thou our country save
    By Thy great might!

2 For her our prayers shall rise
  To God above the skies;
    On Him we wait.
  Thou Who art ever nigh,
  Guarding with watchful eye,
  To Thee aloud we cry,
    God save the State!

God of Our Fathers, Whose Almighty Hand 363

NATIONAL HYMN. 10 10, 10 10.

DANIEL C. ROBERTS, 1876

GEORGE W. WARREN, 1892

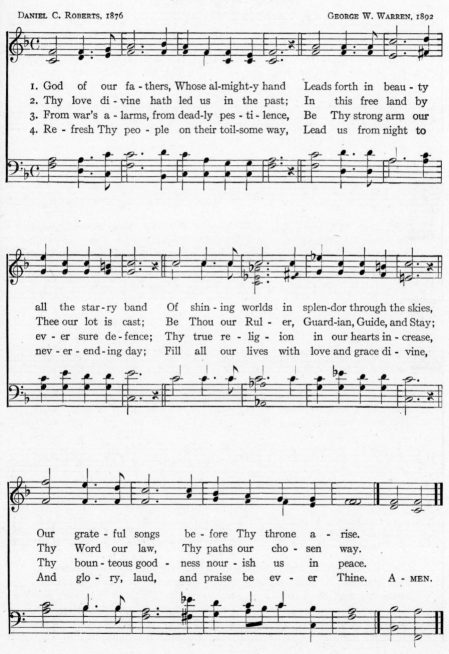

1. God of our fa-thers, Whose al-might-y hand Leads forth in beau-ty
2. Thy love di-vine hath led us in the past; In this free land by
3. From war's a-larms, from dead-ly pes-ti-lence, Be Thy strong arm our
4. Re-fresh Thy peo-ple on their toil-some way, Lead us from night to

all the star-ry band Of shin-ing worlds in splen-dor through the skies,
Thee our lot is cast; Be Thou our Rul-er, Guard-ian, Guide, and Stay;
ev-er sure de-fence; Thy true re-lig-ion in our hearts in-crease,
nev-er-end-ing day; Fill all our lives with love and grace di-vine,

Our grate-ful songs be-fore Thy throne a-rise.
Thy Word our law, Thy paths our cho-sen way.
Thy boun-teous good-ness nour-ish us in peace.
And glo-ry, laud, and praise be ev-er Thine. A-MEN.

364 From Ocean Unto Ocean

WEBB. 7 6, 7 6. D.

ROBERT MURRAY, 1880

GEORGE J. WEBB, 1837

1. From o - cean un - to o - cean   Our land shall own Thee Lord,
2. O   Christ, for Thine own glo - ry,   And for our coun-try's weal,
3. Our   Sav - iour King, de - fend   us,   And guide where we should go;

And, filled with true de - vo - tion,   O - bey Thy sov-'reign word,
We hum - bly plead be - fore   Thee,   Thy - self in us re - veal;
Forth, with Thy mes - sage send   us,   Thy love and light to show;

Our prai - ries and our moun - tains,   For - est and fer - tile field,
And may we know, Lord Je - sus,   The touch of Thy dear hand;
Till, fired with true de - vo - tion   En - kind - led by Thy word,

Our riv - ers, lakes, and foun - tains,   To Thee shall trib - ute yield.
And, healed of our dis - eas - es,   The tempter's pow'r with-stand.
From o - cean un - to o - cean   Our land shall own Thee Lord. A-MEN.

O Beautiful for Spacious Skies

AMERICA, THE BEAUTIFUL. C. M. D.

KATHERINE LEE BATES, 1893, 1910

WILLIAM W. SLEEPER, 1908

1. O beau - ti - ful for spa-cious skies, For am - ber waves of grain,
2. O beau - ti - ful for pil - grim feet, Whose stern, impassioned stress
3. O beau - ti - ful for he - roes proved In lib - er - at - ing strife,
4. O beau - ti - ful for pa - triot dream That sees be - yond the years,

1. O beau - ti - ful for spa-cious skies,

For pur - ple moun-tain maj - es - ties, A - bove the fruit - ed plain;
A thor - ough-fare for free - dom beat A - cross the wil - der - ness;
Who more than self their coun - try loved, And mer - cy more than life!
Thine al - a - bas - ter cit - ies gleam Un-dimmed by hu - man tears;

A - mer - i - ca! A - mer - i - ca! God shed His grace on thee,
A - mer - i - ca! A - mer - i - ca! God mend thine ev - 'ry flaw,
A - mer - i - ca! A - mer - i - ca! May God thy gold re - fine,
A - mer - i - ca! A - mer - i - ca! God shed His grace on thee,

And crown

And crown thy good with broth-er-hood, From sea to shin - ing sea.
Con - firm thy soul in self con - trol, Thy lib - er - ty in law.
Till all suc - cess be no - ble-ness, And ev - 'ry gain di - vine.
And crown thy good with broth-er-hood From sea to shin - ing sea. A - MEN.

thy good with broth - er - hood,

366 Before the Lord We Bow

DARWALL'S 148th. 6 6, 6 6, 4 4, 4 4.

FRANCIS SCOTT KEY, 1832

JOHN DARWALL, 1770

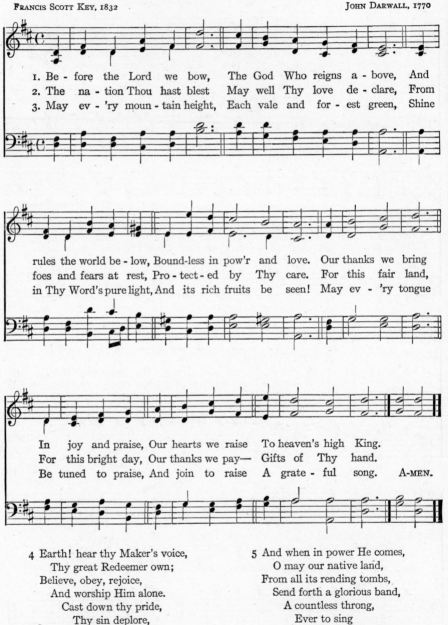

1. Be - fore the Lord we bow, The God Who reigns a - bove, And
2. The na - tion Thou hast blest May well Thy love de - clare, From
3. May ev - 'ry moun - tain height, Each vale and for - est green, Shine

rules the world be - low, Bound-less in pow'r and love. Our thanks we bring
foes and fears at rest, Pro - tect - ed by Thy care. For this fair land,
in Thy Word's pure light, And its rich fruits be seen! May ev - 'ry tongue

In joy and praise, Our hearts we raise To heaven's high King.
For this bright day, Our thanks we pay— Gifts of Thy hand.
Be tuned to praise, And join to raise A grate - ful song. A-MEN.

4 Earth! hear thy Maker's voice,
   Thy great Redeemer own;
   Believe, obey, rejoice,
   And worship Him alone.
       Cast down thy pride,
       Thy sin deplore,
       And bow before
   The Crucified.

5 And when in power He comes,
   O may our native land,
   From all its rending tombs,
   Send forth a glorious band,
       A countless throng,
       Ever to sing
       To heaven's high King
   Salvation's song.

God the All-Merciful

RUSSIAN HYMN. 11 10, 11 9.

Arr. from HENRY F. CHORLEY, 1842
and JOHN ELLERTON, 1870

ALEXIS T. LWOFF, 1833

1. God the All - mer - ci - ful! earth hath for - sa - ken
2. God the All - right - eous One! man hath de - fied Thee;
3. God the All - wise! by the fire of Thy chas - tening
4. So shall Thy chil - dren with thank - ful de - vo - tion

Thy ways of bless - ed - ness, slight - ed Thy Word;
Yet to e - ter - ni - ty stand - eth Thy Word;
Earth shall to free - dom and truth be re - stored;
Praise Him Who saved them from per - il and sword,

Bid not Thy wrath in its ter - rors a - wak - en:
False - hood and wrong shall not tar - ry be - side Thee:
Through the thick dark - ness Thy king - dom is hast - ening:
Sing - ing in cho - rus from o - cean to o - cean,

Give to us peace in our time, O Lord!
Give to us peace in our time, O Lord!
Thou wilt give peace in Thy time, O Lord!
"Peace to the na - tions, and praise to the Lord." A - MEN.

368 O Lord, Our God, Thy Mighty Hand

PRESBYTER. C. M. D.

HENRY VAN DYKE, 1912

WALTER O. WILKINSON, 1895

Firmly and in exact time

1. O Lord, our God, Thy might-y hand   Hath made our coun-try free;
2. The strength of ev-'ry state in-crease   In Un-ion's gold-en chain,
3. O suf-fer not her feet to stray;   But guide her un-taught might,
4. Thro' all the wait-ing land pro-claim   Thy gos-pel of good-will;

From all her broad and hap-py land   May wor-ship rise to Thee;
Her thou-sand cit-ies fill with peace,   Her mil-lion fields with grain.
That she may walk in peace-ful day,   And lead the world in light.
And may Thy sweet and sav-ing Name   In ev-'ry bos-om thrill.

Ful-fill the prom-ise of her youth,   Her lib-er-ty de-fend;
The vir-tues of her min-gled blood   In one new peo-ple blend;
Bring down the proud, lift up the poor,   Un-e-qual ways a-mend;
O'er hill and vale, from sea to sea,   Thy ho-ly reign ex-tend;

By law and or-der, love and truth,   A-mer-i-ca be-friend!
By u-ni-ty and broth-er-hood,   A-mer-i-ca be-friend!
By jus-tice, na-tion-wide and sure,   A-mer-i-ca be-friend!
By faith and hope and char-i-ty,   A-mer-i-ca be-friend!   A-MEN.

The Ocean Hath No Danger

ST. CHRISTOPHER. 7 6, 7 6. D.

GODFREY THRING, 1862

FREDERICK C. MAKER, 1881

1. The o - cean hath no dan - ger / For those whose prayers are made
2. If fierce the tem - pest round us, / And white the an - gry deep,
3. Though life it - self be wan - ing, / And waves shall o'er us sweep,
4. Then, Ho - ly Je - sus, hear us, / And keep us free from harm,

To Him Who, in a man - ger, / A help - less babe was laid;
Yet He, Whose love hath found us, / Can still His treas - ure keep;
The wild wind's sad com - plain - ing / Shall lull us still to sleep;
Have pit - y, Lord, and bear us / On Thy sup - port - ing arm,

Who, born to trib - u - la - tion / And ev - 'ry hu - man ill,
Nor wind nor wave can harm us, / Nor hope it - self grow dim,
For, as a gen - tle slum - ber, / E'en death it - self shall prove
Should storm or calm be - fall us, / What - e'er our lot may be,

Yet, Lord of His cre - a - tion, / The wild - est waves can still.
No tem - pest need a - larm us, / If peace we seek in Him.
To those whom Christ doth num-ber / As wor - thy of His love.
When all is o'er,—then call us / Home, Saviour,—home to Thee. A-MEN.

370   Eternal Father! Strong to Save

MELITA. 8 8, 8 8, 8 8

WILLIAM WHITING, 1860, 1869   JOHN B. DYKES, 1861

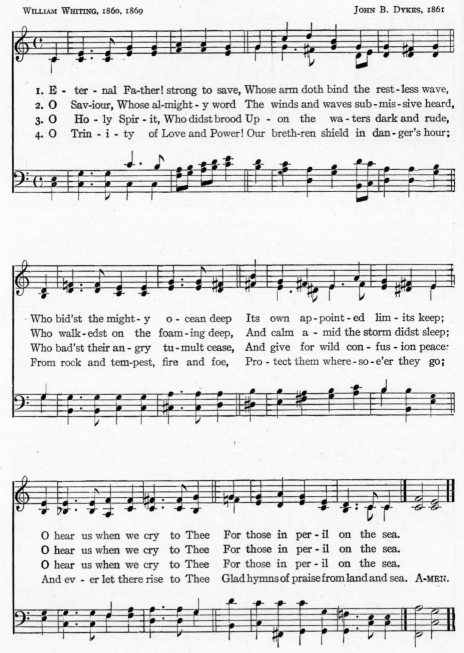

1. E - ter - nal Fa-ther! strong to save, Whose arm doth bind the rest-less wave,
2. O Sav-iour, Whose al-might - y word The winds and waves sub-mis-sive heard,
3. O Ho - ly Spir - it, Who didst brood Up - on the wa - ters dark and rude,
4. O Trin - i - ty of Love and Power! Our breth-ren shield in dan-ger's hour;

Who bid'st the might- y o - cean deep   Its own ap-point-ed lim - its keep;
Who walk-edst on the foam-ing deep,   And calm a - mid the storm didst sleep;
Who bad'st their an - gry tu-mult cease,   And give for wild con - fus - ion peace:
From rock and tem-pest, fire and foe,   Pro - tect them where-so-e'er they go;

O hear us when we cry to Thee   For those in per - il on the sea.
O hear us when we cry to Thee   For those in per - il on the sea.
O hear us when we cry to Thee   For those in per - il on the sea.
And ev - er let there rise to Thee   Glad hymns of praise from land and sea. A-MEN.

Almighty Father, God of Love

371

SAXBY. L. M.

HESTER P. HAWKINS, 1885

TIMOTHY R. MATTHEWS, 1883

1. Al-might-y Fa-ther, God of love, Hear from Thy Throne of light a - bove
2. Our loved ones we com-mend to Thee, Who cross-ing o'er the rest - less sea,
3. It is Thy world wher-e'er they go, Thy sun that shines on all be - low;

The pray'r that now to Thee as-cends, For blessings on our ab-sent friends.
Or wand'ring through a for-eign land, Are still with-in Thy might-y hand.
And we may still be one in Thee, Whose love en-cir-cles land and sea. A-MEN.

4 Thou seest, even whilst we pray,
Our absent loved ones far away;
O shield them with a Father's care,
And all their joys and sorrows share.

5 Be with them when the day is bright,
Be near them in the gloom of night,
And guide until the end shall come
Of life's full day, then lead them home.

Now unto Him that is able to do exceeding
abundantly above all that we ask or
think, unto Him be glory in the
Church by Christ Jesus
throughout all ages,
world without end.
Amen.

The Services

of the

Common Service Book

with

Music

The Service

¶ *The Congregation shall rise, and the Minister shall say:*

IN the Name of the Father, and of the Son, and of the Holy Ghost.

¶ *The Congregation shall sing or say:*

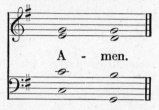

A - men.

The Confession of Sins

¶ *The Minister shall say:*

BELOVED in the Lord! Let us draw near with a true heart, and confess our sins unto God our Father, beseeching Him, in the Name of our Lord Jesus Christ, to grant us forgiveness.

Versicle. Our help is in the Name of the Lord.

Response.

Who made heaven and earth.

℣. I said, I will confess my transgressions unto the Lord.

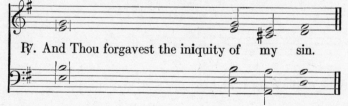

℟. And Thou forgavest the iniquity of my sin.

Additional directive and permissive rubrics are appointed in the General Rubrics, p. 290.

9

The Service

¶ Then shall the Minister say:

ALMIGHTY GOD, our Maker and Redeemer, we poor sinners confess unto Thee, that we are by nature sinful and unclean, and that we have sinned against Thee by thought, word, and deed. Wherefore we flee for refuge to Thine infinite mercy, seeking and imploring Thy grace, for the sake of our Lord Jesus Christ.

¶ The Congregation shall say with the Minister:

O MOST Merciful God, Who hast given Thine Only-begotten Son to die for us, have mercy upon us, and for His sake grant us remission of all our sins: and by Thy Holy Spirit increase in us true knowledge of Thee, and of Thy will, and true obedience to Thy Word, to the end that by Thy grace we may come to everlasting life; through Jesus Christ our Lord. Amen.

¶ Then shall the Minister say:

ALMIGHTY God, our Heavenly Father, hath had mercy upon us, and hath given His Only Son to die for us, and for His sake forgiveth us all our sins. To them that believe on His Name, He giveth power to become the sons of God, and bestoweth upon them His Holy Spirit. He that believeth, and is baptized, shall be saved. Grant this, O Lord, unto us all.

¶ The Congregation shall sing or say:

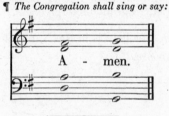

A - men.

¶ The Congregation shall stand until the close of the Collect.

The Introit

¶ The Introit for the Day (Pages 51–127) with the Gloria Patri shall be sung or said.

Gloria Patri

I

J. L. ROGERS.

GLORY be to the Father, and to the Son, and to the Ho-ly Ghost:

10

As it was in the be-
ginning, is now, and } ev - er shall be, world with-out end. A - men.

For use in Lent.

II

Arranged by J. STAINER.

GLO - RY . . be to the Fa - ther, and to the Son, and

to . . the Ho - ly Ghost: As it { was in the beginning, is now, } and

ev - er shall be, world with-out end. A - - - men.

The Service

¶ *Then shall be sung or said the* Kyrie.

The Kyrie

℣. Lord, have mercy upon us.

℟. Lord, have mer - cy up - on . . us.

℣. Christ, have mercy upon us.   ℣. Lord, have mercy upon us.

℟. Christ, have mer-cy up-on . . us. ℟. Lord, have mer-cy up-on . . us.

¶ *Then shall be sung the* Gloria in Excelsis.

The Gloria in Excelsis

¶ *The Minister shall say:*

Glory be to God on high!

¶ *The Congregation shall sing:*

COMPOSITE.

GLORY be to | God on | high, || and on earth | peace, good | will toward | men. ||

We praise Thee, |
we bless Thee, we | wor-ship | Thee, ||

we glorify Thee, we |
give thanks to Thee for | Thy great | glory, ||

12

O Lord God, |heav'n-ly | King, ||God the |Father Al- | might - y. ||

O Lord, the Only-
begotten Son, | Je - sus | Christ;|| O Lord God, Lamb of God, Son | of the |Father,||

that takest
away the | sin of the|world,||have mercy|up - on | us. ||Thou that takest away the |

sin of the | world,|| re- | ceive our | prayer.|| Thou that sittest
at the right hand of |

God the |Father,||have mercy| up - on | us. || For Thou|only art |holy; |

Thou| on - ly |art the |Lord; || Thou only, O
Christ, with the | Ho - ly |Ghost, ||

art most high in the| glory of |God the | Fa - |ther. A-men.

¶ Then shall the Minister say:

The Lord be with you.

¶ The Congregation shall sing or say:

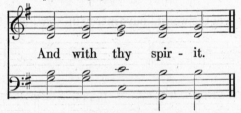

And with thy spir - it.

¶ The Minister shall say:

Let us pray.

¶ Then shall the Minister say the Collect for the **Day.**

The Collect

¶ The Collect ended, the Congregation shall sing or says

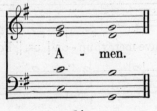

A - men.

The Communion

¶ *Then shall the Minister announce the* Epistle *for the Day saying :* The Epistle for (*here he shall name the Festival or Day*) is written in the ——— Chapter of ———, beginning at the ——— Verse.

The Epistle

¶ *The Epistle ended, the Minister shall say :* Here endeth the Epistle for the Day.

¶ *Then may the* Gradual *for the Day be sung.*

The Gradual

¶ *When the Gradual is omitted, the* Hallelujah *or the* Sentence *for the Season may be sung.* (Sentences, pp. 47–50.)

The Hallelujah

Hal - le - lu - jah, Hal - le - lu - jah, Hal - le - lu - jah.

¶ *In Lent this* Sentence *shall be sung instead of the* Hallelujah:

Adapted from MERBECKE, 1550.

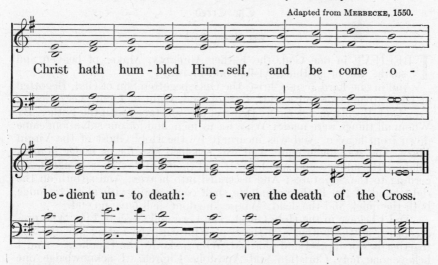

Christ hath hum - bled Him - self, and be - come o -

be - dient un - to death: e - ven the death of the Cross.

¶ *Then shall the Minister announce the* Gospel *for the Day, saying :* The Holy Gospel is written in the ——— Chapter of St. ———, beginning at the ——— Verse.

15

I

The Service

¶ *The Congregation shall rise and sing or say:*

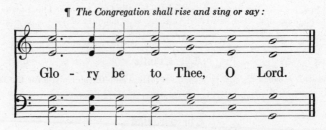

Glo - ry be to Thee, O Lord.

¶ *Then shall the Minister read the Gospel for the Day.*

The Gospel

¶ **The** *Gospel ended, the Minister shall say:* Here endeth the Gospel for the **Day.**

¶ *The Congregation shall sing or say:*

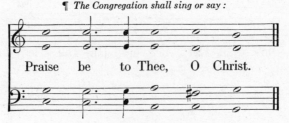

Praise be to Thee, O Christ.

¶ *Then shall be said or sung the* Creed.

The Creed

The Nicene Creed

I BELIEVE in one God, the Father Almighty, Maker of heaven and earth, And of all things visible and invisible.

And in one Lord Jesus Christ, the Only-begotten Son of God, Begotten of His Father before all worlds, God of God, Light of Light, Very God of very God, Begotten, not made, Being of one substance with the Father, By Whom all things were made; Who, for us men, and for our salvation, came down from heaven, And was incarnate by the Holy Ghost of the Virgin Mary, And was made man; And was crucified also for us under Pontius Pilate. He suffered and was buried; and the third day He rose again, according to the Scriptures; And ascended into heaven, And sitteth on the right hand of the Father; And He shall come again with glory to judge both the quick and the dead; Whose kingdom shall have no end.

And I believe in the Holy Ghost, The Lord and Giver of Life, Who proceedeth from the Father and the Son, Who with the Father and the Son together is worshipped and glorified, Who spake by the Prophets. And I believe one holy Christian and Apostolic Church. I acknowledge one Baptism for the remission of sins; And I look for the Resurrection of the dead; And the Life of the world to come. Amen.

The Communion

The Apostles' Creed

I BELIEVE in God the Father Almighty, Maker of heaven and earth. And in Jesus Christ His only Son, our Lord; Who was conceived by the Holy Ghost, Born of the Virgin Mary; Suffered under Pontius Pilate, Was crucified, dead, and buried; He descended into hell; The third day He rose again from the dead; He ascended into heaven, And sitteth on the right hand of God the Father Almighty; From thence He shall come to judge the quick and the dead.

I believe in the Holy Ghost; The holy Christian Church, the Communion of Saints; The Forgiveness of sins; The Resurrection of the body; And the Life everlasting.   Amen.

¶ *Then shall be sung the* Hymn.

The Hymn

¶ *Then shall follow the* Sermon.

The Sermon

¶ *After the Sermon the Congregation shall rise and the Minister shall say:*

THE Peace of God, which passeth all understanding, keep your hearts and minds through Christ Jesus.

¶ *Then shall the* Offertory *be sung, at the close of which the Congregation shall be seated.*
¶ *One of the Offertories here following, or any other suitable Offertory, may be used.*

The Offertory

TONUS REGIUS.

I

THE sacrifices of God are a | broken | spirit:
  A broken and a contrite heart, O God, | Thou wilt | not de- |spise.
Do good in Thy good plea**sure** | unto | Zion:
  Build Thou the | walls . of Je- | rusa- | lem.
Then shalt Thou be pleased with the sacrifices of | righteous- |ness:
  With burnt-offering and | whole burnt- | offer- | ing.

II

CREATE in me a clean | heart, O | God:
  And renew a right | spirit . with- | in— | me.
Cast me not away | from Thy | presence:
  And take not Thy | Holy | Spirit | from me.
Restore unto me the joy of | Thy sal- | vation:
  And uphold me with | Thy free | Spir- | it.

17

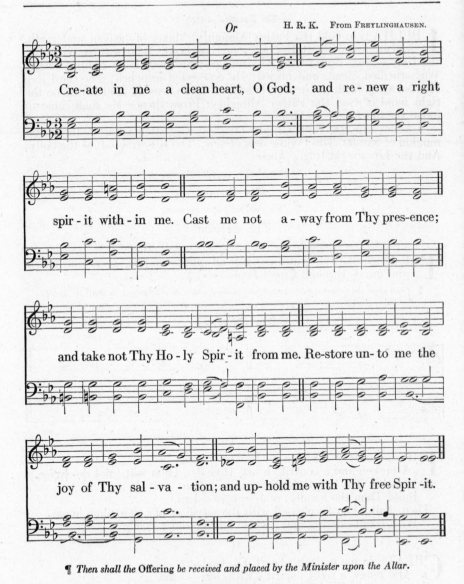

Or   H. R. K.   From Freylinghausen.

Cre-ate in me a clean heart, O God; and re-new a right spir-it with-in me. Cast me not a-way from Thy pres-ence; and take not Thy Ho-ly Spir-it from me. Re-store un-to me the joy of Thy sal-va-tion; and up-hold me with Thy free Spir-it.

¶ *Then shall the* Offering *be received and placed by the* Minister *upon the* Altar.

The Offering

¶ *Then shall follow the* General Prayer.

¶ *At the end of each paragraph the Congregation may say:* We beseech Thee to hear us, good Lord.

18

The Communion

The General Prayer

Let us pray.

ALMIGHTY and most Merciful God, the Father of our Lord Jesus Christ: We give Thee thanks for all Thy goodness and tender mercies, especially for the gift of Thy dear Son, and for the revelation of Thy will and grace; and we beseech Thee so to implant Thy Word in us, that, in good and honest hearts, we may keep it, and bring forth fruit by patient continuance in well doing.

Most heartily we beseech Thee so to rule and govern Thy Church universal, that it may be preserved in the pure doctrine of Thy saving Word, whereby faith toward Thee may be strengthened, and charity increased in us toward all mankind.

Send forth Thy light and Thy truth unto the uttermost parts of the earth. Raise up faithful pastors and missionaries to preach the Gospel in our own land and to all nations; and guide, protect and prosper them in all their labors.

Bless, we pray Thee, the institutions of the Church; its colleges, its seminaries, and all its schools; that they may send forth men and women to serve Thee, in the Ministry of the Word, the Ministry of Mercy, and all the walks of life.

Let the light of Thy Word ever shine within our homes. Keep the children of the Church in the covenant which Thou hast made with them in Holy Baptism; and grant all parents grace to bring them up in faith toward Thee and in obedience to Thy will.

Grant also health and prosperity to all that are in authority, especially to the President (and Congress) of the United States, the Governor (and Legislature) of this Commonwealth, and to all our Judges and Magistrates; and endue them with grace to rule after Thy good pleasure, to the maintenance of righteousness, and to the hinderance and punishment of wickedness, that we may lead a quiet and peaceable life, in all godliness and honesty.

All who are in trouble, want, sickness, anguish of labor, peril of death, or any other adversity, especially those who are in suffering for Thy Name and for Thy truth's sake, comfort, O God, with Thy Holy Spirit, that they may receive and acknowledge their afflictions as the manifestation of Thy fatherly will.

And although we have deserved Thy righteous wrath and manifold punishments, yet, we entreat Thee, O most Merciful Father, remember not the sins of our youth, nor our many transgressions; but out of Thine unspeakable goodness, grace and mercy, defend us from all harm and danger of body and soul. Preserve us from false and pernicious doctrine, from war and bloodshed, from plague and pestilence, from all calamity by fire and water, from hail and tempest, from failure of harvest and from famine, from anguish of heart and despair of Thy mercy, and from an evil death. And in every time of trouble, show Thyself a very present Help, the Saviour of all men, and especially of them that believe.

19

Cause also the needful fruits of the earth to prosper, that we may enjoy them in due season. Give success to all lawful occupations on land and sea; to all pure arts and useful knowledge; and crown them with Thy blessing.

¶ Here special Supplications, Intercessions, and Prayers may be made.

These, and whatsoever other things Thou wouldest have us ask of Thee, O God, vouchsafe unto us, for the sake of the bitter sufferings and death of Jesus Christ, Thine only Son, our Lord and Saviour, Who liveth and reigneth with Thee and the Holy Ghost, ever One God, world without end.

¶ Then shall the Minister and the Congregation say the Lord's Prayer.

The Lord's Prayer

OUR Father, Who art in heaven; Hallowed be Thy Name; Thy kingdom come; Thy will be done on earth, as it is in heaven; Give us this day our daily bread; And forgive us our trespasses, as we forgive those who trespass against us; And lead us not into temptation; But deliver us from evil; For Thine is the kingdom, and the power, and the glory, for ever and ever. Amen.

¶ Then shall be sung a Hymn.

Hymn

¶ If there be no Communion, the Minister standing at the Altar, shall say the Benediction.

The Benediction

THE Lord bless thee, and keep thee.
The Lord make His face shine upon thee, and be gracious unto thee.
The Lord lift up His countenance upon thee, and give thee peace.

¶ The Congregation shall sing or say:

A - - men.

The Communion

The Holy Communion

¶ *When there is a Communion, the Minister shall go to the Altar during the singing of the Hymn. After Silent Prayer, he shall uncover the Vessels and reverently prepare for the Administration of the Holy Sacrament.*

¶ *The Congregation shall rise and stand until the end of the* **Agnus Dei.**

The Preface

¶ *The Minister shall say:*

The Lord be with you.

¶ *The Congregation shall sing or say:*

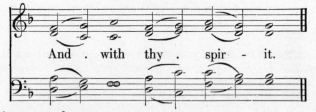

And . with thy . spir - it.

℣. Lift up your hearts.

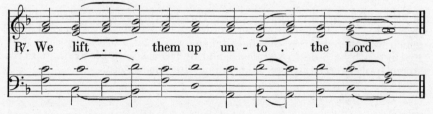

℟. We lift . . . them up un - to . the Lord. .

℣. Let us give thanks unto the Lord our God.

℟. It is meet . . and right so . to do. . .

¶ *Then shall the Minister turn to the Altar and say:*

IT is truly meet, right, and salutary, that we should at all times, and in all places, give thanks unto Thee, O Lord, Holy Father, Almighty Everlasting God.

¶ *Here shall follow the* Proper Preface *for the Day or Season. If there be none especially appointed, there shall follow immediately,* Therefore with Angels, etc.

The Service

For Christmas.

FOR in the mystery of the Word made flesh, Thou hast given us a new revelation of Thy glory; that seeing Thee in the person of Thy Son, we may be drawn to the love of those things which are not seen. Therefore with Angels, etc.

For Epiphany.

AND now do we praise Thee, that Thou didst send unto us Thine Only-begotten Son, and that in Him, being found in fashion as a man, Thou didst reveal the fullness of Thy Glory. Therefore with Angels, etc.

For Lent.

WHO on the Tree of the Cross didst give salvation unto mankind; that whence death arose, thence life also might rise again: and that he who by a tree once overcame, might likewise by a Tree be overcome, through Christ our Lord; through Whom with Angels, etc.

For Easter.

BUT chiefly are we bound to praise Thee for the glorious Resurrection of Thy Son, Jesus Christ, our Lord: for He is the very Paschal Lamb, which was offered for us, and hath taken away the sin of the world; Who by His death hath destroyed death, and by His rising to life again, hath restored to us everlasting life. Therefore with Angels, etc.

For the Festival of the Ascension.

THROUGH Jesus Christ our Lord, Who after His Resurrection appeared openly to all His disciples, and in their sight was taken up into Heaven, that He might make us partakers of His Divine Nature. Therefore with Angels, etc.

For the Festival of Pentecost.

THROUGH Jesus Christ, Thy dear Son, our Lord and Saviour; Who ascending above the heavens and sitting at Thy right hand, poured out [on this day] the Holy Spirit as He had promised, upon the chosen disciples; whereat the whole earth rejoices with exceeding joy. Therefore with Angels, etc.

For the Festival of the Holy Trinity.

WHO with Thine Only-begotten Son, and the Holy Ghost, art One God, One Lord. And in the confession of the only true God, we worship the Trinity in Person, and the Unity in Substance, of Majesty Co-equal. Therefore with Angels, etc.

The Communion

¶ *After the Preface shall follow immediately:*

THEREFORE with Angels and Archangels, and with all the company of heaven, we laud and magnify Thy glorious Name; evermore praising Thee, and saying:

¶ *Then shall the* Sanctus *be sung or said.*

The Sanctus

Ascribed to J. S. BACH.

Ho - ly, Ho - ly, Ho - ly, Lord God of Sa - ba - oth;

Heaven and earth are full of Thy glo - ry; Ho - san - na

in the high - est. Bless - ed is He that com - eth in the

Name of the Lord. Ho - san - na in the high - est.

The Service

The Lord's Prayer

¶ Then shall the Minister say:

Let us pray.

OUR Father, Who art in heaven; Hallowed be Thy Name; Thy kingdom come; Thy will be done on earth,as it is in heaven; Give us this day our daily bread; And forgive us our trespasses, as we forgive those who trespass against us; And lead us not into temptation; But deliver us from evil; For Thine is the kingdom, and the power, and the glory, for ever and ever.

¶ The Congregation shall sing or say:

A - men.

¶ Then shall the Minister say the Words of Institution.

The Words of Institution

OUR Lord Jesus Christ, in the night in which He was betrayed,[a] took bread; and when He had given thanks, He brake it and gave it to His disciples, saying, Take, eat; this is My Body, which is given for you; this do in remembrance of Me. *(a) Here he shall take the Paten, with the* BREAD, *in his hand.*

After the same manner also He [b] took the cup, when He had supped, and when He had given thanks, He gave it to them, saying, Drink ye all of it; this cup is the New Testament in My Blood, which is shed for you, and for many, for the remission of sins; this do, as oft as ye drink it, in remembrance of Me. *(b) Here he shall take the* CUP *in his hand.*

¶ Then shall the Minister turn to the Congregation and say:

The Peace of the Lord be with you alway.

¶ The Congregation shall sing or say:

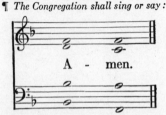

A - men.

¶ Then shall be sung or said the Agnus Dei.

The Communion

The Agnus Dei

BRAUNSCHWEIG, 1528.

O   Christ, Thou Lamb   of   God, that   tak - est a - way the

sin   of   the world,   have mer - cy up - on   us.

O   Christ, Thou Lamb of   God, that tak - est a - way the

sin   of   the world,   have mer - cy up - on   us.

O   Christ, Thou Lamb of   God, that   tak - est a - way the

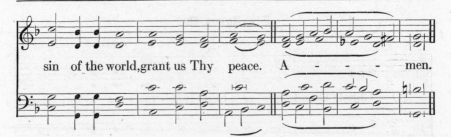

sin of the world, grant us Thy peace. A - - - men.

¶ *Then shall the Communicants present themselves before the Altar and receive the Holy Sacrament.*

The Administration of the Holy Sacrament

¶ *When the Minister giveth the* BREAD *he shall say :*

Take and eat, this is the Body of Christ, given for thee.

¶ *When he giveth the* CUP *he shall say :*

Take and drink, this is the Blood of the New Testament, shed for thy sins.

¶ *After he hath given the Bread and the Cup, the Minister shall say :*

The Body of our Lord Jesus Christ and His precious Blood strengthen and preserve you in true faith unto everlasting life.

¶ *Then shall the Congregation rise, and the* Nunc Dimittis *may be sung or said.*

The Nunc Dimittis

W. HINE.

LORD, now lettest Thou Thy servant de- | part in | peace:
　　Ac- | cording | to Thy | word;
For mine eyes have seen | Thy sal- | vation:
　　Which Thou hast prepared before the face of | all | peo- | ple;
A light to | lighten . the | Gentiles:
　　And the glory of Thy | peo-ple | Isra- | el.
GLORY be to the Father, and | to the | Son:
　　And | to the | Holy | Ghost;
As it was in the beginning, is now, and | ever | shall be:
　　World | without | end. A- | men.

¶ *Then shall be said the* Thanksgiving.

26

The Communion

The Thanksgiving

℣. O give thanks unto the Lord, for He is good.

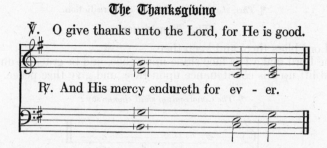

℟. And His mercy endureth for ev - er.

WE give thanks to Thee, Almighty God, that Thou hast refreshed us with this Thy salutary gift; and we beseech Thee, of Thy mercy, to strengthen us through the same in faith toward Thee, and in fervent love toward one another; through Jesus Christ, Thy dear Son, our Lord, Who liveth and reigneth with Thee and the Holy Ghost, ever One God, world without end.

¶ *The Congregation shall sing or say:*

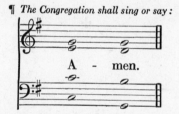

A - men.

¶ *Then may be sung or said the* Salutation *and the* Benedicamus.

℣. The Lord be with you.

℟. And with thy spir - it.

℣. Bless we the Lord.

℟. Thanks be to God.

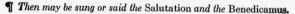

¶ *Then shall the Minister say the* Benediction.

The Benediction

THE Lord bless thee, and keep thee.
The Lord make His face shine upon thee, and be gracious unto thee.
The Lord lift up His countenance upon thee, and give thee peace.

¶ *The Congregation shall sing or say :*

A - - - - men.

✠

Matins

The Versicle

O LORD, open Thou my lips.

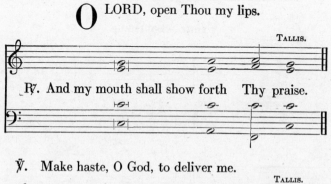

℟. And my mouth shall show forth Thy praise.

℣. Make haste, O God, to deliver me.

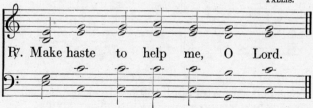

℟. Make haste to help me, O Lord.

℣. Glory be to the Father, and to the Son, and to the Holy Ghost:

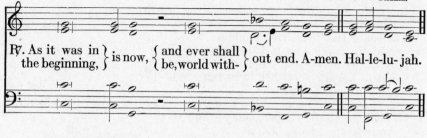

℟. As it was in the beginning, } is now, { and ever shall be, world with- } out end. A-men. Hal-le-lu-jah.

Additional directive and permissive rubrics are appointed in the General Rubrics, p. 290.

Matins

¶ *Then may follow the* Invitatory *with the* Venite.

The Invitatory

℣. O come, let us worship the Lord.

℟. For He is our Mak - er.

Venite Exultemus

I

W. RUSSELL.

II

P. HAYES.

O COME, let us sing | unto . the | LORD:
　Let us make a joyful noise to the | Rock of | our sal- | vation.
Let us come before His presence | with thanks- | giving:
　And make a joyful | noise . unto | Him with | psalms.
For the LORD is a | great | God:
　And a great | King a- | bove all | gods.
In His hand are the deep places | of the | earth:
　The strength of the | hills is | His | also.
The sea is His, | and He | made it:
　And His hands | formed the | dry | land.
O come, let us worship | and bow | down:
　Let us kneel before the | LORD our | Mak- | er.
For He | is our | God:
　And we are the people of His pasture, and the | sheep of | His | hand.
GLORY be to the Father, and | to the | Son:
　And | to the | Holy | Ghost;
As it was in the beginning, is now, and | ever | shall be:
　World | without | end. A- | men.

30

Matins

¶ *Then shall be sung the* Hymn.

The Hymn

¶ *Then, all standing, shall be sung or said one or more* Psalms.

The Psalm

¶ *At the end of each Psalm the Congregation shall sing or say the* Gloria Patri.

Gloria Patri

I

R. GOODSON.

II

R. WOODWARD.

GLORY be to the Father, and | to the | Son:
And | to the | Holy | Ghost;
As it was in the beginning, is now, and | ever | shall be:
World | without | end. A- | men.

For Lent.

III

Arranged by J. STAINER.

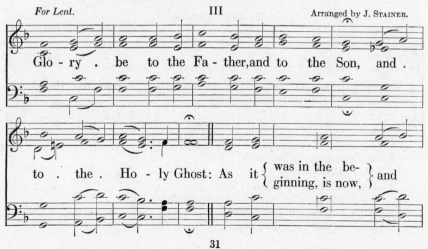

Glo - ry . be to the Fa - ther, and to the Son, and .

to . the . Ho - ly Ghost: As it { was in the be- ginning, is now, } and

31

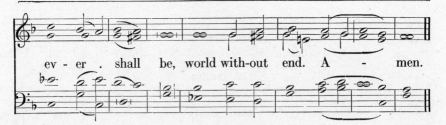

ev - er . shall be, world with-out end. A - men.

The Lesson

¶ *The* Scripture Lessons *shall then be read. After each* **Lesson** *shall be sung or said the* Response.

℣. O Lord, have mercy upon us.

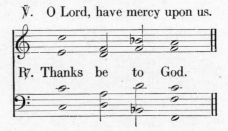

℟. Thanks be to God.

¶ *After the Lesson a* Responsory *or a* Hymn *may be sung.*

¶ *A brief* Sermon *may then follow.*

The Canticle

¶ *The Congregation shall rise and sing or say* the Canticle.

Te Deum Laudamus

FREDERICK ILIFFE (1847———).

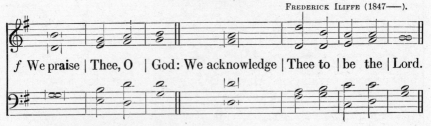

f We praise | Thee, O | God: We acknowledge | Thee to | be the | Lord.

All the earth doth | worship | Thee:
   The Father | ever- | last- | ing.
To thee all Angels | cry a- | loud:
   The heavens, and | all the | powers there- | in.
To Thee Cherubim and | Sera- | phim:
   Con- | tinual- | ly do | cry,

Matins

Ho - ly, Ho - ly, Ho - ly: Lord God of Sa - ba - oth;

Heaven and earth are full of the | Ma-jes- | ty: Of | Thy — | Glo- — | ry.

The glorious company | of the A-| postles: Praise . . . . Thee.

The goodly fellowship | of the | Prophets:
   Praise | — | — | Thee.
The noble | army . of | Martyrs:
   Praise | — | — | Thee.
The holy Church throughout | all the | world:
   Doth | — ac- | knowledge | Thee;
The | Fa- | ther:
   Of an | infin-ite | Majes- | ty;
Thine a- | dora-ble, | true:
   And | on- | — ly | Son;
Also the | Holy | Ghost:
   The | Com- | — fort- | er.

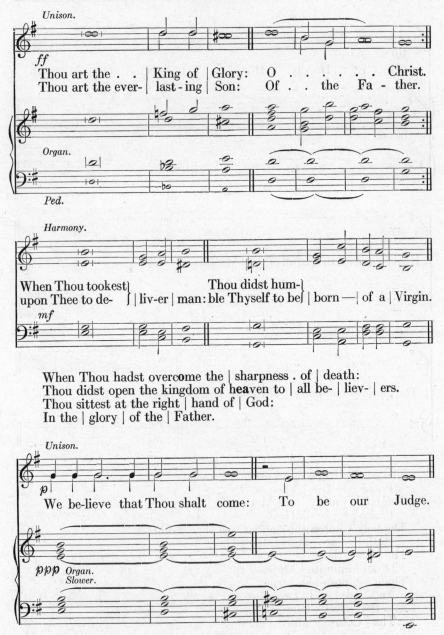

Thou art the . . | King of | Glory: O . . . . Christ.
Thou art the ever- | last-ing | Son: Of . . the Fa - ther.

When Thou tookest | | liv-er | man: ble Thyself to be | | born — | of a | Virgin.
upon Thee to de-

When Thou hadst overcome the | sharpness . of | death:
Thou didst open the kingdom of heaven to | all be- | liev- | ers.
Thou sittest at the right | hand of | God:
In the | glory | of the | Father.

We be-lieve that Thou shalt come: To be our Judge.

Matins

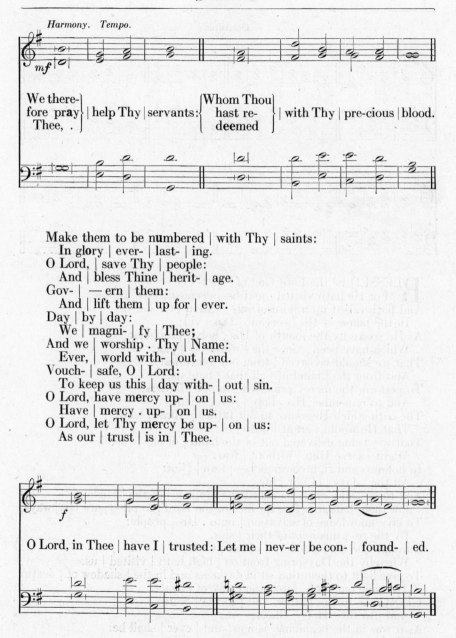

Harmony. Tempo.

mf

We there-
fore pray } | help Thy | servants: { Whom Thou
hast re-
deemed } | with Thy | pre-cious | blood.
Thee, . }

Make them to be numbered | with Thy | saints:
  In glory | ever- | last- | ing.
O Lord, | save Thy | people:
  And | bless Thine | herit- | age.
Gov- | — ern | them:
  And | lift them | up for | ever.
Day | by | day:
  We | magni- | fy | Thee;
And we | worship . Thy | Name:
  Ever, | world with- | out | end.
Vouch- | safe, O | Lord:
  To keep us this | day with- | out | sin.
O Lord, have mercy up- | on | us:
  Have | mercy . up- | on | us.
O Lord, let Thy mercy be up- | on | us:
  As our | trust | is in | Thee.

f

O Lord, in Thee | have I | trusted: Let me | nev-er | be con- | found- | ed.

Matins

Benedictus

I

W. CROTCH.

II

TRENT.

BLESSED be the Lord God of | Isra- | el:
  For He hath visited | and re- | deemed . His | people;
And hath raised up a horn of sal- | vation | for us:
  In the house of His | servant | Da- | vid;
As He spake by the mouth of His | holy | prophets:
  Which have been | since the | world be- | gan;
That we should be saved | from our | enemies:
  And from the | hand of | all that | hate us;
To perform the mercy promised | to our | fathers:
  And to remember His | holy | cove- | nant;
The oath which He sware to our father | Abra- | ham:
  That He would | grant | unto | us;
That we, being delivered out of the hand | of our | enemies:
  Might | serve Him | without | fear,
In holiness and righteousness be- | fore | Him:
  All the | days | of our | life.
And thou, child, shalt be called the prophet | of the | Highest:
  For thou shalt go before the face of the Lord | to pre- | pare His | ways;
To give knowledge of salvation | unto . His | people:
  By the re- | mission | of their | sins.
Through the tender mercy | of our | God:
  Whereby the Dayspring from on | high hath | visited | us;
To give light to them that sit in darkness and in the | shadow of | death:
  To guide our feet | into . the | way of | peace.
GLORY be to the Father, and | to the | Son:
  And | to the | Holy | Ghost;
As it was in the beginning, is now, and | ever | shall be:
  World | without | end. A- | men.

Matins

The Prayer

¶ *Then shall be said the* Prayers.

¶ *The Minister shall say :*

Lord, have mercy upon us.

¶ *The Congregation shall sing or say :*

I

Matins

¶ *Then shall all say the* Lord's Prayer.

OUR Father, Who art in heaven; Hallowed be Thy Name; Thy kingdom come; Thy will be done on earth, as it is in heaven; Give us this day our daily bread; And forgive us our trespasses, as we forgive those who trespass against us; And lead us not into temptation; But deliver us from evil; For Thine is the kingdom, and the power, and the glory, for ever and ever. Amen.

¶ *Then may be sung or said:*

℣.　The Lord be with you.

℟.　And　with　thy　spir - it.

Let us pray.

¶ *Then shall be said the* Collect for the Day.

The Collect for the Day

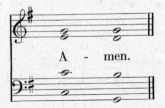

A - men.

¶ *Other Collects may then be said, and after them this* Collect for Grace, *with which a* Versicle *may be used.*

℣.　Let my mouth be filled with Thy praise.

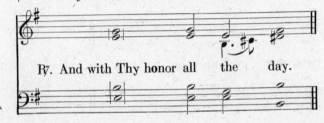

℟.　And with Thy honor all　the　day.

Matins

The Collect for Grace

O LORD, our Heavenly Father, Almighty and Everlasting God, Who hast safely brought us to the beginning of this day: Defend us in the same with Thy mighty power; and grant that this day we fall into no sin, neither run into any kind of danger; but that all our doings, being ordered by Thy governance, may be righteous in Thy sight; through Jesus Christ, Thy Son, our Lord, Who liveth and reigneth with Thee and the Holy Ghost, ever One God, world without end.

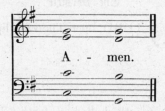

A - men.

¶ *Then may be sung or said the* Benedicamus.

℣. Bless we the Lord.

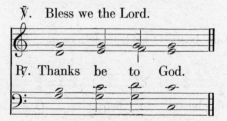

℟. Thanks be to God.

¶ *Then shall the Minister say the* Benediction.

THE Grace of our Lord Jesus Christ, and the Love of God, and the Communion of the Holy Ghost, be with you all.

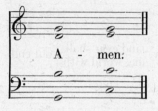

A - men.

39

Vespers

¶ *The* Versicles *with the* Gloria Patri *shall be sung or said, the Congregation standing until the end of the* Psalm.

¶ *The* Hallelujah *shall be omitted in Lent.*

The Versicle

O LORD, open Thou my lips.

TALLIS.

R︢. And my mouth shall show forth Thy praise.

V︢. Make haste, O God, to deliver me.

TALLIS.

R︢. Make haste to help me, O Lord.

V︢. Glory be to the Father, and to the Son, and to the Holy Ghost:

TALLIS.

R︢. As it was in the beginning,} is now, {and ever shall be, world with-} out end. A-men. Hal-le-lu - jah.

Additional directive and permissive rubrics are appointed in the General Rubrics, p. 290.

Vespers

¶ *Then shall be sung or said one or more* Psalms.

The Psalm

¶ *At the end of each Psalm the Congregation shall sing or say the* Gloria Patri.

Gloria Patri

GLORY be to the Father, and | to the | Son:
 And | to the | Holy | Ghost;
As it was in the beginning, is now, and | ever | shall be:
 World | without | end.   A- | men.

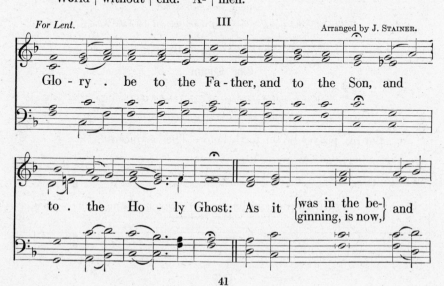

41

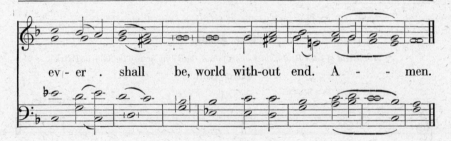

ev - er . shall be, world with-out end. A - - men.

The Lesson

¶ *The* Scripture Lessons *shall then be read.* *After each Lesson shall be sung or said the* Response.

℣. O Lord, have mercy upon us.

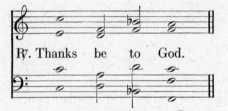

℞. Thanks be to God.

¶ *After the Lesson a Responsory or a Hymn* may be sung.

¶ *A* Sermon *may then follow.*

¶ *The* Offering *may then be received and placed upon the Altar.*

¶ *Then shall be sung the* Hymn.

The Hymn

¶ *The* Congregation *shall rise and sing or say the* Canticle.

¶ *A* Versicle *shall be used with the Canticle.*

℣. Let my prayer be set forth before Thee as incense.

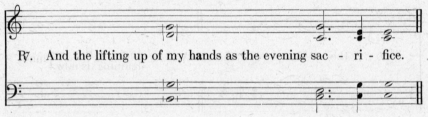

℞. And the lifting up of my hands as the evening sac - ri - fice.

Vespers

The Canticle.

Magnificat

I

E. G. MONK.

II

ANON.

MY SOUL doth magni- | fy the | Lord:
  And my spirit hath re- | joiced . in | God my | Saviour.
For He | hath re- | garded:
  The low es- | tate of | His hand- | maiden.
For behold, | from hence- | forth:
  All gener- | ations . shall | call me | blessed.
For He that is mighty hath done to | me great | things:
  And | holy | is His | Name.
And His mercy is on | them that | fear Him:
  From gener- | ation . to | gener- | ation.
He hath showed strength | with His | arm:
  He hath scattered the proud in the imagin- | ation | of their | hearts.
He hath put down the mighty | from their | seats:
  And exalted | them of | low de- | gree.
He hath filled the hungry | with good | things:
  And the rich He | hath sent | empty . a- | way.
He hath holpen His servant Israel, in remembrance | of His | mercy:
  As he spake to our fathers, to Abraham, and | to his | seed, for | ever.
GLORY be to the Father, and | to the | Son:
  And | to the | Holy | Ghost;
As it was in the beginning, is now, and | ever | shall be:
  World | without | end . A- | men.

43

Vespers

Nunc Dimittis

I

J. GOLDWIN.

II

J. MEDLEY.

L ORD, now lettest Thou Thy servant de- | part in | peace:
Ac- | cording | to Thy | word;
For mine eyes have seen | Thy sal- | vation:
Which Thou hast prepared before the face of | all | peo- | ple;
A light to | lighten . the | Gentiles:
And the glory of Thy | peo-ple | Isra- | el.
GLORY be to the Father, and | to the | Son:
And | to the | Holy | Ghost;
As it was in the beginning, is now, and | ever | shall be:
World | without | end. A- | men.

The Prayer

¶ *Then shall be said the* Prayers.

¶ *The Minister shall say:*

Lord, have mercy upon us.

¶ *The Congregation shall sing or say:*

I

TALLIS.

Lord, have mer-cy up-on us. Christ, have mer-cy up-on us.

44

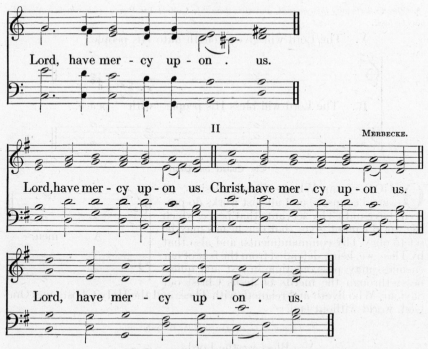

Lord, have mer - cy up - on . us.

II

MERBECKE.

Lord, have mer - cy up - on us. Christ, have mer - cy up - on us.

Lord, have mer - cy up - on . us.

¶ *Then shall all say the* Lord's Prayer

OUR Father, Who art in heaven; Hallowed be Thy Name; Thy kingdom come; Thy will be done on earth, as it is in heaven; Give us this day our daily bread; And forgive us our trespasses, as we forgive those who trespass against us; And lead us not into temptation; But deliver us from evil; For Thine is the kingdom, and the power, and the glory, for ever and ever. Amen.

¶ *Then may be sung or said:*

℣. The Lord be with you.

℟. And with thy spir - it.

Let us pray.

¶ *Then shall be said the* Collect for the Day.

The Collect for the Day

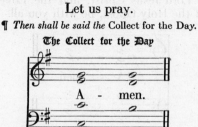

A - men.

45

Vespers

¶ *Other Collects may then be said, and after them this* Collect for Peace *with which a* Versicle *may be used.*

℣. The Lord will give strength unto His people.

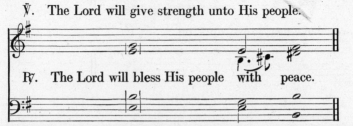

℞. The Lord will bless His people with peace.

The Collect for Peace

O GOD, from Whom all holy desires, all good counsels, and all just works do proceed: Give unto Thy servants that peace, which the world cannot give; that our hearts may be set to obey Thy commandments, and also that by Thee, we, being defended from the fear of our enemies, may pass our time in rest and quietness; through the merits of Jesus Christ our Saviour, Who liveth and reigneth with Thee, and the Holy Ghost, ever One God, world without end.

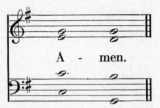

A - men.

¶ *Then may be sung or said the* Benedicamus.

℣. Bless we the Lord.

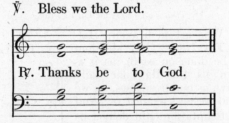

℞. Thanks be to God.

¶ *Then shall the Minister say the* Benediction.

THE Grace of our Lord Jesus Christ, and the Love of God, and the Communion of the Holy Ghost, be with you all.

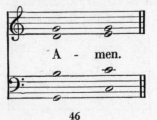

A - men.

INDEX OF TUNES

i

INDEX OF TUNES

INDEX OF TUNES

INDEX OF TUNES

INDEX OF TUNES

INDEX OF TUNES

INDEX OF FIRST LINES

INDEX OF FIRST LINES

INDEX OF FIRST LINES

INDEX OF FIRST LINES

CHRISTMAS CAROLS

INDEX OF FIRST LINES

EPIPHANY CAROLS

EASTER CAROLS

INDEX OF SUBJECTS

xii

INDEX OF SUBJECTS

INDEX OF SUBJECTS